*Swedish research in a changing society*

# Swedish research in a changing society

The Bank of Sweden

Tercentenary Foundation

1965-1990

Edited by Kjell Härnqvist and Nils-Eric Svensson

Gidlunds bokförlag · Hedemora

© *The Authors, 1990*

*ISBN 91 7844 168 4 (Swedish edition)*

*ISBN 91 7844 169 2 (English edition)*

*Fälths tryckeri, Värnamo 1990*

# Contents

# Foreword

The autumn of 1990 will witness the 25th anniversary of the Bank of Sweden Tercentenary Foundation. The Foundation was established in connection with the commemoration of the Bank of Sweden's 300 years of existence. By comparison, a mere 25 years is a short period of time indeed, but this particular quarter century encompassed wide-ranging developments in Swedish scientific research, developments to which the Foundation has contributed in different ways. So a birthday celebration for this latter-day spin-off of the Bank of Sweden's activities is warranted even after only 25 years.

The Foundation decided to commemorate its 25th anniversary by publishing an anthology containing papers from different fields. This anthology offers examples of research supported by the Foundation. Because of space limitations, a selection had to be made. This selection is certainly not representative of the total volume of research awarded Foundation grants. But it does exemplify the breadth of Foundation activities and its emphasis on research fields of importance to society's development.

The invitation to contributors to this anthology indicated that the starting point for papers should be projects supported by the Foundation. Authors were otherwise able to exercise great freedom in their approaches. But the invitation also noted that project impact on the public debate, social development, graduate training, research environments and national and international research contacts might be appropriate aspects to cover, in addition to research results.

Since projects were chosen from numerous disciplines and were started at different times, different aspects were accentuated in different papers. However, the papers should collectively supply an informative picture of research in the selected fields from 1965 on, with some emphasis on earlier phases in the Foundation's history. This is also why most authors are senior scholars in their field. A brief presentation of the authors will be found in an Appendix.

The Foundation's director since 1974, Nils-Eric Svensson, begins the anthology with a description of the Foundation's establishment and development over the 25 years. As this paper shows, the Swedish Riksdag is the Foundation's principal. So it seemed appropriate to have two political scientists commence the cavalcade of research accounts. Nils Stjernquist describes research on the Swedish Riksdag, and Leif Lewin, using examples of several central issues in the Riksdag's work, discusses the driving forces impelling political decision-makers.

Erik Allardt (sociology), Torsten Hägerstrand (human geography), Bo Gustafsson (economic history) and Assar Lindbeck (economics) examine processes in modern society's development from the point of view of the respective disciplines. Sten Carlsson (history), Birgitta Odén (history) and Lars Furuland (literature) shed light on social changes as viewed from the humanities research horizon.

The next theme concerns the environment and is expounded by Erik Dahmén and Karl-Göran Mäler (economics), Anders Rapp (physical geography) and Jan-Erik Kihlström (biology). David Ingvar (neurophysiology) and Bengt Pernow (clinical physiology) review two important fields of medicine: alcohol usage and cardiovascular disease, fields that have a central position in the Foundation's research support.

These contributions are followed by papers from three researchers with behavioral science backgrounds. David Magnusson (psychology) presents his longitudinal studies of individual development from the early school years to adulthood. Torsten Husén (international education) and Kjell Härnqvist (educational psychology) provide examples of educational evaluation in international and longitudinal perspectives.

Another theme brings together Gunnar Fant (speech communication technology) who studies speech and voice within an interdisciplinary framework, Inger Rosengren (German), Sture Allén (computational linguistics) and Bengt Sigurd (general linguistics). They jointly provide a picture of aspects of contemporary language research.

The final contributions come from history of science. Svante Lindqvist describes the emergence of the new discipline "history of technology". Tore Frängsmyr addresses a general theme in the book: the internationalization of Swedish science.

As noted above, the authors approached their material in different ways. The topics also varied too much to permit coordination to any great extent. So the editors adopted a cautious line and concentrated mainly on achieving a certain degree of formal and typographical uniformity.

Eva Andersson edited the reference lists in the Appendix. Margareta Bulér helped us prepare the manuscripts for printing. The book's publisher, Krister Gidlund, is responsible for the graphical design.

The book appears both in a Swedish and an English version. The original papers were written in Swedish and translated by William P. Michael. Some papers refer to information not readily available to a non-Swedish audience. Many of the examples in the linguistic papers had to remain in Swedish. Hopefully, readers of the English version will still be able to follow the authors' lines of argument despite these complications.

Our warm thanks for devoted work and fine team effort by all the people who participated in the production of this book – the authors, the editorial and technical staff and the translator.

*Kjell Härnqvist    Nils-Eric Svensson*

*Nils-Eric Svensson*

# The Tercentenary Foundation's establishment and development

## Commemorative bequest

The Bank of Sweden, the world's oldest central bank, was founded in 1668. Thus, it was to celebrate its 300th anniversary in 1968. The Bank's board of directors (governors) wrote to the Riksdag's Committee on Banking on March 1, 1962 and suggested that an "anniversary this unique" should be "commemorated and celebrated in some manner commensurate with the Bank's position and long history".

As the Bank is a Parliament entity a parliament decision was necessary. One "attractive idea" was to "set aside a significant part of the Bank's profit" (in 1961) "as a major bequest in commemoration of the Bank of Sweden's 300-year existence while simultaneously promoting an important national objective".

The letter suggested that "the Committee on Banking propose to the Riksdag"... that the sum of SEK 250 000 000 ... be set aside for a special Bank of Sweden bequest for the promotion of scientific research related to Sweden ... and to give a special Riksdag committee the task of performing a study to result in a proposal to the Riksdag on detailed regulations concerning the bequest's management and utilization".

The letter also noted the following: "With a view to the special national character the Governors wish to give the proposed commemorative bequest, the Governors take the liberty of suggesting that the Prime Minister serve as the chairman of this committee".

The basic idea in the letter was that bequest capital be allocated as soon as possible to an independent fund managed by the Bank and then allowed to appreciate until 1968 when disbursement of the yield could commence.

The man who conceived the idea and the author of large parts of the letter, which displayed considerable understanding of research issues, was undoubtedly the Governor of the Bank of Sweden at the time, Per Åsbrink. As might be expected, the scientific community responded very positively to the proposal. Grants for research had indeed been awarded in the past, but the need for funds was regarded as far greater than the supply. For the 1962/63 fiscal year, a total of more than SEK 20 million (equivalent to about SEK 125 million in the 1989 value of money) were granted to government councils for research in the humanities, social sciences, medicine and natural sciences.

The annual yield on the proposed bequest was expected to be SEK 15-20 million. Such an amount would represent an enormous reinforcement of research resources. In view of the great need for research funds, many people felt that the yield on the bequest should be put to use at once and not deferred until the tercentenary year, 1968.

Several bills were brought before the Riksdag as a result of the proposed commemorative bequest. One of these bills advocated payment of the bequest capital, SEK 250 million, to the Ministry of Finance and deposited in a special government research fund. However, these bills were rejected. In a report issued on April 3, 1962, the Committee on Banking proposed that the Riksdag rule in accordance with the original suggestion.

The Riksdag reached a decision on April 11, 1962 after a debate lasting nearly three hours. The decision was not unanimous. One of the disputed issues concerned the appropriateness of an *independent* fund with resources large enough to finance research other than the programs supported by government grants. Some members pointed out that severe coordination and priority problems could develop. However, most Members of the Riksdag agreed that research was in need of an immediate increase in funding. The yield on the fund capital should therefore be utilized before the tercentenary year, 1968, it was felt.

The 1962 Riksdag ruling created prerequisites for the establishment of an independent "Bank of Sweden Tercentenary Fund". But a great many preparations remained before it could begin to support research.

## *Guidelines*

The Prime Minister Tage Erlander was appointed chairman of the committee that was to draw up guidelines for Fund activities. The committee had its first meeting on December 5, 1962. A total of six formal meetings were ultimately held, the last one on April 3, 1964.

The committee report submitted to the Riksdag on April 14, 1964 contained proposals on the Tercentenary Fund's aims, financial management, board of directors and administration. Special attention was devoted to the Fund's "incorporation in the total research support system and the drawing up of demarcation lines between various forms of support".

In the committee's view, it was important for the Fund's resources to be placed at the disposal of research in 1965. However, it felt that "... utilizing the entire allocation amount available the first year would entail considerable difficulties and risks".

As far as the aims of the Fund were concerned, the committee concurred with all the important points in the bequest proposal. Grants would be awarded without restriction to any particular subject field or type of costs. Activities were to be conducted with great flexibility, and no discipline would be "excluded from the possibility of receiving a grant from the Fund".

Major, long-term research projects and contacts with international research would be promoted. The committee assumed that the Fund's initial support would concentrate on "research aimed at expanding knowledge about the impact of technical, economic and social changes on the society and on individual citizens".

According to the committee, research should devote greater attention than hitherto to problems "related to the adaptation of society and individuals" to the drastic changes in life over "the past fifty years". It also supplied some examples of important research subjects, such as "job satisfaction", the "adaptation to occupational life and society", the "effect of social reforms on health" and certain issues concerning "criminality".

The need for studies dealing with the "position and circumstances of young people" was cited, as well as research in modern and political history and "in business administration, advertising psychology and advertising methodology". Research "concerning problems caused by the effect of modern technology on our natural resources, such as the effects of air and water pollution, preservation of flora and fauna and conservation practiced in a way satisfying e.g. the increasing need for recreational areas", was also mentioned.

The proposed aims for the Fund's activities were felt to be in close harmony with its original concept. "The idea of a fund, established as a result of the Riksbank's work on central economic issues, for support to research promoting and developing knowledge on the impact of ongoing changes in society is most appealing".

The general discussion on the emphasis in Fund activities advocated coordination with other research-support bodies. This probably seems natural enough in a small country like Sweden with limited staff and economic resources for research. However, the committee felt that many strong arguments indicated that this coordination should not be too far-reaching. Research funds should not be centralized too much but "be allocated by organizations competing with one another". So the Fund should have an independent position enabling it "to actively determine research needs in fields important from society's point of view". However, this was not to lead to any reduction in the standards of the scientific projects supported by the Fund.

The proposal suggested that the Bank of Sweden Tercentenary Fund be a foundation, in the legal sense of the word. It was to be led by a board of directors with "representatives of the Riksdag and the Bank of Sweden in numbers jointly giving them the majority". Scientists from different fields were also to be included. Periods of office would be limited to six years. The head of the fund's executive organization was to be a full-time "scholar with sound, all-round experience of research work".

The assessments and comments in the committee's report, as stated above, are also reflected in the draft bye-laws for the prospective Bank of Sweden Tercentenary Foundation.

The committee's report was studied by the Committee on Banking in the autumn of 1964. Prior to that, comments had been procured from a large number of Swedish research-support organizations. In every essential respect, the Committee followed the report proposals in its own report to the Riksdag dated November 24, 1964.

The Riksdag's ruling on the matter occurred on December 2nd after extensive debate, especially in the lower house. The issue attracting the greatest interest this time concerned the number of members on the Foundation's board of directors. The final number was two more than had been proposed. Demands were also made for e.g. more concrete objectives for Foundation activities. The committee's guidelines were felt to be too general in nature. However, the committee's guidelines were the ones finally used in the adopted bye-laws.

As a result of a ruling in December 1964, the independent Bank of Sweden Tercentenary Foundation became a reality.

## The initial years

According to the Riksdag ruling, the Foundation's board of directors was to consist of eleven persons, i.e. four representatives of scientific research, one representative of the Bank of Sweden and six representatives of the Riksdag, plus personal substitutes for all eleven. The chairperson and other board members were appointed on March 31, 1965.

The first board meeting was held on May 6, 1965. In addition to electing a deputy-chairperson, the board discussed the Foundation's work forms, including procedures for reviewing applications and selecting the first grant recipients that autumn. The board also received a report on the state of the Foundation's finances. The market value of its securities amounted to almost SEK 340 million (equivalent to about SEK 2 000 million in the 1989 value of money). The board also appointed a delegation with the task of preparing the employment of a chief executive officer for the Foundation and other requisite staff.

Grants were awarded for the first time at the board's second meeting on October 7, 1965. The board reviewed 21 applications seeking a total of about SEK 7 million. Two of these applications were awarded grants totalling SEK 0.3 million, one was rejected, eight were sent to the Swedish Council for Social Science Research for priority ranking and the others were tabled.

By the next meeting on December 3rd, applications requesting an additional SEK 8 million had arrived, SEK 2 million of which were approved (12 separate grants). So in the Foundation's first year, applications for more than SEK 15 million (equivalent to about SEK 85 million in the 1989 value of money) were submitted. SEK 2.2 million (equivalent to about

SEK 12 million in 1989) was approved. The following year, i.e. in 1966, 61 grants totaling more than SEK 16.5 million (nearly SEK 90 million in the 1989 value of money) were awarded.

Examination of the distribution of grants the first two years (a total of SEK 18.8 million) shows that about 55% went to social science and behavioral science research projects, 10% to the humanities and 30% to medicine, natural science and technology.

In addition, the Nobel Foundation was awarded a major grant enabling it to hold international symposia two or three times a year. (In 1979, this resource was made permanent through the establishment of a special symposium fund at the Nobel Foundation. The Knut and Alice Wallenberg Foundation and the Nobel Foundation itself contributed to this fund, in addition to the Foundation.)

The Swedish Academy of Engineering Sciences (IVA) also received a grant during the first year for the purpose of surveying and establishing contacts with scientific and technological activities in Japan.

Many of the projects receiving grants at the beginning of the Foundation's activities were large and lasted for several years. Most of these projects would probably have found it very hard to obtain funding elsewhere. The average size of awarded grants amounted to nearly SEK 85 000 (equivalent to about SEK 450 000 in the 1989 value of money) a year.

The following project examples should give some idea of the way Foundation resources were initially utilized. Only their titles (in English translation) are listed. They supply a rather good picture of the problems viewed as important in the middle of the 1960's and deemed accessible for scientific study. They also illustrate the wide-ranging nature of the Foundation's activities. Hardly any area was "excluded from the possibility of receiving a grant from the Foundation". Several of the projects will be described in special papers presented elsewhere in this volume.

*In the field of economic research, precedence was given to research on e.g.*
"The Development of Swedish Welfare from 1925 to 1960",
"Nordic Industrial Integration",
"The Problems of Regional Resource Allocation",
"Cost-Benefit Analyses of Labor Market Policy Measures",
"The Urbanization Process",
"Service Problems in Rural Areas",
"Natural Resources, Environment and Society".

*The following projects can serve to exemplify grant awards to the behavioral and social science fields:*
"Future Prospects of Stockholm's Youths",
"Social Structure and Social Change in the Nordic Countries",
"The Attitude of Workers to Work and Working Conditions in Various Technological Environments",
"Structure and Processes in the Swedish Trade Union Movement",
"Physical Work Capacity, Subjective Exertion and Mental Performance",
"Achievements in the Educational Systems of Different Countries",
"The Criminality of Foreigners",
"Municipal Subdivision – Municipal Self-Government",
"The Structure and Function of Swedish Political Parties".

*The following were some of the large projects in the humanities:*
"Computational Investigation of Newspaper Prose",
"Sweden During World War II",
"Sweden and America After 1860. Emigration, Remigration, Political and Social Debate",
"The Role of Scientists and Technicians in the Swedish Industrial Revolution",

"State and National Boundaries as Conflict-generating/ Contact-dissipating Factors",
"Socially Oriented Musicology".

\* *Some of the grants awarded to the projects in the medical, natural science and technical fields were as follows:*
"Measurement of Stress in Working Life",
"Initiative Program for Alcohol Research",
"Clinical and Experimental Studies of Addiction",
"Attempts to Prevent Myocardial Infarction",
"Links Between Mental Illness and Social Conditions and Changes",
"Primary Protein Production",
"Study of the Impact of Man's Activities on the Chemical Composition of Seabed Sediment and Sedimentation in the Göteborg Archipelago",
"The Hydrology of Lakes",
"Magnetic Containment of Hot, Ionised Gas",
"Man-Machine Speech Communication".

As previously noted, most of the listed projects would probably never have been conducted without the funds granted by the Foundation. They were too large and long-term for their time. Many were in the borderland between traditional disciplines. They therefore played a major role in the training of scholars in these fields and contributed to the emergence of new, important knowledge.

## Resource for Swedish research

Government grants to the research councils for sectors in which the Foundation mainly came to be active, i.e. social science, the humanities, medicine and natural science, amounted to more than SEK 42 million (SEK 3.2, 3.5, 17.4 and 18.2 million respectively) in the 1965/66 fiscal year. This amount is equivalent to about SEK 230 million in the 1989 value of money.

As far as private grants to research are concerned, only the Knut and Alice Wallenberg Foundation was awarding large grants at this time. This foundation awarded SEK 8 million in 1965 and SEK 11 million the following year (equivalent to SEK 45 and SEK 60 million respectively in 1989). Most of these funds were used for different purposes at universities.

At the beginning of its activities, the Tercentenary Foundation was of greatest importance to social and behavioral science research; this is still the case. The Swedish Council for Social Science Research (SFR) and the Swedish Council for Research in the Humanities (HFR) jointly disbursed SEK 6.7 million in 1965/66. During the same period, the Foundation awarded twice as much in grants to research in the fields covered by the SFR and HFR. So the additional funding made an important contribution.

Foundation grants, amounting to SEK 17-19 million a year (equivalent to SEK 85-90 million in 1989), were obviously viewed as a very considerable improvement in the funding of Swedish research. The Foundation became the largest independent research-support organization in Sweden.

Twenty-five years later, conditions are rather different. Government grants to the aforementioned research fields, the now merged Swedish Council for Research in the Humanities and Social Sciences (HSFR), the Swedish Medical Research Council (MFR) and the Swedish Natural Science Research Council (NFR) amounted to a total of SEK 720 million (SEK 125, 250 and 346 million respectively) in the 1989/1990 fiscal year, i.e. three times more, in real terms, than in 1965/66. The Wallenberg Foundation, which passed the Foundation in size in 1981, awarded SEK 164 million (also a tripling in real terms) in 1989. The same year, research grants awarded by the Foundation amounted to SEK 71 million (a real decline by about SEK 20 million compared to the initial years).

Thus, the economic importance of the Foundation's support to Swedish research is far different today (1990) than at the start of activities (1965). In addition to the national research councils, there are now a number of other government and non-government grant-giving bodies that finance research with similar objectives.

However, the demand for research grants is just as great as ever. Competition for grants from the Foundation has actually increased. This is because there are more researchers and research institutions. Modern society has become increasingly dependent on research. In view of this development, it is probably a good thing for society and researchers that research grants are not too heavily centralized but supplied "by organizations in competition with one another", one of the Erlander committee's arguments for giving the Foundation an independent position enabling it "to actively determine research needs in fields important from society's point of view".

## Competition for research funds

Figure 1 shows how the total amount of funds (nominal) sought from the Foundation changed from SEK 19 million/year (in 1966) to SEK 230 million (in 1989). The grants awarded over the same period increased from SEK 17 to 71 million a year, a change actually representing a decline. The sums expressed in the 1989 value of money roughly correspond to SEK 100 to 230 million (amount sought) and SEK 90 to SEK 71 (amount granted) respectively.

Figure 2 shows how competition for funds developed from 1965 to 1989. With the exception of the very first years, only about one-third of the amounts sought were granted. These figures apply to all the applications, i.e. both applications for continuation grants and applications for new research projects. Competition for new projects alone is shown from 1974. Only

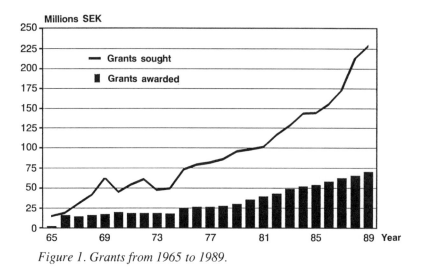

*Figure 1. Grants from 1965 to 1989.*

10-12% of the total sums sought for new grants were awarded. According to available statistics from other research-support organizations in Sweden and elsewhere, competition for Foundation grants is harder than for grants from any other organization. The Foundation's importance to research appears therefore to be as great today as it was at the Foundation's inception. In contrast to the government research councils, each of which active in a relatively narrow sector, the Foundation is to work in all sectors. And scientific standards are to be high.

The bye-laws prescribe, among other things, "that Foundation funds especially be used for supporting major, long-term projects" and that "no field of research is to be excluded from the possibility of receiving a Foundation grant".

During its 25-year existence, the Foundation has approved about 4 000 research grants. The total value of these grants amounts to about SEK 1 800 million in the 1989 value of money. The average value of a grant therefore amounted to about SEK 450 000 (also in the 1989 value of money).

About half of the approved grants were awarded to projects in the social sciences and behavioral sciences, one-fourth to

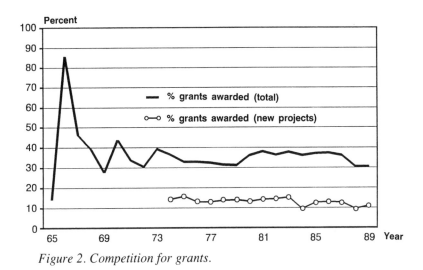

*Figure 2. Competition for grants.*

humanities and one-fourth to medical, natural science and technical disciplines. On the average, the financed research projects have lasted four years or more.

On the basis of these data it is fair to say that the guidelines ("major, long-term projects") laid down for the Foundation's activities have been followed.

These data also show that the Foundation has disbursed an average of more than SEK 70 million a year (in the 1989 value of money) in its 25 years of existence to date.

Figure 3 illustrates the magnitude of annual grants, in both nominal and real (in the 1989 value of money) terms from 1965 to 1989. After being on a real level of SEK 85-90 million a year the first years, the size of grants declined considerably up to 1974. Thereafter, it remained on about the same level (in real terms). I will explain the reasons for this real decline in the next section.

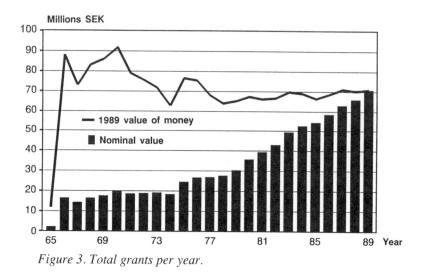

*Figure 3. Total grants per year.*

## Capital management

According to the original proposal, the bequest sum was to be deposited in an independent fund to be administered by the Bank of Sweden. The bequest was to be invested in the same kind of securities that are a normal part of the Bank's portfolio. The Riksdag's 1962 ruling also transferred a special bond portfolio with a book value of SEK 250 million (equivalent to more than SEK 1 500 million in the 1989 value of money). The market value of this portfolio was reported to be SEK 340 million (equivalent to about SEK 2 000 million) at the board's first meeting in 1965.

Yield on the bond portfolio, i.e. interest on the securities, was the asset the Foundation would be able to use for awarding grants to research. The first few years, yield amounted to SEK 17-19 million a year, an amount equivalent to SEK 95 million in the 1989 value of money (peaking at SEK 98 million in 1967 and 1968).

As Figure 3 shows, the Foundation awarded grants of the same nominal magnitude until 1974, i.e. around SEK 19-20 million a year. In real terms, however (i.e. in the 1989 value of money), awards dropped from SEK 92 million to SEK 63 million). This was because e.g. investments were in bonds with long maturities and a low yield. In many instances, interest rates were only one-fourth of the rates prevailing in the middle of the 1970's. The real value of revenue dropped continuously as a result of annual cost rises. The market value of the portfolio declined to the same degree as interest rates rose on newly floated bonds. New acquisitions were only made when some bond matured.

At the 1973/74 turn of the year, the situation was deemed to be highly unsatisfactory. The Foundation's vice-chairperson at the time, the Governor of the Bank of Sweden Krister Wickman, therefore proposed that the Bank transfer SEK 100 million to the Foundation for the purpose of improving the latter's real grant capacity for the next few years. This was also the case. Bonds with a book value of SEK 100 million were transferred in the late spring of 1974 following a ruling by the Riksdag.

The improvement was only expected to be temporary. The Foundation's interest revenue did indeed rise, and grants for research could increase in nominal terms. However, the distance to the real level of the initial years remained considerable. So the Foundation's future was discussed by the board on a number of occasions. Proposals for long-term improvements in grant disbursement on the real level were submitted to the Bank of Sweden in the autumn of 1976. As a result of two Riksdag bills, bonds with a book value of SEK 100 million were then transferred to the Foundation in 1978.

But even after this capital injection, the Foundation's long-term problems remained. However, the new capital did give the Foundation a respite for the next few years. This respite was also utilized in different ways.

Instead of immediately utilizing all of the increased yield, the board decided to increase grant awards only in step with general cost rises. So until further notice, grant awards were locked to the real level of the preceding few years. And in order to keep grants on this level as long as possible, the board decided to transfer unallocated money to a grant reserve fund. Withdrawals could subsequently be made from this fund if interest revenue dropped below the specified grant level in a few years, as was expected.

The board also decided to budget revenue and costs for the same budget year from 1982. Previously, a given year's revenue had been utilized for grants awarded the following year. The decision made it possible for the Foundation to transfer a full year's revenue to the grant reserve (buffer) fund. The idea was to achieve an annual grant-giving capacity on about the same level as in 1980 over the next 7-8 years. Figure 3 shows that we achieved this goal. From 1980 to 1989, grants for research remained on virtually the same real level.

However, measures other than those described so far were needed in order to protect the Foundation's long-term support to research. A number of different proposals were submitted during discussions over the years. The primary aim of most of these proposals was to restore the foundation bequest's real value and the grant distribution capacity of the initial years.

Following highly constructive and committed efforts by the Governor of the Bank of Sweden, Bengt Dennis, vice-chairperson of the Foundation at the time, the Bank of Sweden's governors were able to submit a proposal in the spring of 1987 that would enable the Foundation to achieve the desired objectives. According to the proposal, the Bank would buy the Foundation's bonds for SEK 600 million (an amount roughly equal to their market value) at turn of the year and, following a ruling by the Riksdag, inject an additional SEK 900 million in cash. From 1st January 1988, the Foundation would be allowed to manage its assets independently. The Riksdag ruled in accordance with this proposal.

New bye-laws were drawn up, adopted by the board and approved by the Riksdag in December 1987. The new bye-laws increased the number of board members to twelve, two of whom with special experience of asset management. Thereafter, the Bank of Sweden would not be represented on the board.

In the middle of May 1988, SEK 900 million were transferred to the Foundation. Thus, Foundation capital amounting to SEK 1 500 million could be listed in the 1988 Annual Report. This sum is roughly equivalent to the 1962 bequest capital of SEK 250 million. The real value of the bequest donation was accordingly restored.

Investment regulations in the new bye-laws are highly modern and functional. In principle, they permit any kind of investment deemed to be in accordance with rational, efficient assets management. This creates prerequisites for retention of the Foundation's research support on the same level as in the past few years. It is then up to the Foundation to make the most of things.

Our goals for the next few years are to increment annual research grants by general cost increases, if possible, and to transfer enough funds from revenue so Foundation capital can retain its real value. We do not believe that the grant-giving capacity of the Foundation's initial years is attainable in the foreseeable future. Any additional capital transferred to the Foundation would of course change the picture. The new bye-laws allow the Foundation to accept donations from companies and private persons.

## The Foundation's present importance

As previously shown, the Foundation's economic importance as a research-support organization has declined over the past 25 years. But has its importance also declined in other respects? In my view, this has not been the case. Here are some of the reasons why:

\* Information based on scientific research is playing an increasingly important role in a society whose complexity is increasing in many respects.

\* International collaboration and the exchange of knowledge are increasing. The number of scholars, specialties and research institutions is greater today than ever before.

\* New research methods and research equipment are constantly being introduced. New, important problem areas (often multidisciplinary) are constantly emerging.

\* The cost of research in certain fields is increasing more rapidly than in other activities of benefit to society.

\* For the results of research to be transformed into practical reform work and political decisions, representatives of other activities in society must acquire greater insight into and greater understanding of research's conditions, needs and opportunities.

Even this incomplete listing of observations make it easy to see that the need for research and research grants is not likely to decline in the future. Quite the opposite! Funds for scientific research should continue to be supplied "by organizations in competition with one another" (the Erlander committee's recommendation in conjunction with the Foundation's establishment).

Even if the Foundation's grant-giving capacity is less today, relatively speaking, than 25 years ago, it remains large enough to have an impact of the Swedish research community. In 1989, 222 research grants averaging more than SEK 300 000 were approved.

Most research-support organizations operate in relatively narrow sectors. But the Foundation supports and promotes research in all scientific disciplines. People with differing specialties participate in the reviewing procedure assigning priority to all grant decisions. This facilitates the evaluation of and support to new or multidisciplinary research fields.

The advantage of multiple grant-giving organizations with different staff constellations is that no single scientific philosophy can ever predominate. The Foundation's board has included representatives of many scientific disciplines over the years. In addition to scholars, the board also has members with special experience of asset management and members of the Riksdag. Every three years, half of the members of boards and priority assignment committees are up for election for six-year terms of office.

To my knowledge, no other Swedish research organization has a board of directors whose majority consists of top-level people outside the scientific sphere. Experience suggests that this circumstance has opened up completely new opportunities for a valuable, multifaceted exchange of experience between representatives of research and representatives of other, important activities in society. In the past 25 years, 149 people, 72 of whom scholars, 64 members of the Riksdag and 13 economic experts, have served on the Foundation's board and priority assignment committees. This spread in experience and periodic renewal should promote all-round, top-quality decisions firmly anchored in realities of today.

Organizations operate within different international contact networks. In contrast to the position for government research councils, the Foundation has its international contacts mainly with private or non-governmental, grant-making institutions. This encourages the acquisition of information and experience that might otherwise be missed. Contacts have been extensive in recent years. Agreements on the co-financing of certain projects and on the financing of the mutual exchange of scholars are examples of activities in this context.

Any review of the Foundation's annual reports, published each year in Swedish and English, will disclose many examples of activities in which the Foundation has strived to achieve the exchange of knowledge and experience between scholars and other interests in society. For example, the Foundation has organized a number of special committees over the years. Their task has been to shed light on research needs and propose measures for the purpose of stimulating scientific research and the exchange of information in important but neglected problem fields. The groups have consisted of scholars from relevant disciplines and representatives of important public interests.

Most of the activities conducted by the special committees have also been documented in the Foundation's publications series. The publications comprise research overviews or reports from symposia and conferences. A cumulative list, now comprising 36 publications, is found in each year's Annual Report from the Foundation.

The composition of the special committees has been of major importance to the impact of the research results obtained and to the transformation of those results into reform work. One example is the committee on taxation research that operated from 1979 to 1986. Its work resulted in comprehensive taxation research at different Swedish universities and in different disciplines. The contents or results of this research were passed on in a natural way to relevant recipients. After the committee concluded its work, several of the committee members became involved in the reform and planning work conducted by the Ministry of Finance that ultimately led to an autumn 1989 proposal on a major tax reform.

In various contexts, the Swedish Riksdag has expressed opinions similar to the above. The view of the Foundation's Board can be summarized as follows:

* The Foundation has played and should continue to play an important role for Swedish research in the future.
* It is important for research to be financed by different sources. The expansion of government research councils does not mean that the Foundation's importance is less now than at its inception. The tasks assigned in 1964 are as important today as then.

* The Foundation's multidisciplinary activities, its independent position and the board's composition are unparalleled. It is a unique contact point for scholars, members of the Riksdag and other representatives of important public interests.

* Restoration of the Foundation's original grant-making capacity should be possible in time. The Foundation would then improve its ability to make active contributions to the promotion of high-level Swedish research.

*Nils Stjernquist*

# The Riksdag from
# a research point of view

## In the beginning was the Arboga Meeting

Back in our good old school days, we learned that the Arboga
Meeting in 1435 was Sweden's first Riksdag and that Swedish
representative government was of ancient date, something we
had every right to be and were proud of. So the Riksdag planned
a magnificent commemoration of its 500th anniversary for
1935.

But all good things come to an end! Just before celebrations
were due to start, two Swedish historians belonging to different
schools, Gottfrid Carlsson and Erik Lönnroth, independently
arrived at the conclusion that the famous assembly in Arboga
was no parliament. However, preparations for the commemoration had advanced too far to be stopped, a thought no one
seriously considered anyway. The culmen in celebrations was
in Arboga itself on 27th May 1935. H.M. the King, the government, Riksdag members, all resplendent in uniforms or morning
coats and top hats, travelled from Stockholm in two special
trains to this historic meeting place. There, the famous history
professor and vice-chancellor of the University of Stockholm,
Sven Tunberg, held a "grandiose speech on Engelbrekt and the
Riksdag", as it was described in one contemporary newspaper
account. Engelbrekt was depicted as the creator of the Swedish
Riksdag.

## What exactly is the Riksdag?

In fact, a question about what was the "first Riksdag" is rather pointless, as Herman Schück (1987) showed. The Swedish Riksdag, like parliaments in other countries, evolved over a long period of time. A "Riksdag" is actually a matter of definition. This definition depends on standards and criteria. A view previously held was that the Four Estates, as well as the entire realm, should be represented at one, i.e. even the peasants. This was where the Arboga meeting fell short of the mark. It should be noted that the 1319 election of a king and the summons issued by Magnus Eriksson in Lund on 29th August 1359 to an assembly in Kalmar on 13th October the same year have been cited in discussions on the first Riksdag.

However, other criteria should be met in defining a "Riksdag", as Herman Schück emphasized. Having all the Estates and the entire realm represented is obviously important (cf. Jansson 1989). But is this enough? Shouldn't a certain degree of competence for the legislature be another criterion? This was the case relatively early in dynastic matters and in foreign and defense policies. However, rulings on taxes had long been made at regional sessions.

Moreover, the legislature should have the right to take initiatives and participate in decision-making, not merely a right to attend assemblies and listen to proceedings. In this respect, circumstances varied from one era to another.

If regular sessions of the legislature is another criterion, then there was no true Riksdag until the 1660's, the preview of the Age of Liberty in the 18th century.

If democratic representation based directly on the citizenry and not the Estates nor other special interests is the criterion, we must look for a Riksdag in a period after the constitutional reform in 1866. When the criterion is equality in the form of universal suffrage, no such Riksdag held a session until 1922.

If the assumption is that the Swedish people are sovereign on election day in the sense that they elect all members of the Riksdag at one and the same election, then this situation did not occur until the election to the unicameral Riksdag whose first session was in 1971.

The present brief review, made on the basis of answers to several questions, can serve to illustrate the difficulties in designating a year in which it is proper to say that the Swedish parliament was born. Claiming that the Arboga Meeting was the beginning of Swedish Riksdag is wrong. However, the statement "In the beginning was Arboga" is at least correct from one point of view, i.e. if the issue is considered from the Riksdag research perspective (cf. Holmberg and Esaiasson 1988). The 500th anniversary of the Meeting should be celebrated, it was felt,with a major commemorative work on the Swedish Riksdag. This triggered intense research on the institution.

## Older research on the Riksdag

Earlier research on the Riksdag was relatively limited. Historians had indeed published reviews analyzing the role of the Riksdag in various situations but hardly in any systematic manner. However, important contributions had been made by e.g. Wilhelm Carlgren ("Riksdagsutskott före 1680 med särskild hänsyn till sekreta utskottet", 1909 – Riksdag committees before 1680 with special regard to the secret committee), Erik Naumann ("Om sekreta utskottet under den tidigare frihetstiden 1719-1734", 1911 – On the secret committee in the earlier Age of Liberty 1719-1734) and Fredrik Lagerroth ("Frihetstidens författning", 1915 – The Age of Liberty's constitution).

Political scientists had only occasionally studied the Riksdag. The far and away most important contributions were Sigfrid Wallengren's works on the subject ("Tvåkammarsystemet i belysning av den danska författningsrevisionen 1912-15", 1915 – The bicameral system in the light of the Danish constitutional revision 1912-15; "Förstakammarfrågan inför svenska riksdagen efter 1866" – The Upper House issue in the Riksdag after 1866; "Första kammaren i nutida författningar", 1919 – The Upper House in contemporary constitutions). The thesis which Carl Malmroth, subsequently a minister of defense in the Trygger government 1923-24, published in 1900: "Kamrarnas inbördes ställning i stater med tvåkammarsystem" (The interrelationship of parliamentary houses in states with bicameral systems) is typical of its time.

From the point of view of research on the Riksdag, comments on the constitution, and other documents published by jurists, were even more important. However, the first commentary on the 1809 constitution was written by a physician, Pehr Gustaf Cederschjöld, initially a lecturer in anatomy and teacher of pastoral medicine at Lund, subsequently active in Stockholm as a highly regarded obstetrician. He wrote a widely used "Handbok för barnmorskor" (Handbook for midwives) published in seven editions from 1822 to 1868. He was a member of the Riksdag from 1815 to 1845 and played a major role there. To assist his colleagues, he published a "Handbok för riksdagsmän" (Handbook for Members of the Riksdag) in 1822 (final edition in 1860) and "Försök att bringa Sweriges grundlagar i system; med anmärkningar, till hjelpreda för riksdagsmän" (Attempt to systematize Sweden's constitution; plus comments, as an aid for Members of the Riksdag) that he published in 1828.

The most well-known name in the middle of the 19th century was Christian Naumann, attached to the office of the Peasants Estate during Riksdag meetings in 1834-35 and 1840-41. He was the one who produced the basic material underlying the 1809 constitution, material referred to as the "Håkanson proposal", thereby dispelling some of the myths about Hans Järta's role in the development of this constitution, not the least through Järta's own promotional efforts. Naumann was a Lund professor of constitutional law and law relating to legal procedures. He thence served for many years as a supreme court justice in Stockholm. In 1854 he published an annotated commentary to the constitution (3rd edition in 1866). However, his magnum opus is "Sveriges statsförfattningsrätt" (Sweden's constitutional law) 1-4 (1847-1874; new edition 1879-1884). His "Svenska statsförfattningens historiska utveckling" (The Swedish constitution's historical development) in 1864 with new editions in 1866 and 1875 is noteworthy.

Herman Ludvig Rydin was active in the latter part of the 19th century. He was a professor (in Uppsala) of constitutional law, canon law, the rules of war and international law from 1855 to 1890 and a member of the Riksdag from 1867 to 1890 (with only one minor break). Rydin also enjoyed a considerable reputation as a constitutional expert. He wrote an interesting article in the Svensk Tidskrift in 1876 "Om det parlamentariska styrelsesättet och dess förenlighet med svenskt statsskick" (On parliamentary government and its compatibility with the Swedish constitution). His main work is "Svenska riksdagen, dess sammansättning och verksamhet" (The Swedish Riksdag, its composition and activities), 1-2 (1873-1879). This became a standard work.

The 1920's witnessed the appearance of two new commentators on constitutional matters: Robert Malmgren, a Lund professor of constitutional law, administrative law, canon law and international law, and his Uppsala colleague Carl Axel Reuterskiöld, the latter also a member of the Riksdag for the Agrarian Party and long-term chairperson of the Committee on the Constitution. The first edition of Malmgren's comments on the constitution appeared in 1921. The work was ultimately published in eleven editions, the latter editions by other publishers and the most recent edition in 1971. It became a widely read book on the subject. Reuterskiöld's comments were published in three parts from 1924 to 1926. Second editions of parts 1 and 3 were published in 1934 and 1937 respectively. Despite the work's stringent legal nature, Reuterskiöld included a considerable amount of information on practice, so the work remains important to research. In addition to his comments on the constitution, Malmgren published an outstanding book on Swedish constitutional law, "Sveriges författning" 1-2 (1929-1941); second editions of 1 and 2:1 were published (1945-1952).

## *500 years since the Arboga Meeting: Commemorative work in 1935*

It was in the 1920's that the Arboga Meeting entered the picture in the history of Riksdag research. When planning for a major commemorative work began, it was soon found that information on the celebrant, i.e. the Riksdag, was not merely patchy but even obsolete in many important historical, political science and constitutional law respects.

Work got off to an early start. The initiative came from Värner Rydén, a primary school teacher and Minister of Education in the Edén government 1917-19. As early as 1925, he introduced a bill in the Lower House on the publication of a large, historical and constitutional work on the Swedish Riksdag. Rydén wrote as follows in the bill:

"The 500th anniversary of the first known Riksdag in Swedish history will occur in 1935. As we know, representatives of the Nobility, Clergy, Burghers and Peasants gathered, during the Engelbrekt's liberating uprising, at a national assembly in Arboga in 1435. As far as we can determine from available historical records, the Peasants as an Estate were there represented at a Swedish national assembly for the first time. ...

"Apart from the English parliament, the Swedish Riksdag is the world's oldest surviving legislature. In every essential respect, it has developed on the basis of Swedish ideals and represents, by virtue of numerous remarkable features, a subject of particular interest to historians, experts in constitutional law, politicians and statesmen. Since the Swedish Riksdag's emergence is linked to one of our history's most precious memories, the event most properly designated as the birth of Swedish national awareness, commemorating the 500th anniversary of the Arboga assembly in a suitable manner would be only right and proper."

In Rydén's view, the "most important measure" would be to create a "truly standard work on the Swedish Riksdag". "There could be no more worthwhile way" for the Riksdag to "celebrate the 500th anniversary of its existence than by the realization of such a work". Rydén pointed to the disparate and inadequate picture provided by available research.

The Riksdag decided, after a proposal by the Committee on Banking, to have the National Debt Commissioners study the matter. In a memo sent to the Committee and published in its report, Värner Rydén sketched a plan for the work. It is remarkable to note how this plan served as the basis of subsequent efforts. The study ordered by the Riksdag was conducted by a committee chaired by the chairperson of the National Debt Commissioners, Karl Hildebrand. The results were submitted to the Committee on Banking the following year. At the Committee's suggestion, the Riksdag gave the National Debt Commissioners the task of publishing a historical and political science work, primarily in accordance with the study's plan, on the Swedish Riksdag.

The National Debt Commissioners immediately appointed an editorial committee with the county governor and former prime minister, Nils Edén, in charge of and responsible for the editorial work.

The editorial committee recruited a large number of the country's leading historians, political scientists and experts on constitutional law as contributors. The Riksdag's siren call was irresistible. However, some changes were made. The former prime minister and minister of finance, Rickard Sandler, had been asked to write about the preparation of a budget but had more important things to think about after becoming foreign minister in the autumn of 1932. As a result of increasing involvement in the work of the National Unemployment Commission, Arthur Thomson, whose assignment had been to write about compromises and joint voting, was forced to relinquish this task to someone else.

Edén carried out his assignment with energy and scrupulousness. Fredrik Lagerroth, who produced almost two volumes on his own, told the author of these lines that Edén and he sat day after day on opposite sides of a desk while Edén closely edited page after page in Lagerroth's manuscript. The two men never became on a first name basis and unfailingly addressed one another with the titles "governor" or "professor".

Fifteen of the 17 volumes had been completed by the anniversary year, 1935.

It should be noted that Edén somehow found time to write an excellent, 332-page summary in the book "Den svenska riksdagen under femhundra år" (The Swedish Riksdag over 500 years).

The commemorative work bears the title "Sveriges riksdag, historisk och statsvetenskaplig framställning" (Sweden's Riksdag, a historical and political science presentation). It is divided into two sections: one section deals with the Riksdag's history up to 1865 (volumes 1-8) and one section deals with the Riksdag from 1866 (volumes 9-17).

It is generally agreed that the commemorative collection maintains a consistently high standard. Several of the volumes remain standard works, for example Fredrik Lagerroth's analysis of the parliamentary system during the Age of Liberty, Georg Andrén's depiction of the bicameral system's emergence and development, Nils Herlitz's analysis of the Riksdag's financial power and Edvard Thermænius' pioneering work on the Riksdag parties.

The 17-volume work never became a best-seller. It was too compact and scholarly. But it was of considerable and lasting importance to our knowledge of the Swedish Riksdag's history, operations and procedures up to the middle of the 1930's. However, the absence of footnotes and references was a problem for scholars. To increase its usefulness, a comprehensive index volume, i.e. volume 18, prepared by the Riksdag's chief librarian Lars Frykholm, was published 30 years later.

## Bicameral Riksdag 100 years old; commemoration in 1966

But times insist on changing. Over the years, the knowledge acquired on the Riksdag up to the middle of the 1930's was accorded increasingly limited importance. Moreover, historical and political science research constantly polished, refined, altered and amended the picture depicted by the commemorative volumes. The elucidation of parliamentarism (in Sweden in particular and even in other countries) which had long been pursued in Uppsala under the leadership of Axel Brusewitz and a program of election research conducted at the Department of Political Science in Göteborg in the 1950's under the leadership of Jörgen Westerståhl, Bo Särlvik and (subsequently) Sören Holmberg were of major importance. However, this research scarcely touched on the Riksdag's operations and procedures.

A new anniversary was needed as an "excuse" for bringing Riksdag research up to date. No anniversary of the Arboga assembly was conveniently imminent. And waiting until the assembly's 550th anniversary in 1985 did not seem feasible. So the centennial of the bicameral system became the "excuse". The initiative came from Hemming Sten, at one time a radical socialist but now a social-democratic member of the Riksdag from Gävle and a person with an intense interest in the roots of representative government. He got off to an early start. In 1954, he introduced a bill in the Upper House suggesting that the Riksdag prepare some appropriate commemoration of the constitutional reform's centennial. The bicameral Riksdag had indeed achieved a notable age but Sten was convinced that the bicameral system was likely to survive until its 100th birthday. He proved to be right.

Hemming Sten's idea – conveyed in the form of a proposal – was the publication of a concentrated chronicle on the work of the bicameral Riksdag during its 100 years, a chronicle which would report on the Riksdag's contributions to social developments. So his intention was not to supplement the commemorative work from the 1930's. The Committee on Banking agreed that the centennial should be celebrated in some way. The Riksdag, at the Committee's suggestion, gave the National Debt Commissioners the task of investigating the "forms" in which the centennial should be commemorated.

Two years later, the National Debt Commissioners appointed a committee including the Speakers of both houses. The committee really took its time. Four years later it submitted a proposal on the publication of a far more comprehensive work than Hemming Sten had envisaged. A memo prepared by the political science professor and Riksdag member, Elis Håstad, and subsequently revised by his colleague in both respects, Gunnar Heckscher, served as the basis of the proposal. At the suggestion of the Committee on Banking, the Riksdag decided, in principle, to adopt the proposed program. The former Chancellor of the Swedish Universities and county governor, Arthur Thomson, assisted by the lower house's secretary, Sune K. Johansson, was appointed editor.

The aim was to supplement the old commemorative work in different respects. However, the perspective was broadened, as the new title, "Samhälle och riksdag" (Society and Riksdag), shows. The editor pursued his work with great diligence and efficiency, and all the volumes, apart from the index volume, were ready in time for the anniversary on 12th May 1966. It was celebrated in the Stockholm Concert Hall with speeches by H.M. The King, the Prime Minister, the Archbishop and Speakers of both houses. The festivities were concluded with a banquet in the Blue Hall of the Stockholm City Hall.

The 1966 commemorative work comprised five volumes. A sixth volume was originally planned. It was to have described the development of parliamentarism. But nothing came of it. The author assigned the task, Gunnar Gerdner, passed away in 1964. Finding a replacement for him in the brief amount of time left proved to be impossible.

## 550th anniversary of the Arboga Meeting: 1985 commemorative book

The years passed quickly, and many things happened in and to the Swedish Riksdag. A new electoral system and a unicameral Riksdag were introduced in 1969. The first unicameral Riksdag held its initial session in 1971. In 1974, Sweden acquired a new constitution and a new Riksdag Act. In addition, a great many general political prerequisites were changed.

Research was unable to keep up or was preoccupied with other subjects. One foreign observer noted to his surprise that Swedish political science, even though highly developed, did not accord the Riksdag much interest (Arter 1984). A number of studies were conducted by the committees dealing with the constitutional revision, but these studies were generally "slanted" within the examined framework. The situation was unsatisfactory to say the least.

However, the Arboga Meeting once again extended a helping hand. 1985 would mark the 550th anniversary of that meeting. As before, a commemoration initiative was in the form of a bill, this time an all-party bill in 1982 signed by all eleven members from Västmanland County with Olle Göransson from Arboga as the first name and main "actor". The bill's authors suggested that the Riksdag take the necessary steps to commemorate the Riksdag's 550th anniversary in Arboga in 1985. They dutifully pointed out that historical research "questioned" whether the Arboga Meeting really had been a Riksdag. But the tradition of citing Arboga as the "birthplace of Swedish democracy" was powerful, and it was felt that the democratic system's genesis should be celebrated in Arboga.

But the idea was rejected. The Standing Committee on the Constitution said no on rather formal grounds: "The nature of the issue is such that it can be considered by the Speaker without a particular assignment from the Riksdag." There was no debate on the matter in the House. This happened just before Christmas

1982 and did not generate much holiday cheer in Västmanland County. Even some people in Arboga itself were doubtful about taking on the responsibilities a commemoration might entail.

But no one "threw in the towel". Olle Göransson had other options. He was a member of the Social-Democratic party's Riksdag group steering committee and got Olof Palme interested in the matter. He had also been the chairperson of RIFO (an association of members of the Riksdag and university people) for many years and, as a result, had close contacts with the scientific community. He discussed the idea of a commemorative book with the director of the Bank of Sweden Tercentenary Foundation, Nils-Eric Svensson. The latter, in turn, took up the matter with the secretary of the Council for Research in the Humanities and Social Sciences, Pär-Erik Back, who promised, after some hesitation, to write a memo on a commemorative book.

Back's memo is dated 8th March 1983. It outlines a commemorative book in two parts. The first part would deal with the Riksdag from its earliest days to 1950. The second part would cover the period thereafter. The Riksdag's Speaker the Rt. Hon. Ingemund Bengtsson, Pär-Erik Back, Olle Göransson and Nils-Eric Svensson met the same day as the memo's date. The Speaker was in favor of a commemorative work, provided the Foundation took on the job.

Not much time was available, but things moved quickly. Only two days later, the Foundation's board of directors decided to "appoint a reference committee to investigate, in collaboration with the Speaker, Olle Göransson, Pär-Eric Back and Nils-Eric Svensson, the possibility of producing a book, based on research, on the Swedish Riksdag, to commemorate the 550th anniversary of the Arboga Riksdag in 1435". Each of the parties with members on the Foundation's board would be represented on the reference committee.

The author of these lines was invited to serve as the editor of this commemorative book. An informal meeting with Nils-Eric

Svensson, Pär-Eric Back and two professors of history took place on 21st June. It was then apparent that coming to grips with the Riksdag's functions and procedures over the past few decades would not be possible without comprehensive studies. Something was needed to stimulate research here, but the results of this research would not be available by 1985. It was also apparent, as the historians pointed out, that there were gaps in our knowledge even regarding earlier times. But in general, it was felt that the publication of a commemorative book would be possible by 1985, although based on existing research findings.

Work on the Riksdag's history was the most urgent task. Collaborators were selected by the summer of 1983. For the period up to 1921, we were able to recruit the historians of primary interest, viz. Herman Schück, Göran Rystad, Michael F. Metcalf and Sten Carlsson. I accepted the task of writing about the period after 1920. It is unusual to note that one of these authors is an American, proof as much as anything of the interest in Swedish history in other countries.

The formal decision on publication of the commemorative book was made by the Foundation's board of directors on 12th October. On 22nd November the next year, the Foundation's board of directors appointed an editorial committee, chaired by the Riksdag's Speaker, and with the Riksdag's chief administrator Gunnar Grenfors plus representatives of all Riksdag parties as members.

Olle Göransson got what he wanted. A commemorative book on the Riksdag, "Riksdagen genom tiderna" (The Riksdag through the ages) was published – and on schedule too. So there was an anniversary ceremony in Arboga on 24th May 1985, attended in the same way as the event 50 years earlier by H.M. The King, members of the government and the Riksdag (all conveyed by a special train from Stockholm), although participants were more mundanely dressed this time than in 1935. Arboga was again at center stage. Speeches were held by the chairperson of the municipal council, the King and the Speaker and the Prime Minister. The speeches made extensive mention of medieval Arboga. However, the Middle Ages were superseded in the afternoon by the present day. The defense industry demonstrated its activities in Arboga while Viggen fighter aircraft overhead put on a display no one could avoid hearing. When it was time for the guests to leave Arboga, many of them were flown to Stockholm-Arlanda Airport, like airborne commandos, in two of the Royal Swedish Air Force's Hercules transport planes.

The "Riksdagen genom tiderna" was published two years later in an English-language version, translated and edited by Michael F. Metcalf, under the title "The Riksdag, a History of the Swedish Parliament". In April 1988, the Foundation held a symposium in Stockholm on the book. It was attended by a number of experts on parliamentary history from various countries. The lectures were published in the report "The Riksdag in an International Perspective" (Bank of Sweden Tercentenary Foundation 1989:1).

## Study of Parliament Group

As things were, it seemed natural for the Foundation to assume responsibility not only for publishing the commemorative book but even to encourage scientific research on the present Riksdag's operations and procedures. On 12th October 1983, at the same meeting at which the board decided to commission the commemorative book, the Foundation appointed a study group for "Research on the Riksdag's operations and procedures". It was chaired by the Foundation's director and had six members of the Riksdag and three scholars as members.

The study group decided that an appropriate starting point would be to convene a meeting (ultimately held on 17th January 1984) for general discussions by members of the Riksdag and political scientists. A memo, written by me, on appropriate subjects for research served as the basis of discussions. At a meeting on 6th February 1984, the study group reached one important decision. The group would not strive to achieve an all-encompassing analysis of the field but would concentrate on encouraging research viewed as being particularly important. The group also agreed that grant applications would be processed by the Foundation in the usual manner.

There was no difficulty in identifying important research tasks. But recruiting suitable scholars proved to be more difficult. The shortage of well-trained scholars was even greater than the shortage of funds. This circumstance was not unique to Swedish political science but also applied to broad sectors of the Swedish research community. All because society's research needs have grown!

The study group launched a number of research projects, viz. "The Riksdag and mass-media" (led by Folke Johansson, Göteborg), "The Riksdag, elections and representative democracy" (led by Sören Holmberg, Göteborg), "Social development and consensus democracy, problem perception and strategies for conflict resolution in Sweden's Riksdag in the 1970's and 1980's" (led by Lars-Göran Stenelo, Lund) and "The Riksdag and organized interests" (led by Leif Lewin, Uppsala). The intention is also for Magnus Isberg to begin a project in the near future on the party groups in the Riksdag. At some later date, Björn von Sydow will probably commence a project on parliamentarism in Sweden.

A comparison of ongoing research on the Riksdag's operations and procedures with studies previously published, the 1935 commemorative work in particular but even the 1966 work, might prove to be fruitful. New techniques and methods are now being used, such as polling, interviews, computerized data processing, analysis of variance and correlation, and there is greater general awareness of methods and theory. This rather accurately reflects developments in political science. By the same token, relatively little remains of the legal issues, their importance to policies and interest in the Riksdag's operations. The committee's original planning also included studies of the Riksdag's legislative powers, budgeting powers and supervisory powers plus the procedures of the unicameral Riksdag. In all these areas, striking changes have occurred in recent decades: framework legislation, designation of objectives instead of concrete legal provisions, program budgets, framework budgets, public committee hearings (Johansson 1989), the scrutiny work of the Standing Committee on the Constitution (Fiskesjö 1987) and changes in the work of committees and the legislature. My hope is that studies of these fields will be able to start once the ongoing studies no longer encumber the Foundation.

I might add that the study group and the Foundation had a number of prominent former members of the Riksdag describe their "experiences, recollections and lessons" in a series of programs called "Politik och riksdagsarbete" (Politics and Riksdag work). They were held in the Riksdag building at meetings to which all members of the Riksdag were invited. Lecturers in this series have been: former Speakers Ingemund Bengtsson and Torsten Bengtson, the former ministers Erik Holmqvist, Svante Lundkvist, Torsten Nilsson and Nils G. Åsling, the former party leaders Gunnar Helén, C.-H. Hermansson and Jarl Hjalmarson and the former county governor Astrid Kristensson. In conjunction with the publication of their respective biographies, Olof Ruin held a talk about the late Prime Minister Tage Erlander, and Paul Lindblom and Nine Christine Jönsson spoke about the late Minister of Social Affairs Gustav Möller. The sessions were popular and well-attended. The lectures will be published.

The study group for "research on the Riksdag's operations and procedures" is by no means unique. It has an equivalent in the parliaments of many other countries. For example, the Swedish group is in touch with the Study of Parliament Group in the British House of Commons.

Study groups like the present one were an interesting innovation, broadening the Foundation's role. The Foundation no longer only passively awaited the arrival of applications and then selected projects to be awarded grants. In its new role, the Foundation took the initiative in encouraging research on a relatively wide-ranging front. Through its study groups, it explores the avenues and byways of the scientific community to convince, persuade, exert pressure on and induce top-quality scholars to undertake particular projects. This study group is a mixed group comprising members of the Riksdag and scholars. The Riksdag members are interested in research, and the scholars are interested in the Riksdag. They are able to speak one another's language. The group has had discussions with project leaders and project members. The group's Riksdag members have actually facilitated project work by arranging e.g. interviews and access to records. It is my understanding that this has been highly beneficial to projects.

The Foundation's study group on "Research on the Riksdag's operations and procedures" has also made a contribution by directing the attention of scholars to the importance of not forgetting central public organs. The media do claim, and occasionally even the public debate, that the influence of central public organs has declined in recent years. At the same time, some maintain (paradoxically) that the public sector has become too expansive. These views have an inherently political basis. But even when the views are held, investigation of the extent to which and reasons why developments have proceeded along these lines should be a subject of major research interest.

## Arboga Meeting's 600th anniversary: What will the year 2035 be like?

The study group is not a permanent group. It may be dissolved once it has achieved its objectives. Conditions will also change. Weeds can easily take root even in a well-raked research landscape. After the turn of the century, as in previous centuries, some scholars will file claims on part of this landscape and may even work those claims. But our knowledge of the Swedish Riksdag's operations and procedures is still likely to seem sketchy and inadequate at some future date. So a new research project on the Riksdag will probably be needed in time. Certainly by 2035 (if not before) when the Arboga meeting will celebrate its 600th anniversary and when the event will again be commemorated in Arboga by the King and members of the government and the Riksdag. From the point of view of research on the Riksdag, we will then once again proclaim that "In the beginning was the Arboga meeting". At the same time, fresh proof will show us that tradition is sometimes more powerful than science, provided (of course) that science does not adopt a new stance once again.

*Leif Lewin*

# Rationality and selfishness

Being rational without being selfish is quite possible. This is a trivial truth in everyday life. But when scientists address the issue, the assertion often becomes remarkable and provocative. This quickly became apparent to us in the major research project "Politik som rationellt handlande" (often referred to by the abbreviation of its English name, "Politics As Rational Action, PARA") which had a major impact on the Department of Government in Uppsala at the end of the 1970's and beginning of the 1980's. The significance of the project can be summed up by noting that it returned the scientific debate on politics to this simple distinction, i.e. that the rationality assumption does not lead to any conclusion about the motives dictating the adoption of political positions. In fact, the contrary is true. Social scientists should assume as little as possible in advance (although *some* assumption is necessary for any scientist) and leave as much as possible open for empirical examination.

## Theory of action

PARA evolved from the convulsions of Sweden's student revolt. Claiming that politicians, their implementing proxies (i.e. the bureaucrats) and principals (i.e. the voters) are rational with the free will to adopt different positions and an ability to transform at least some of these positions into action was regarded at the beginning of the 1970's as an obsolete view of history. Politicians were mere agents of economic structures. In "Das Kapital" Karl Marx had found one such superindividual explanatory factor. The belief that politics had any independent impact on developments in society was naive. Sociologists and (some) economists acquired a better understanding of the decisive importance of the structures to the course of events and a clearer view, following Hegel, of the march of the *Zeitgeist* over time. Our department's board seriously considered the question of whether to close the department and link up with more progressive, adjacent disciplines. After new findings were obtained from the French structuralists, doctoral candidates reluctantly admitted that politics could be accorded a certain amount of "leeway" but (as the magic formula expressed it), "economics was the ultimate determinative factor" (Althusser 1968, Poulantzas 1970).

These proclamations resounded so shrilly in our ears because they contradicted what was a little pompously referred to as departmental tradition in the analysis of ideas and decisions. For decades, political scientists at our department had shown how ideas and interests conflicted in Swedish politics, the way ideologies were changed by new experience and the way programs were transformed from party congress declarations of intent into implemented bureaucratic realities. The scientists had discovered individual actions behind every change. Thus, we both agreed with our predecessors' distaste for "system thinking" while supporting "methodological individualism". Rational argumentation on value issues and rational choices between alternatives in politics were possible subjects for political science inquiry (Brusewitz 1951, Tingsten 1941, Hessler 1956, Brecht 1959, Hessler 1964, cf. Popper 1963, Rawls 1971).

Departmental tradition was based on the theory of action. But I must admit that this was not a particularly well-developed theory of action. The legacy of the Weibulls (Swedish historians) lived on, explanations were often *ad hoc* in nature and intuition was allowed to prevail instead of systematic theory. Viewed in a self-critical light, the position was as described in the final sentence of this paper's initial paragraph: there were virtually no theoretical premises upon which our research could be based.

So a period of soul-searching ensued. I recall collecting white stones in strolls along the beaches of Öland Island during the chilly summer of 1974 and badgering my house guests into designating their preferences about which wine I should serve by stacking the stones in piles of varying numbers. I then tried to show how the rankings could go in a circle so no alternative could be said to express the group's preference (Riker and Ordeshook 1973).

If the need for a better theory of action was one of the prerequisites for PARA, the other comprised certain departmental conditions. A new generation had taken over at the department. The assistant professors and research assistants were my contemporaries. We were all paradoxically filled with enthusiasm and a belief in the future, despite the severe attacks to which we were being subjected. At the same time, most of us happened to be available for new research assignments after recently concluding major studies. The question I then raised was whether we should tackle some joint project or move on to individual work.

We decided to try and agree on a common program. Research projects are often devised in a decision situation, which can be described as "idyllic dictatorship", to use a term we encountered when we began studying the modern theory of action: i.e. "This is what I want to do if no one else decides". This is an unrealistic starting point for a large research program. Strategic consideration of others is essential in the launching of any large research program including virtually all of a department's scientists with doctorates. Reaching agreement on a program can be as important to a department as carrying out the research itself. Agreeing on a program is a difficult, time-consuming task demanding psychological insight and diplomatic skill by the chairperson. If anyone attempts to force issues or play the dictator, however "idyllically", there is a great risk of a breakdown and resistance to the presumed oppression. In any case, we finally succeeded, with the aid of recently published literature, in agreeing on a theoretical framework which was broad enough to suit everyone but still sufficiently stringent to be scientifically fruitful. Everyone found a niche which suited his particular research personality. At the same time, we succeeded in arriving at a program which, as a whole, was uniform and coherent. The program's scale was a major advantage: a dozen scientists collaborated through the merger of departmental funds with generous grants from the Bank of Sweden Tercentenary Foundation. The project attained the "critical mass" often sought, thereby at best freeing intellectual resources, creating cumulative knowledge and stimulating exchange of concepts and analytical tools among project scientists.

## Model Platonism

The project was called "Politics As Rational Action". The name was quickly selected under pressure from the university president who insisted that we should decide, well in advance, on the program for the international symposium we were asked to arrange to commemorate the Uppsala University's 500th anniversary in 1977. The wording proved to have a greater governing effect than we had assumed. "Rationality" was obviously the central concept. The theory of action we began addressing was "rational choice" as the English term runs. After various improvisations we decided to call the Swedish equivalent "rationalistisk teori" ("rational choice theory"). Game theory is the formalized, central core in the formation of rational choice theory.

We also decided to use the concept "action" rather than behavior. The thrust was to be towards some other theory of structure than the Marxist version, the most prestigious branch of political science prior to the student revolt: behavioral theory.

It entails the study of politics with scientific method, the starting point being the assumption that the behavior of voters is governed by socioeconomic circumstances. Voters were not viewed as either rational or equipped with free will. I criticized this view in an early work (Lewin 1970, cf. Key 1966).

A remarkable world then unfolded before our eyes, a world populated by prisoners who behaved so incompetently in court that they incurred unnecessarily heavy sentences; by California kids playing "chicken" in their cars (driving straight at one another at high speed) to see who is cowardly enough to veer to one side first; by free riders who let other passengers pay for their travel; by a disappointed boy stuck with the smallest apple after misjudging a friend's politeness and letting him pick first; by short-sighted farmers who graze too many animals on common land so that land is destroyed; field commanders using anachronistic weaponry etc. But real politics were nowhere to be seen.

"Model Platonism", we proclaimed when studying the examples in the literature and fictitious cases. We were aware that our objective was to refine and elucidate but we felt that the model approach probably obscures more than it explains. It circumvents difficult issues. Protagonists displayed intellectual laziness by "manipulating" rather than studying reality. In contrast, our research would entail empirical application of the rational choice theory. Long-term method development was essential, as the theory had not been applied to domestic politics (which is what we wished to address) in any significant study anywhere in the world. International relations had been better served by research.

Many concrete issues were examined during this method development phase. In the investigation of the "leeway" available to politicians, the contrafactual alternatives must be devised with some degree of realism. Claiming that Napoleon would have won the Battle of Waterloo if nuclear weapons had been available to him would be a bizarre and irrelevant notion.

Rankings are often the only reliable way to identify the preferences of actors. The literature is full of ranking scales of higher dignity which, in the guise of precision, merely express arbitrariness and thoughtlessness. We found every reason to avoid what the theorists usually identify as the goals of politics; in their analyses, matrices are filled with votes. Quantitative measures here are as exact as the sums cited by economists. But departmental tradition once again raised doubts. Earlier research had taught us that "program realization" was more important than "vote maximization", despite everything. In our matrices we entered conceivable evaluations by politicians of different game results. Winning votes is only one instrument for realizing a program. The theorists advanced the counter-hypothesis that politicians actually strive to maximize votes for the purpose of coming to power rather than for forming a government with which their programs could be implemented (Downs 1957). However, their arguments in support of this view were very meager, compared to their sophisticated choice analyses, and were, as usual, not based on empirical findings.

One of the experts used by the Foundation for evaluating our project application commented with gentle irony about our attempts to link up with departmental traditions. But this was not mere coquetry on our part. The application was the first draft of an attempt to make a fundamental distinction between rationality and selfishness. The mere fact that we regarded politicians as rational, i.e. capable of ranking their preferences and then acting so that as many as possible of these preferences could be realized without impairment of long-term goal achievement, did not necessarily mean that their preferences had to be egotistical in nature. If the preferences were altruistic, acting to achieve as much of the altruism as possible would be rational behavior.

There are two concepts which should not be confused in this context: "selfishness" and "strategy". In rational choice theory, "selfishness" is exactly what the term implies: egotistical preferences. However, "strategy" is an instrument for achieving a goal, whatever the nature of that goal. For example, a person can sometimes improve her/his position by supporting other candidates and issues than those she/he personally favors. Politics is full of "strategy". Politics may well *be* strategy. But the presence of "strategy" says no more about selfishness than the presence of "rationality". A bureaucrat may work with e.g. a strategy for her/his budget requests in order to improve the public agencies she/he represents or a committee chairperson could form coalitions in order to save a bill, but the preference of neither need be egotistical.

When in a subsequent book and in the debate which followed it I reviewed rational choice research (Lewin 1988a), I found cause to consider the deep and emotional antagonisms prevailing in social science in this field. Emotions were aroused because the debate was actually about what generates the greatest prestige in the world of science. Some people feel that this is theory. We prefer putting it in another way: non-theory produces the least prestige. That is why it was essential for us to depart from the non-theoretical, intuitive theory of action. But opinions vary on the way to view empirical work. We feel that the hard – and exciting – part really begins with empirics. Our opponents appear to have a nonchalant attitude to the need for adequate evidence. Empirics produce the unexpected, i.e. circumstances giving us cause to revise our theories. The refutation of false theories, the main task of science, can only be achieved through empirical work (Popper 1963).

Everything would be acceptable, though, if the model Platonists practiced what they preached in their philosophical declarations: that selfishness, and not merely rationality, is declared to be just a model you should judge on the basis of its inherent explanatory power. But in fact, their books and articles abound with reality assertions in which data are often as crude as the theory is refined. Hypotheses are presented as results and premises as conclusions.

My retrospective book noted the paucity of empirical support for the hypothesis on selfishness in politics. There are elements of both self-interest and public interest in western politics. But there should be no doubt about the predominant element. Voters do not vote with their pocket-books but mainly according to assessments of the abilities of parties to manage the country's economy. Politicians generally strive to achieve program realization rather than maximizing the number of votes. Bureaucrats usually find decision implementation more important than budget maximization.

So we settled on the following design. Politicians have ideological preferences and devise strategies for achieving as many of them as possible. They may be successful or unsuccessful. Our research task was to explain decisions in a number of areas with the aid of the actors' ideological and strategic motives.

## *"Log-rolling"*

Now it is high time to exemplify and describe the research program's results.

200 years ago, the French Age of Enlightenment philosopher Condorcet asked the question: how would decisions be made in practice if the democracy he and his sympathizers advocated ever prevailed? Contrasting the "will of the people" to "autocracy", as was usually the case, seemed overly simple to him. As a theory of action advocate, he discerned the presence of individual actors behind the "will of the people", individuals who might well entertain different personal views. Let us envisage three actors, A, B and C, with different ways of ranking their preferences, Condorcet said:

$$
\begin{array}{cccc}
A & x & y & z \\
B & y & z & x \\
C & z & x & y
\end{array}
$$

There is no "will of the people" here. The actors disagree. And there is no "majority". Each alternative has one vote (A votes for "x", B for "y" and C for "z"). How do they arrive at a decision? Condorcet proposed that paired comparisons be made between the preferences, the winner eliminating the other preferences. If we begin by comparing "x" and "y" we find that A and C prefer "x" to "y", whereas B prefers "y" to "x". So "x" garners two votes and "y" one. If we compare "z" in the corresponding manner, we find that "z" wins by two votes (B and C) to one for "x" (A). The third comparison, i.e. between "y" and "z", produces a surprise. Two actors (A and B) prefer "y" to "z" which only gets one vote (C). Even though "z" was preferred to "x" which, in turn, was preferred to "y", "z" loses in a comparison with "y"! Ranking appears to go in a circle. The winning choice depends on the order in which they are compared. There is a technical term for designating the sequence of preferences which go in a circle without any fixed hierarchy: it does not meet the requirement of "transitivity", i.e. if someone prefers "x" to "y" and "y" to "z", then she/he must also prefer "x" to "z" (Condorcet 1785).

Condorcet's voting paradox was an unpleasant insight which did not suit the more fanatical advocates of democracy based on the will of the people. So it was forgotten during a century-long battle "for" and "against" universal suffrage. One of the people who did not forget this paradox was the lecturer in mathematics at Oxford and author of "Alice's Adventures in Wonderland", Lewis Carroll (Black 1958). Serious discussion of the voting paradox began in earnest in our time after it was re-formulated by Kenneth Arrow, a subsequent Nobel laureate (Arrow 1963). However, the predominant view in the middle of the 1970's was that the voting paradox was indeed an elegant mathematic game for eccentric professors but was of no relevance to decision-making in contemporary democracies.

In PARA we decided to investigate whether or not this was the case and began our hunt for an "abominable snowman". And we found him in the most internationally renown Swedish political decision, the 1933 crisis agreement which laid the foundation for the Social-Democratic Party's long period in power in Sweden. At the beginning of the 1930's, preference rankings in the most important domestic policy issues can be described as follows (I have to simplify things here and refer the reader to the detailed description in the final PARA report, Lewin 1984). For the Social-Democrats, the new unemployment policy was the main preference. The Conservatives and Liberals rejected it on ideological grounds, as did the Agrarians although less for reasons of principle. The farmers mainly demanded tariffs as protection for agriculture, something opposed by the Social-Democrats who by tradition were advocates of free trade. But the Conservatives and Liberals were divided on this issue. However during maneuvers in the welfare committee in the spring of 1933, they did succeed in reaching an agreement on a "semiprotectionistic" line. This gives us the following rankings:

| | | | |
|---|---|---|---|
| A | t | u | R |
| S | u | R | t |
| C+L | R | t | u |

*A = Agrarians; S = Social-Democrats; C+L = Conservatives and Liberals; t = tariffs on agricultural imports; u = the new unemployment policy; R = rejection of both.*

Here was intransitivity, as the reader will note. What then was the result?

It was "by the book" (Buchanan and Tullock 1962), i.e. a decision was reached by two actors exchanging issues with one another and forming a majority coalition: the Agrarians backed the Social-Democratic policy on unemployment. In return, the Social-Democrats abandoned their free trade stance and agreed to tariffs on agricultural imports. "Log-rolling" was a fact. In relation to their original preferences, this was not a decision anyone actually wanted. But the winning actors had still acted rationally, since each party had gained approval for a policy important to it at the expense of concessions on issues regarded as being less important.

So using a well-known example we were able to show that the voting paradox really did exist and had a major impact on Swedish policies. I was able to abandon my role as a bizarre host, handing out white stones, and again become a political scientist with an eye for the essence of decision (Allison 1971).

We were also able to point to several circumstances which explain why the merry-go-round (i.e. roundabout) stopped at the point it did. One was the time factor. In principle, rankings could have continued in a circle indefinitely. Actor C+L could have e.g. made A an even better offer. In practice, though, horse-trading never proceeds indefinitely. The adroit politician displays her/his ability by "waiting for the right moment" (Machiavelli 1513). Despite the long duration of negotiations, Per Albin Hansson ultimately surprised his opponents with an agreement proposal.

Another was the actors' long-term strategies. K.G. Westman and Pehrsson in Bramstorp felt that it would be more advantageous to get the Social-Democrats to abandon their free trade stance and adopt protectionism than seek support from the fragile C+L alliance which had been such strong adversaries only a few years earlier that the Liberals had brought down the Conservative government on the tariff issue. Elites always circulate, so what rational actors should do is to form alliances with people on the way up (Mosca 1896). The Agrarians felt that the wisest policy for the future was to support the Social-Democrats.

## Sectors

"Log-rolling" is one of eight decisions examined in the final

PARA report. This report is chronologically arranged and deals with the biggest issues in Swedish politics over the past century.

Other reports were sectorized, dealing with different sectors of Swedish society in the 1970's. Our project meetings began resembling "cabinet" sessions in which each participant represented a departmental field (a conference table like the one used in the Swedish government's cabinet room was installed during a renovation of our department). Let me briefly mention a few of the substantive issues we investigated in PARA.

A new dimension emerged in energy policies at this time, in addition to the familiar right-left scale. Disagreements had arisen on the "growth" and "ecology" issues; they cut across non-Socialist party lines. Not unlike California teenagers, party leaders played "Chicken" with one another on the issue of nuclear power, whereupon Fälldin's strategy of "binding himself" led to his election victory in 1976 and his fall in 1978 (Vedung 1979, Lewin 1984).

The subsequent government crisis provided a good example of political calculation. Here, *different* strategic motives were weighed against one another. The Social-Democratic Party leadership decided to let the Liberal Party form a government, aware that they could sustain losses among the electorate and in the internal arena. The government formed in 1978 also subjected the new constitution to its first severe test (Petersson 1979).

The book dealing with the major industrial policy decision on "Steel mill 1980" did not examine a government's rise and fall but an issue's. The author ascribed strategic considerations major importance in the course of developments (Henning 1980).

Politics comprise a continuous process, and current Swedish tax policies are an excellent "thermometer" in any attempt to study them. One study analyzed a number of taxation decisions up to the "wonderful night" in 1981 when the Social-Democrats, to the annoyance of the Conservatives, succeeded in splitting the non-Socialist government and reached an agreement with the Liberal and Center parties. However, these parties soon began feeling cheated – just like the disappointed boy who ends up with the smallest apple (Hadenius 1981).

One and the same political position can sometimes be justified with different arguments. Traffic policies are a striking example. Despite different ideologies, politicians agreed on market-oriented solutions in two decisions on traffic policies from 1963 to 1979 (Wedin 1982).

Making a distinction between motives (*motiv* in Swedish) and reasons (*motiveringar* in Swedish) is a main task in theory of action research. Riksdag publications and other official material are far more useful for this purpose than we had reason to believe after reading the handbooks, more often written by philosophically oriented scholars than empirically experienced scientists. The motives of Swedish politicians can be revealed to a great degree by careful analysis of their positions on the respective issues. One study of Swedish agricultural policies showed how the parties acted to ensure that ownership legislation was tailored to suit the owner interests each wished to favor (Holmström 1983).

A special method study discussed these evidence problems further and examined different ways of mastering circularity problems encountered by empirical research when studying the motives of actors (Hadenius' paper in Hadenius, Henning and Holmström 1984, and Hadenius (in English) 1983b).

The introduction of the Co-determination Act was explained in another report with the aid of game theory analysis (Hadenius 1983a).

One study considered the well-known conflict in the theory of action between individual and collective rationality, this time in the guise of the "prisoners" of industrial policies of the 1970's, actors who never considered any other options except those arising from negotiations between companies and officials of the Ministry of Industry. With never a thought to the future, the politicians instituted a process, costing hundreds of millions of Crowns, a development everyone later had cause to regret (Henning's paper in Hadenius, Henning and Holmström 1984).

When decisions are implemented, considerable departures are often made from original objectives. But, as an analysis of the Swedish civil service's relocation to towns outside the capital for regional policy reasons showed, "failures" of this kind are more closely related to an excessively vague view, at the time the decisions are made, of the desired goals of the decision rather than to tactical behavior or political ignorance (Holmström's paper in Hadenius, Henning and Holmström 1984).

In the 1970's, the Left and Green waves swept over society with full force. The work environment issue, technically hard to understand and politically advocated by strong special interests, was brought to the fore in the intersection of these waves. One research report analyzed the ability of politicians to represent a conviction of the common good against this background (Nordfors 1985).

"Disappearance of the family doctor", exciting as a detective story, was the name of a study showing why the Liberal Party's proposal on family doctors, popular with everyone, was still rejected by the Riksdag one year, only to be adopted by the Riksdag a year later when another government was in power (Johansson 1985).

Finally, the basic problem in housing politics is the view of the State's responsibility for the housing standard. Is it the task of the State to specify minimums, plan for optimums or support an *avant garde* which contributes to placing an increasingly higher housing standard within reach of most of the population? In 1946, 1967 and 1974 these three basic options were studied in relation to one another. A description and explanation of the combination of these three positions, which the Government and Riksdag actually adopted, were the goals of one study (Gustavsson 1985).

## Continued research. Impact on teaching

Our international research contacts were greatly promoted by the 500-year anniversary symposium (Lewin and Vedung 1980). The fact that two symposium participants, Graham Allison from Harvard and William Riker from Rochester, were awarded honorary doctorates at Uppsala did not make it harder for us to disseminate our results during sabbatical leave abroad, in workshops held by the European Consortium for Political Research and in journals. The Foundation financed translation of our research results into English (Hadenius 1983b, Lewin 1988b).

However, it is important for me to point out that rational choice research has been continued at our department by younger scientists after PARA was concluded; a driving force was to make PARA a *major* research program in cumulative respects. A game theory analysis of Rousseau's philosophy on the general will, an explanation of the way the market is undermined, like the way grazing animals devastate common pastureland, by increasing demands on public services and an analysis of free rider problems in tax avoidance are examples of such studies.

The efforts we have been making to achieve incorporation of PARA research into teaching programs is conceivably more interesting. This work is being conducted in three ways. Firstly, several young teachers are holding a course on rational choice research in the doctoral program. This course is in the form of a secondary analysis of the PARA material and asks questions about alternative interpretations by offering the best "carrot" anyone could offer an ambitious student: find faults in the professor's book!

Secondly, in a special school for prospective scientists we copied the attempts by American colleagues, using a laboratory format and computer tournaments, to revive interest in the famous "prisoners" and their attempts to arrive at collectively rational decisions (Axelrod 1984). Tit-for-tat – "Begin by collaborating and then act the same way as your opponent in her/his previous move" proved to be the most successful strategy.

Finally, we developed a teaching game for basic training (Lewin 1979). During the first term of political science studies, students play the roles of members of the Riksdag. They are instructed about their ideological preferences, derived from the different empirical studies in the PARA program, but there are no restrictions on strategies they can use in forming governments and implementing programs. A computer-simulated Riksdag election, whose outcome depends on the way Riksdag members vote on various issues, concludes the game. An excessive number of unrealistic, tactical maneuvers were corrected in later versions of this game by increasing "costs" in the form of lost votes when positions changed, vacillated or were betrayed. Ideology is regarded as a constraint on strategy.

The frequency with which we arrived at the same conclusions as the Americans in these training games is striking. Politics is an iterative process. Iteration teaches the students to collaborate, and collaboration means that one cares about one's opponents. Since contacts will also be necessary in the future, I must be able to trust my opponent in order to reach binding agreements with him. In politics, working for the common good generally proves to be the rational line of action as well.

*Erik Allardt*

# Social structure and social change in the Nordic countries

A society's social structure comprises the social groupings which evolve due to differences in inherited privileges, cultural background, geographic location, work tasks or economic standing and which reflect the entire society's mode of operation. In the estate society, geographic subdivision of the country into units called provinces, in addition to the division into estates, was a major factor. The main social categories in the estate society were the nobility, clergy, bourgeoisie and peasants, as well as the inhabitants of the various provinces who differed from one another in terms of economic structure, traditions and lifestyle.

After the breakthrough of industrialism, the subdivision into social classes and occupational sectors acquired decisive importance. Social classes have been defined in different ways, but property, income and work have been the central classification factors. Even more refined classifications have been based in some way on the subdivision into three categories, i.e. the working class, middle class and upper class. An important trinity has also been used in describing occupational sectors, i.e. the primary sector (agricultural and related fields), the secondary sector (industry) and the tertiary sector (services).

# Emergence and transformation
# of the industrial society

A distinguishing feature of structure in the industrial society was undoubtedly the emergence of a working class whose main task was to produce goods in industry. Up to the first few decades after World War II, both the working class and the secondary employment sector continued to grow in developed countries with a market economy. The working class also became a major political force, and political stances were adopted mainly because they were assumed to be either for or against the interests of the working class. In the Nordic countries, the expansion of the welfare state was an important phase of industrial development. The Nordic model differed from the welfare models in most other countries by being universal in coverage and by rejecting means-tested social assistance schemes as reflecting negative discrimination. They also placed the emphasis on political mechanisms for achieving social equalization and on institutionalization instead of time-oriented programs (Esping-Andersen and Korpi 1987, pp. 40-43).

Until the middle of the 1960's, industrial societies functioned about the same way as they had done up to that point in the 20th century. The traditional working class grew, and the number of people employed in industry increased. The welfare state expanded but its system of rules and institutions had more or less assumed its present form in the Nordic countries by 1965. Some social policies and subsidies have indeed been changed since then, but these changes have only been adjustments, marginal improvements or implementation of previous decisions. The studies of the level of living performed at the end of the 1960's and beginning of the 1970's in all the Nordic countries concentrated on measuring and describing well-being as defined by traditional Nordic welfare policies (Erikson, Hansen, Ringen and Uusitalo 1987). A comparative study of Nordic welfare, described in the book "Att ha, att älska, att vara" (Allardt

1975), was performed at the beginning of the 1970's by the Research Group for Comparative Sociology at Helsinki University with financial support from the Bank of Sweden Tercentenary Foundation and research councils in all the Nordic countries. It expanded the "welfare" concept to encompass social relationships (Loving) and personal development (Being) and not merely the material standard of living (Having). The study's findings suggested that new problems were developing. The correlations between the material standard of living (Having) and the quality of life, as manifested in social relationships, were weak. Nor were discontent attitudes correlated with external material circumstances. With the benefit of hindsight, we can now see that the comparative study failed to analyze the reasons for the weak correlations or to take into account the new social groupings being formed. Nor did it analyze new problems, such as pollution of the environment and increased bureaucracy at the middle echelons of the civil service.

In fact, the social fabric of Nordic countries has undergone an extraordinarily comprehensive, qualitative change over the past 25 years (from 1965 to 1990). The working class and the secondary sector have not only stopped expanding but have also declined in relative terms. In the past few decades, completely new social categories and groups have become large, central units in the social structure. New political tensions have also emerged and are therefore hard to describe with accuracy.

Changes from and after 1965 can be viewed from many angles but summarized by three, partially related processes: (1) expansion of the public sector, (2) the rapid increase in the percentage of women in the work force and (3) evolution of the tertiary (service) and quaternary (information occupations) sectors into the largest employment sectors.

## Growth in the public sector

After World War II, the public sector has grown in every developed country. Comparisons are complicated by the circumstance that the "public sector" is defined in different ways in different contexts (Furuåker 1985, pp. 19-21, Alestalo, Bislev and Furuåker 1990). Some economic definitions are based on the public sector's percentage of the gross national product. In an analysis of social structure, it is natural to base the definition on the number of employees in the public sector. Even with this delineation, several definitional options are available. Two of these definitions are of particular relevance. One, i.e. a restrictive definition, is usually employed by the OECD and counts the number of people employed by public agencies. Thus, employees in ministries, administrative boards and offices in state, municipal and county council facilities belong to the public sector, but not employees in state-owned and municipal enterprises. The number of public servants has grown rapidly, especially in Sweden, as Table 1 shows.

It should be noted that Sweden had a lower percentage of public servants than the U.S., the United Kingdom and Australia in 1960, even if Sweden was still on a higher level then than most OECD member countries. At the same time, Finland's figure was substantially under the average percentage of public servants. By 1980, Sweden had moved up to first place in the OECD in respect to the percentage of public employees. In 1985, Sweden was still first with 33.1%, Denmark was in second place, Norway and Finland were above average and Iceland had a lower-than-average percentage of employees in public agencies. Expressed another way, one-third of the work force in Sweden, nearly one-third in Denmark, one-fourth in Norway and one-fifth in Finland were in public service.

Even if the OECD definition used above has its merits, this definition of public service is by no means unequivocal. Bengt Furuåker (1985, p. 20), who used Statistics Sweden's work

Table 1. The number of employees in public agencies as a percent of the total number of people employed in OECD countries from 1960-1985.

| Country | 1960 | 1970 | 1975 | 1980 | 1985 |
|---|---|---|---|---|---|
| Denmark | .. | 16.8 | 23.6 | 28.3 | 29.8 |
| Finland | 7.7 | 11.8 | 14.6 | 17.8 | 20.4 |
| Iceland | .. | 11.2 | 13.9 | 15.7 | 16.4 |
| Norway | .. | 16.4 | 19.3 | 21.9 | 23.8 |
| Sweden | 12.8 | 20.6 | 25.5 | 30.7 | 33.1 |
| | | | | | |
| Austria | 10.5 | 13.7 | 16.4 | 18.2 | 20.5 |
| Belgium | 12.2 | 13.9 | 15.7 | 18.6 | 19.9 |
| France | 13.1 | 13.4 | 14.3 | 15.6 | 17.8 |
| Ireland | .. | 11.2 | 13.3 | 14.5 | 16.1 |
| Italy | 8.7 | 11.8 | 14.0 | 15.0 | 15.8 |
| Luxembourg | .. | 9.4 | 9.7 | 10.8 | 11.2 |
| Netherlands | 11.7 | 12.1 | 13.6 | 14.9 | 16.1 |
| Portugal | 3.9 | 6.8 | 8.1 | 10.3 | .. |
| Spain | .. | 7.1 | 10.0 | 11.9 | 14.3 |
| Switzerland | 6.4 | 7.9 | 9.5 | 10.7 | 11.2 |
| United Kingdom | 14.8 | 18.0 | 20.8 | 21.1 | 21.8 |
| West Germany | 8.0 | 11.6 | 13.9 | 14.9 | 16.0 |
| | | | | | |
| Canada | .. | 19.5 | 20.3 | 18.9 | 20.0 |
| United States | 15.7 | 18.1 | 17.8 | 16.5 | 15.8 |
| | | | | | |
| Australia | 23.0 | 22.9 | 26.2 | 26.0 | 26.4 |
| Japan | .. | 5.8 | 6.5 | 6.7 | 6.4 |
| New Zealand | 17.9 | 18.2 | 18.9 | 19.2 | 18.1 |
| | | | | | |
| Mean | 11.9 | 13.6 | 15.7 | 17.2 | 18.6 |

(Alestalo 1989, p. 128)

force studies and included Church of Sweden parish offices and certain foundations in figures for the public service, arrived at a somewhat higher percentage of public servants in Sweden than the OECD figure. According to him, the percentage of employees in the public sector amounted to 38% of the Swedish work force by 1983. However, trends are virtually identical, irrespective of how the number of public servants is calculated.

When the public sector is discussed, there is often reason to use another definition than the OECD's rather restrictive version. State-owned and municipal commercial enterprises often have functions similar to state and municipal agencies offering service at no charge and are supervised and run by representative bodies. The "public sector" then even encompasses employees of state-owned and municipal commercial enterprises. So a distinction is made between two different categories, i.e. between employees in public agencies, on the one hand, and employees in the public sector comprising both public agency employees and employees of state-owned and municipal commercial enterprises, on the other hand. The latter definition comprising both categories is the main one used here.

## Expansion of the public sector

As shown in Table 2, the ranking order of the Nordic countries is not affected by the inclusion of employees of state-owned and municipal commercial enterprises.

*Table 2. The number of public sector employees as a percent of all the people employed in the Nordic countries from 1960-1985.*

| Country | 1960 | 1965 | 1970 | 1975 | 1980 | 1985 |
|---------|------|------|------|------|------|------|
| Denmark | .. | .. | 23.2 | 27.5 | 36.5 | 37.1 |
| Finland | 15.5 | .. | 21.2 | 25.0 | 29.7 | 31.6 |
| Norway | .. | .. | 26.5 | 27.8 | 31.7 | 34.7 |
| Sweden | .. | 22.2 | 28.6 | 34.3 | 40.9 | 42.8 |

(Alestalo 1989, p. 132)

The rapid expansion of the work force in the public sector obviously reflects the way public agencies have taken over many services previously supplied by the private sector, especially in families. The public sector's expansion has had many consequences, but identifying cause and effect is difficult. Total employment increased in all the Nordic countries in the 1970's and 1980's. The increase is mainly ascribable to the growth in employment in the public sector (Alestalo, Bislev and Furuåker 1990). However, no one can claim with any certainty that the private sector would have been unable to operate the services that have expanded in the public sector. A public debate on privatization and allowing market forces take over certain public services has paralleled growth in the public sector. Certain steps towards increased privatization were taken in the Nordic countries (Norway and Denmark in particular) in the 1980's. In Norway, fees for some social services, previously almost "free", have been raised considerably, and in Denmark certain previously universal social benefits have been linked to income and need (Johansen and Kolberg 1985, pp. 168-169). Despite these measures, changes in the Nordic welfare model have only been modest and marginal. Here, it seems appropriate to share the view that the public sector has become so large that its sheer size constitutes an effective impediment to a general transfer of welfare services from the public to the private sector (Kosonen 1987, p. 285).

In their report on political resources in the Norwegian standard of living study, Hernes and Martinussen begin their analysis (1980, p. 9) by pointing out that one of the most striking features of the Norwegian society's development after 1814 has been the growth of the public sector. From an international point of view, however, it can still be claimed that the public sector's expansion in the Nordic countries was greatest in the period after 1965. As Table 1 shows, Sweden in 1960 still had a smaller percentage of employees in public service than the heavily market-oriented United States. The welfare state's expansion did not have a noticeable impact on the public sector until after 1960.

After that year, the public sector not only expanded but changed in essence. The welfare state's central sectors, i.e. public health, social welfare and education, accounted for most of the expansion.

*Table 3. The number of employees in welfare administration (public health, social welfare, education) in the Nordic countries as a percent of all the employees in the public sector from 1970-1985.*

| Country | 1970 | 1975 | 1980 | 1985 |
|---|---|---|---|---|
| Denmark | .. | 61.3 | 63.4 | 66.9 |
| Finland | 31.7 | 36.3 | 40.9 | 45.2 |
| Norway | 46.4 (1973) | 49.5 | 54.5 | 55.9 (1984) |
| Sweden | 49.9 | 53.5 | 55.9 | 58.6 |

(Alestalo, Bislev and Furuåker 1990)

During the entire period, less than 20% of the employees in the public sector of the Nordic countries were employed in general administration, the armed forces and public safety agencies. This represents a rather radical change in the tasks of the state. The public sector's expansion and conversion into a guarantor of security and welfare comprises both a structural change and a drastic transformation of culture and lifestyle. Or as Gudmund Hernes and Willy Martinussen (1980, p. 17) put it:

"People today are in contact with public institutions more hours of the day, more days a year and more years in life than at any time in our history. The individual wage-earner places about half of his income at the disposal of the public sector whose activities she/he constantly encounters in the form of offers, orders or bans".

As Table 3 shows, two-thirds of Danish public sector employees in 1985 worked in welfare institutions, whereas the corresponding figure for other Nordic countries was 59% in Sweden, 56% in Norway and 45% in Finland. The welfare sector was also large in relation to the respective country's total labor force. In 1985, welfare administration employees in Denmark and Sweden accounted for about one-fourth of the total labor force; the figure for Norway was one-fifth and for Finland only one-sixth. However, the welfare sector even in Finland was much larger than the number of employees in general administration, the armed forces and public safety.

## Growth of the middle class

Growth in the public sector has obviously affected both society's class structure and political strength relationships. The consequences of the public sector's expansion has led to debate and discussion in all the Nordic countries. The importance of the increase in civil servants has been both blindly denied and heavily overemphasized. As early as 1973, the Danish professor of economics, Jørgen Dich (1973, pp. 76-136) referred to the new cadre of civil servants as "the ruling class" (the title of his much debated book).

The difficulty in evaluating the impact on society's class structure is due in part to the fact that so many different traditions are still employed in analyzing and assessing the structure of social classes. Demarcations of the social class to which individual occupational groups belong often seem arbitrary to people outside these analysis traditions. However, the difficulties are by no means merely theoretical but are even due to concrete, readily observable circumstances. One Norwegian analysis (Rogoff Ramsøy and Kjølsrød 1986, pp. 236-237) noted the ambivalent position of welfare occupations. Today, welfare occupations require special training. Their importance is underlined in the political debate and their practitioners have numerous opportunities to influence the lives of individual citizens. At the same time, representatives of welfare occupations have relatively poor salaries, have heavy workloads, are circumscribed by numerous regulations and risk becoming parties in social conflicts.

Changes in the class structure of the Nordic countries appear to have been discussed with different terms and emphases, even if factual content has apparently been about the same. In Sweden and Swedish sociology, the question has been raised as to whether or not the working class has declined, whereas Finland and Norway have instead tended to question whether or not the middle class has grown. However, countries have generally arrived at about the same conclusions, viz. the working class has shrunk and the middle class or, more accurately, the middle layer of society has grown. After a cautious but scrupulous analysis of developments in Sweden, Robert Erikson (1984, p. 46) presented a conclusion which rather accurately reflects the general view of Nordic scholars:

> "The groups that are growing in size are senior and middle management white-collar workers. We can discern two trends that jointly explain this development. The public sector has increased in relative size. Since the proportion of middle management and senior white-collar workers is greater in the public sector than in the private sector, growth in the public sector (with an unchanged work organization) means that the percentage of white-collar workers increases on these levels. And work organization in the private sector has changed so a larger proportion of white-collar employees have relatively advanced duties. If we view the class structure in the same way as a population pyramid, the different segments atop one another with a width corresponding to their size, class structure will be seen to have changed in the same way as population, i.e. the upper segments have become somewhat broader while the base has narrowed somewhat."

One interesting fact is that the impact of public sector growth on class structure has been the subject of comment and debate, especially in Nordic social science. In international sociology, the leading examiners of the class structure of present-day society, such as Pierre Bourdieu, Anthony Giddens, John Goldthorpe, Frank Parkin and Erik Olin Wright, never make any serious attempts to analyze the effects of public sector growth. However, social scientists in all the Nordic countries have

systematically studied this development (e.g. Ahrne and Leiulfsrud 1984, Alestalo 1989, pp. 127-137, Hoff 1985, pp. 207-226,
Knutsen 1986, pp. 263-287). The political effects of the public
sector's expansion have also been analyzed by Nordic social
scientists (e.g. Kosonen 1987, p. 316, Lafferty and Knutsen
1984, pp. 369-392, Svallfors 1989). Yet at the moment, no
good, comparative studies or data are available on the public
sector's political reactions. The most systematic and also the
most provocative results have been obtained in Norway.

In their analyses, Lafferty (Lafferty and Knutsen 1984, pp.
369-382) and Knutsen (1986, pp. 263-287) have spoken of the
emergence of a special "public sector middle class". It differs
from the private sector's middle class not only in terms of
conditions but even by embracing completely different political
attitudes. Knutsen, who carefully analyzed Norwegian data
from 1981, assumes that his findings are actually applicable to
all the Nordic countries. He shows how the public sector's
middle class, both in respect to its attitudes towards the welfare
state and state regulatory measures, entertains more radical (i.e.
more socialistic) values than the private sector's middle class. In
these matters, the Norwegian public sector's middle class is
really more radical than the working class which, in turn, is
more radical than the public sector's middle class only in
matters directly related to industrial democracy and economic
equality. Knutsen's general conclusion is that the public sector's expansion in Norway has created a large, new middle class
with political attitudes completely different from those held by
the traditional middle class. In Sweden, Hans Zetterberg has
presented analyses in the conservative daily newspaper Svenska Dagbladet (1985) whose contents are generally similar to
Knutsen's empirical studies. Pekka Kosonen (1987, p. 316),
who in a comparative analysis of the welfare state's future
examined several different studies of attitudes towards the
welfare state, maintains that his findings are indicative of a
growing political gap between the middle class in the public and

private sectors. In summary, the public sector's expansion can be said to have had political consequences resulting in the development of political differences between the middle class in the public sector and in the private sector and a clearly more radical middle class in the public sector than their counterparts in the private sector. Definite differences do exist between the Nordic countries, but general trends remain the same.

## Women on the labor market and in society

One of the most important structural changes since the middle of the 1960's has been the increase in women in the work force, an increase which is continuing. In all the Nordic countries, total employment has increased as a result of the increased number of employed women. The ability of women to take jobs outside the home has also been facilitated by reforms in various areas, such as the introduction of separate taxation for spouses and the expansion of day nursery facilities (Erikson 1984, p. 102). There is a definite link between the increased numbers of employed women and the public sector's expansion, as a table prepared by Alestalo, Bislev and Furuåker (1990) clearly shows.

Table 4 shows the increase in the percentage of women in the labor force. It should be noted that the percentage of women in the Nordic labor force is the highest in the world. In 1985, women already constituted nearly half of the labor force employed outside the home in Finland, Norway and Sweden. There is also a definite convergence trend, i.e. increasing similarity between the Nordic countries. The public sector and the percentage of women in it are indeed smaller in Finland than in the other Nordic countries. But in respect to the general degree of women's employment, the Nordic countries are tending to resemble one another to an increasing degree. The same trend towards convergence is also discernible in the higher education field and in politics (Haavio-Mannila 1981, pp. 555-

Table 4. The percentage of women in the total work force and in the public sector work force in the Nordic countries from 1970-1985.

| Women as a percent of all employed | 1970 | 1975 | 1980 | 1985 |
|---|---|---|---|---|
| Denmark | 38.5 | 41.1 | 43.3 | 44.8 |
| Finland | 42.2 | 44.4 | 46.6 | 47.9 |
| Norway | 36.6 (1973) | 37.5 | 41.0 | 47.9 (1984) |
| Sweden | 39.4 | 42.4 | 45.0 | 47.0 |

| Public employees as a percent of all employed women | 1970 | 1975 | 1980 | 1985 |
|---|---|---|---|---|
| Denmark | .. | ... | 44.4 | 44.1 |
| Finland | 23.0 | 29.1 | 35.5 | 38.8 |
| Norway | 35.6 (1973) | 38.6 | 43.5 | 47.2 (1984) |
| Sweden | 38.7 | 45.2 | 52.4 | 54.8 |

| Women as a percent of public employees | 1970 | 1975 | 1980 | 1985 |
|---|---|---|---|---|
| Denmark | .. | .. | 60.9 | 62.3 |
| Finland | 45.8 | 51.7 | 54.5 | 58.9 |
| Norway | 49.0 (1973) | 52.1 | 56.5 | 58.3 (1984) |
| Sweden | 57.9 | 62.1 | 65.6 | 67.4 |

| Women employed in public sector as a percent of all employed | 1970 | 1975 | 1980 | 1985 |
|---|---|---|---|---|
| Denmark | .. | .. | 19.2 | 20.1 |
| Finland | 9.7 | 12.9 | 16.5 | 18.6 |
| Norway | 13.0 (1973) | 14.5 | 17.9 | 20.2 (1984) |
| Sweden | 15.2 | 19.2 | 23.6 | 25.8 |

585, Skard and Haavio-Mannila 1986, pp. 176-199). The percentage of women in the Finnish public sector is smaller and their percentage of the private sector is larger than in other Nordic countries. This is partly due to the fact that the percentage of employed women was traditionally greatest in Finland and relatively large even before the public sector began growing.

Before the women's lib movement began making an impact at the end of the 1960's, women were generally more active outside the home in Finland than in other Nordic countries. In 1960, 46% of the students in Finnish colleges and universities were women. The figure was 33% for Sweden and Denmark and 21% for Norway. Only 10 years later, the situation in these countries had become more similar. In 1970, 48% of newly enrolled university students in Finland were women, 42% in Sweden and 37% in Denmark and Norway.

Yet, Nordic comparisons in the 1970's showed how women have had a more equal status in Finland in many respects than in the other Nordic countries. The Nordic comparison of level of living and the quality of life, performed by the Research Group for Comparative Sociology at Helsinki University, showed that men enjoyed a higher degree of welfare than women according to every indicator of welfare except life expectancy. The differences between men and women were simultaneously the smallest in Finland (Kandolin and Uusitalo 1980, pp. 55-60). Similar findings were reported in "Levnadsnivå och jämlikhet i Norden", published by the Nordic Council and the Nordic Statistics Secretariat on the basis of data for the years 1976-80 (1983, pp. 173-176). This report noted that "women in Finland have generally made the greatest progress as regards equality in many respects". The report also contained a ranking (based on a number of indicators) of the Nordic countries in respect to how favorable gender differences were from the point of view of women. The equality profile ranked the countries in the following order: Finland, Sweden, Denmark and Norway (in last place according to seven of the ten indicators).

In Finland, the equality of women has tended to increase with the distance to Nordic and central European influences. Thus, there has been a greater equality in rural areas than in towns. And equality has been greater in eastern Finland than in western Finland. It has been suggested that the latter difference is related to some basic traits in the social structure. In western Finland, the village was the basic social unit, and village societies tend as a rule to be strongly patriarchal. In eastern Finland, however, the extended family was the central and fundamental social unit. The extended family provides women with a strong position but differentiates on the basis of age so older women, not young women, have power and prestige (Allardt 1987, pp. 63-64).

As regards Nordic comparisons, there is every reason to keep in mind that although various equality indices rank Finland first in respect to women's participation and actual standard of living in relation to men, the picture is different when recent institutional arrangements for achieving sex equality, such as equality legislation, equal pay rules, admission to the priesthood etc., are compared. Here, comment on general differences between the Nordic countries is difficult. In respect to some formal equality guarantees in the respective Nordic countries, Finland has lagged behind. But as regards other criteria, the same thing can be said about all the Nordic countries (Österberg and Hedman 1989, p. 173).

Presenting generally valid comparisons in this field is difficult, since the investigated circumstances are highly variegated in nature. Even if e.g. the increased employment of women is indicative of a decline in welfare differences between men and women, as Robert Erikson (1984, p. 104) noted, the degree of employment is a very blunt measure of such change. The increased degree of employment is due in part to the circumstance that part-time work has increased in all the Nordic countries except Finland. But the most important feature is the fact that the increased degree of women's employment has not led to a corresponding decline in women's household work. Some occupations are also continuously dominated by men and some by women.

Even if women are not equal to men in the Nordic countries according to many welfare criteria and in respect to different forms of participation and career opportunities, developments and efforts to attain equality have been an intense and potent force in all the Nordic countries over the past 25 years. One important question is how and to what extent this force has had any general effect on lifestyle and culture in areas not directly related to equality. This question is hard to answer, since research findings have arrived at different conclusions. However, it is obvious that marriage is being increasingly viewed as a contract (instead of a super-individual institution), the distribution of labor between parents has changed, there are more single-parent households than was previously the case and the number of households containing children born in other nuclear families has increased sharply (Liljeström 1988, pp. 263-289).

The difficulty in evaluating the effects of women's liberation on general lifestyle, culture and social evolution is not only caused by research technicalities but probably due mainly to changes in demands and the intentions expressed regarding efforts to attain women's liberation. Until the 1980's, feminist objectives usually concerned achievement of the same degree of activity, occupation and welfare for women as for men. Now, at the beginning of the 1990's, the system of rules, the so-called gender system, regulating relations between women and men is being criticized and analyzed (Hirdman 1987).

The gender system keeps the sexes apart so that differences between occupations and activities dominated by men and those dominated by women, such as management, on the one hand, and household work, on the other hand, are sustained and emphasized. According to Yvonne Hirdman, the main thrust in women's liberation is occurring in the private sphere of life. Women are economically more independent than before, but their ability to decide whether or not to have children and to control the consequences of sexual activities is even more important. Women can also take the initiative in proposing marriage or divorce to a far greater degree than was previously the case. The impact of these changes on men's lives and general developments in society have yet to be studied and they are also to some extent taboo as research subjects.

## From industrial to service and information society

In the 19th century, the Nordic countries were largely agrarian. Agriculture and its related branches provided the main source of employment. Denmark differed from the other Nordic countries by being fairly urbanized even in the 18th century. According to the oldest Danish census, 20% of Denmark's population lived in urban areas as early as 1769, and half of that population lived in the only major Nordic city, Copenhagen. But Denmark, like the other Nordic countries, was still an agrarian society. Industrialization commenced in the second half of the 19th century, and industry became the largest source of employment in Denmark, Norway and Sweden during the first half of the 20th century. In Finland, industry did not pass agriculture as the main employment sector until the 1960's when Finland underwent very rapid structural change and industrialization.

However, a decline in the number of people employed in the industrial sector and greater employment in the tertiary sector than in the primary and secondary sectors are distinguishing features of developments in the Nordic countries over the past 25 years.

As Table 5 shows, industrial employment declined in all four countries. Commerce, transportation and "services" (the largest category) are included under "Other". In all the Nordic countries, employment in the service sector is now greater than in industry. The decline in industrial employment while the ser-

*Table 5. Employment by business sector in the Nordic countries from 1960 to 1986.*

| Country<br>Year | Agriculture and<br>related sectors | Industry and<br>construction | Other |
|---|---|---|---|
| **Denmark** | | | |
| 1960 | 18.2 | 36.9 | 44.8 |
| 1970 | 11.5 | 37.8 | 50.7 |
| 1980 | 7.1 | 30.4 | 62.4 |
| 1986 | 5.8 | 27.8 | 66.3 |
| *Finland* | | | |
| 1960 | 35.2 | 32.6 | 32.2 |
| 1970 | 26.6 | 34.6 | 38.6 |
| 1980 | 13.5 | 34.6 | 51.8 |
| 1986 | 10.9 | 31.8 | 57.6 |
| *Norway* | | | |
| 1960 | 21.6 | 35.6 | 42.9 |
| 1970 | 13.9 | 37.3 | 48.8 |
| 1980 | 8.5 | 29.7 | 61.8 |
| 1986 | 6.9 | 27.6 | 65.5 |
| *Sweden* | | | |
| 1960 | 15.7 | 40.3 | 44.0 |
| 1970 | 8.1 | 38.4 | 53.5 |
| 1980 | 5.6 | 32.2 | 62.2 |
| 1986 | 4.2 | 30.1 | 65.7 |

("Yearbook of Nordic Statistics", various editions)

vice sector expanded, becoming the biggest employment sector, is one of the reasons for the claim that we have moved from being an industrial society to a post-industrial society. This term is not entirely satisfactory in every respect, since industrial output, despite the drop in employment, has never been larger.

In addition, different occupational sector classifications can be devised on the basis of employment. As a result of ideas about the evolution of market economies into information societies, the terms "quaternary sector" or "information occupations sector" are being used to an increasing degree (Kennessey 1985). Relatively stringent criteria and methods for identifying "information occupations" have been devised (Porat 1977). Application of Porat's criteria to Finland shows that the quaternary sector was larger than the primary, secondary and tertiary sectors in 1985 (Paakkolanvaara 1988, pp. 94-96). Since other data suggest that information occupations are still somewhat more common in Denmark, Norway and Sweden than in Finland, there is justification for referring to the Nordic countries as "information societies". Information processing with computers has spread to every sector of working life. It is fairly arbitrary whether computer-related trades are classified as information occupations or assigned to their traditional sectors. In any event, computer-related occupations play a central role in Nordic societies of today. According to Statistics Sweden's analysis (1985) of the Swedish people's computer habits, one-fifth of gainfully employed persons in Sweden used a computer in her/his work in 1984. The new information technology has triggered a flood of speculations about the nature of work in the future. There are discussions about whether the distribution of work in its traditional forms is likely to disappear, whether we are drifting towards an increasing gap between "winners" and "losers" or whether work will become less strenuous and more attractive for everyone. Torsten Björkman and Åke Sandberg (1988, pp. 253-255) have posed the question whether our society of the future will be post-industrial or super-industrial. The authors themselves tend to support the latter view, with some reservations. Or, as they put it: "the number of employees used for the production of goods will decline, but industry will triumph as a model for production". They noted "that even very knowledge-intensive work processes can be standardized".

In any event, the industrial society has been transformed and extensively changed in qualitative respects compared to the situation only a few decades ago. This structural change has had a major impact on many areas of society. Many of these effects remain hidden to us because there has not been time to analyze them. Some consequences have probably not become manifest as yet. Certain structural changes, and the spread of automation and computerization will probably lead to shifts in political power. However, political institutions are often very stable and resistant to drastic change. The Nordic political party system functioned very well and remained virtually intact after the violent, dramatic changes inflicted by World War II. But there is considerable doubt about whether the current party system in the Nordic countries could again survive afflictions of the same magnitude. The fact is that our party political subdivisions no longer have any clear correspondence in the social structure of society, as was once the case.

# Torsten Hägerstrand

# Urbanization processes

On September 8, 1966, the Board of Directors of the Bank of Sweden Tercentenary Foundation decided to finance a human geography research program under the general heading "The Urbanization Process". Sven Godlund, Olof Wärneryd and I were awarded a grant of SEK 1.1 million (equivalent to about SEK 6 million in the current value of money) for the first three years of the program. A sub-project, headed by Lennart Améen, was appended in 1967.

Access to that much research funding all at once was a new experience for us. We had indeed previously been funded by the Swedish Council for Social Science Research over the years and several other grant suppliers. But relatively modest sums were available for assistants and material. However, the young Foundation was in a position to supply social scientists with grants of a magnitude previously enjoyed only by researchers in the natural sciences. We could now afford to employ full-time researchers and pay them a good salary. Supplementary grants conveyed considerable, wide-ranging freedom of action.

The program was in accordance with the Foundation's task to concentrate grants, at least initially, on "major, long-term projects" whose object was to expand "knowledge about the impact of technical, economic and social changes on the society and individual citizens". Jörgen Westerståhl's program "Kommunal indelning – kommunalt självstyre" (Local government areas – local self-government), commenced one year earlier, also belonged to this category.

There is some irony in the circumstance that Sven Godlund and I, by virtue of our collaboration as experts in the revision into local government areas (SOU 1961:9), contributed to some extent to the emergence of the problems the local government research program intended to examine. In any event, both programs reflected, each in its own way, the fact that the social terrain in Sweden at this time was in the process of radical transformation in several respects. However, it would be an error to assume that studies of urbanization were only organized as a response to the national leadership's need for up-to-date knowledge. The program was actually launched at the intersection of two spheres: the challenges of ongoing social developments, on the one hand, and the intra-scientific situation, on the other hand. Let me describe both these "spheres" before I move on to an account of the way the program was implemented and the role it can be assumed to have had in the way theory and practice were subsequently addressed.

People's economic activities and their settlements are inter-related. They are inter-related in time because of life's daily alternations between work and leisure. They are inter-related in space because movements incur time loss and expenditures. The circumstances sometimes referred to as the "tyranny of space" have obviously eased in the post-war years as a result of motorism. But when the situation is viewed on a national scale, economic activity and settlement remain inseparable twins. The contemporary existence of a few hundred thousand "decision-makers" who make long-distance trips to and from meetings every day, does not invalidate this rule. The extent to which the new forms of telecommunications are able to loosen the links between home and work more radically than motorism remains to be seen.

During Sweden's modern history, i.e. since the beginning of the 19th century, the location of economic activities and settlements have been radically rearranged three times. To begin with, land reforms and the breaking up of farm villages spread out the rapidly growing population to separate farms and a multitude of cottages until virtually all arable land had been utilized.

The second structural change was caused by the building of railways. Stations along railway lines and at railway junctions quickly became crystallization nuclei for trade and industry. The Sweden of numerous non-administrative urban settlements began to take shape, although without any major regional changes in population distribution, despite the fact that the rural population had begun to decline. The loss of nearly a million emigrants belongs to the initial phase of this period.

The third major change took place after World War II. It was stamped by the rapid depopulation of rural communities, stagnation or decline in the numerous small and peripheral urban settlements and an intensive establishment of suburbs around the major cities, Stockholm, Göteborg and Malmö/Lund in particular. During this period, shifts in the country's settlement pattern gradually became a politically charged issue in quite a different way than had previously been the case.

"The world in which our people will live after the restoration of peace must be a new world in many respects." This is the English translation of the first sentence of the Summary in *Arbetarrörelsens efterkrigsprogram* (1943) (The labor movement's postwar program). Its 27 points, written under the supervision of the Swedish politician Ernst Wigfors, became guidelines for Social-Democracy's economic and social policies, although socialization ambitions were abandoned at an early stage. At this time, thinking was limited to a social world of classes, occupations and genders. A spatial perspective did not extend beyond the home and its immediate environs. The document contains nothing suggesting that any thought had been given to the circumstance that the structural transformation, that was not only foreseen but an objective, would give rise to a nationwide, politically intractable "replanting" of both industries and settlements.

When problems began to arise in the two opposite poles of population redistribution, i.e. in depopulating areas and in the metropolises with their housing shortage, labor union economists proclaimed in *"Samordnad näringspolitik"* (Coordinated economic policy) that the task was to "encourage the concentration of economic activity into expansive areas" (Meidner 1961, p. 582). Prevailing hostility to large cities should be dismissed as "emotional", it was felt. This salvo was aimed not only at the spokespersons of the Agrarian Party but even at the Social-Democratic county governor Per Eckerberg because of his attempts to attract industry to small towns and his suggestion to move public agencies out of Stockholm.

Details in the political debate reflected a number of prevailing views about the prerequisites for economic efficiency and a good life. Efficiency was believed to demand a highly mobile labor force with a rising level of competence plus access to input goods and services without time losses. The population's interests were expressed as a demand for full employment and equal access to education, public health, cultural resources and recreation. All this pointed to a completely urbanized society composed of heavily populated urban regions.

On the other hand, settlement stability is greatly valued by people in practice. Moving from a metropolis is as unpopular as moving from a thinly populated countryside. In fact, economic theoreticians have underestimated the economic merit of stable social environments with highly developed informal relationships. This is indicated by the many return migrations from big cities back to places of origin. In any event, there are always strong forces present that attempt to preserve the prevailing population distribution, also including thinly populated districts. A complete evacuation of large regions would also be unreasonable from a national point of view. Such a policy would make utilization of natural assets (including tourism) and defense of the country's territory far more difficult.

The dilemma has been ridiculed by the common assertion that most Swedes dream of living in a red-painted cottage set down on a central square in Stockholm. Things are no different today than in the 60's. People are possibly more inclined now to refrain from equality ideals, supposedly only attainable in cities, in order to create scope for lifestyles closer to nature. Working at home has increased, especially among men in their 40's and 50's with a computer as their work and communications tool. However, the ability of such ideals to survive without the support of motorism and aviation remains an open question.

In the prevailing political climate, a political sector gradually emerged, a sector first called "industrial location policy" and subsequently "regional policy". The report issued by the Näslund Commission, *"Aktiv lokaliseringspolitik"* (Active location policy) (SOU 1963:58) was the beginning of an intensified public debate and action programs (Olsson 1965). The Government appointed an "Industrial Location Committee". In this context, I was asked to write a review called *"Regionala utvecklingstendenser och problem i Sverige"* (Regional development trends and problems in Sweden) for the 1965 Long-term Economic Review. Another subsequent assignment was to outline a research program on "urbanization, issues concerning major cities in particular" for the Industrial Location Committee in April 1966.

Enough said about regional transformations and political understanding of this process at the middle of the 1960's. And now over to the academic situation. At the departments of social and economic geography, we were well-prepared for dealing with the issues. We had an infrastructure of organized data and methods to work with concerning certain purely descriptive aspects of the work.

Sten De Geer's *"Atlas över befolkningens fördelning i Sverige"* (1919) (Atlas of the distribution of population in Sweden) constituted a stable foundation for a nationwide historical perspective, since it made a clear distinction between urban and rural settlements, free of the disturbed picture of these matters as rendered by official population statistics.

William William-Olson had subsequently (1946) modernized De Geer's work and supplemented it with a classification of the economic structure of *tätorterna* (literally: densely populated places). The designation *tätort* (the root noun) was introduced by William-Olsson and subsequently became an accepted term in the Swedish language. His purpose was to mark the distinction between geographic reality and the various legal terms used in Sweden to designate urban agglomerations. Hedbom-Norling-Pålsson performed a third revision (1964) in conjunction with Elis Pålsson's work on the location of new high schools with a view to maximizing the student population basis in each instance. At this time, Statistics Sweden, thanks to the efforts of Gerd Enequist, introduced special census statistics on industries and occupations in densely populated places.

The picture we now possessed of the geographic distribution and redistribution of the Swedish population was rearranged for computer mapping and thereby constituted a basis for index calculations concerning specific social and economic circumstances for all parts of the country. Thus, conditions in Sweden's southernmost province, Skåne, could be compared to conditions in the northernmost province without the distortion found in official statistics as a result of wide ranging differences in the areal size of municipalities.

We had also performed a number of studies of different types of mobility, i.e. the mobility of people, goods and information. Investigations of annual gross migrations out of and into selected places in various parts of the country, and of the geographic life-paths of samples of individuals, had shown how complex migration patterns really are and how poorly traditional statistical figures on net population losses and gains depict underlying processes.

Corresponding information on road traffic patterns in the country had been gathered, under the leadership of Sven Godlund, in conjunction with the preparation of the 1957 national road plan. A few years earlier, Edgar Kant had called attention to the parallel growth of commuting to and from work and motorism, a development creating a need for new understanding of the shape of local labor markets. Walking distances between home and work were less and less the rule. There was then hardly any point in continuing to compare the number of job opportunities in a municipality with the size of the local population.

Gunnar Törnqvist's *"Studier i industrilokalisering"* (Studies in industrial location) (1963) showed that the classical industrial location theories which emphasized the cost for transporting goods had lost a great deal of their explanatory power because of the growing importance of the need by managers for personal contacts and easy access to information. His work drew attention to a new research field of obvious importance to an understanding of emerging features in urbanization.

Primate cities had been introduced as special objects of investigation as early as 1912 by Sten De Geer in his comparative study *"Storstäderna vid Östersjön"* (Primate cities of the Baltic) (Ymer 1912). However, William William-Olsson's two Stockholm studies, *"Huvuddragen av Stockholms geografiska utveckling 1850-1930"* (Main features of Stockholm's geographic development 1850-1930) (1937) and *"Stockholms framtida utveckling"* (Stockholm's future development) (1941) were of even greater importance. Despite being written in Swedish, these works attracted international attention and played a guiding role in subsequent urban and regional planning.

Geographic urban research in Sweden had advanced far enough after the war to warrant the holding of an international symposium in Lund as one part of the International Geographical Union's Nordic congress in 1960. The symposium gave Swedes an opportunity to establish contacts with leading European and American researchers in the field. It also contributed to contacts between scholars in these two parts of the world.

Research mentioned so far had been conducted over a long period of time and in differing contexts. But under the pressure of rapid social changes in the middle of the 1960's, initiatives were taken to achieve more coordinated research measures in respect to urbanization as well as rural depopulation. The Swedish Council for Social Science Research in which Sven Dahl represented geography at that time summoned representatives of the discipline to a meeting on the matter in Stenungsund in May 1966. This meeting drew up a list of priorities for topical sub-projects. These sub-projects were grouped into three scale levels: European, national and local. At the same time, the newly established Expert Committee for Regional Research (ERU), at that time under the Ministry of the Interior, was attempting to induce scholars other than geographers to address the field from their respective points of view.

The result of these various initiatives was that the grant referred to as the "urbanization process" according to Foundation minutes in 1966 was actually only part of a much more broadly based regional research program. In 1966 and 1967, the Foundation awarded grants to a further six projects on the Stenungsund priority list, viz. "growth problems in large cities", "locational changes in trade and industry", "the middle-sized urban region", "Europe's cities and countrysides" and "problems in the regional distribution of resources". The latter topic was dealt with both in economics and in economic geography. In addition, the ERU awarded a grant to a project in Lund called "population thresholds for availability of education and jobs". The aim of this study was to investigate the way life opportunities varied with the size of population living within commuting range of a given place. A number of related projects supported by the Council for Building Research were also conducted. A report I was asked to prepare on regional policy research in Sweden for the Economic Commission of Europe in October 1967 listed 29 projects. The same month, the Foundation convened a meeting (led by Torgny Segerstedt) in Stockholm for a review of prevailing work plans.

Naturally, there is no space here for a description of all the relevant projects conducted at the time of the "great decampment", as *Industria* (1963), a leading journal, called the ongoing transformation. Instead, I will limit myself to brief descriptions of the part of the Stenungsund program with the closest links to the ERU. This link provides cause for a closing discussion on the relationship between research, political decisions and societal development.

The aim of the work program was to view regional changes, urbanization in particular, in a different light than had generally been the case in other disciplines. The idea was to address problems raised in debates emerging from local experience in different parts of the country while simultaneously supplying context and consistency through refinement of the "physicalism" that is characteristic of geographic thinking.

The predominant approach in social science research makes a distinction between three spheres: the economic, the political and the social spheres. National borders are important as the physical framework of events but location and spatial relationships are otherwise ignored. When an attempt is made to adopt a geographic perspective, the nation is subdivided with respect to administrative areas (like a group of nations in miniature) that lend themselves to convenient tabulation but that are not perceived as a continuum of locations. However, the acting person, whether enterpriser, worker or anything else, cannot avoid place-dependency. This interlinks the economic, political and social spheres in configurations no abstract trisection is capable of capturing because it is excluded by definition right from the start. Another alternative, to quote the 1966 project description, is "to attempt to treat society and its tools as a single contiguous "physical" system. The main object of study then becomes the organization and interlinkages of human activities. Time and place must be assigned a prominent role in description and analysis because organizational connections and troublesome goal conflicts are most easily elucidated within the framework of these dimensions".

The program's vision expressed a view that radically differed from views expressed in the main debate at the time.

Politically speaking, the regional issue was identical to acute problems in depopulating areas and in major cities. Economists, for their part, seemed to regard regionally directed measures as a sacrifice from the point of view of national economic development (Bentzel 1972). But when you view the entire population and the entire national territory in their mutual connection, you naturally find that all policies, economic and otherwise, effect changes to varying degrees throughout a country. Juxtaposing national policy versus regional policy is then the same as addressing only a part of a process whose totality is ignored. In the "urbanization process" program, our aim was to get a grip on the country's total regional structure with an emphasis on the system of urban nodes.

In a relatively uncomplicated economy comprising agrarian production, small-scale industry and trade, plus strong distance friction, Christaller's central place theory was a satisfactory starting point for understanding the dynamics in the urban system when things initially began to change (cf. Godlund 1954, pp. 328-333). Post-war mobility, technology and new organizational forms did not obliterate the inherited pattern but added features demanding new, empirical studies.

One aim of the program was to expose relationships previously undetected, at least not in any systematic manner. The first question concerned the extent and way in which the country's urban centers constituted an integral system in a functional sense. They obviously competed for migrants. As William-Olsson had pointed out in the debate on the future of Stockholm, this competition imposed a limit on the extent to which the capital was capable of attracting people. But beyond this, the mechanisms at work when employment expansion or decline in one place produced effects in other places were not equally clear. The second question involved determining in some reasonably precise manner how different labor market areas behaved as frameworks for working and living.

Research that does not consist solely of the descriptive

rendering of data but that attempts to be innovative thrives best when researchers are free to work as they see fit. In accordance with this view, generously shared by the Foundation and the ERU, work was not centrally controlled. The participants formed what we today refer to as a network. At seminars and with the aid of a publication series, members kept one another informed about the progress of their work. Fifty-one issues of the publication series appeared from 1967 to 1972 with Lund, Göteborg, Stockholm and Uppsala as production sites. The reports were distributed to 190 addressees, mainly at university departments. Thirty-six were sent to Denmark, Norway and Finland and eight to other countries. One issue, called *"Individers dygnsbanor i några hushållstyper"* (The daily paths of individuals in some types of households), contained so much new material that it induced colleagues in Amsterdam to publish a Dutch translation. A large number of seminar papers were produced within the program. The final documentation appeared in doctoral theses and appendices to the reports of government commissions.

A program organized in this loose manner must obviously divaricate along unforeseeable lines as new ideas emerge in the course of time. Some plans are also abandoned when they prove to be fruitless or are too work-intensive or for purely personal reasons. It is more important to note that new issues often emerge once a program has been completed on schedule, issues giving rise to new work plans. This was also the case for the "urbanization process" program. Research is still being conducted on the subject, both in geography and in many other disciplines not included from the beginning. At the time of writing, two new perspectives have emerged, viz. one concerning the impact of the Europeization of industry and the other relationships between urbanization and environmental issues.

The nature of social science research is that it can never be finished. It entails continuous monitoring of events, hopefully with increasing acuity and overview. So the "urbanization process" program had a beginning but no end. I will therefore limit my remaining remarks to that beginning, i.e. up to the years around 1970.

The main problem was how to move from traditional statistical cross-sections and simple extrapolations to an understanding of how urban systems worked and were transformed. Issues such as these cannot be addressed in a general way without the aid of variables that place qualitatively different factors, seen from the micro point of view, on an equal footing. Prices and other standard features of the economic game have that property but transform reality into a set of pure symbols. We turned to the underlying, material transactions and restrictions surrounding these features. The flow of goods, people and information was assumed to depict primary, functional characteristics. The economic use of time stood out as an essential component in this picture. But in order to even reveal processes of change, flows had to be viewed in relation to the channeling system formed by physical infrastructure, organizational domains and prevailing behavioral rules.

The new mobility became a *"leitmotif"* in our studies: its consequences but even the opportunities it presented. It offered people and places new situational values in relation to one another. It promoted collaboration in new organizational forms. But it also had a separating effect, since the gap increased between mobile and less mobile people and between densely populated centers and the sparsely populated peripheries.

Because of the complex relationships generated by the new organizational forms and dependencies, simulation models became a useful tool in work on the sorting out of concepts. Olof Wärneryd supplied the first illustrative example in his 1968 thesis *"Interdependence in urban systems"*. The issue concerned the relationship between organizational structures and spatial outcomes. The model was expanded by Lars Nordström in his *"Rumsliga förändringar och ekonomisk utveckling"* (Spatial change and economic development) (1971). Here, he emphasized the link between centralization and the characteristic life-course of organizations.

In 1970, Bo Lenntorp completed the first version of PESASP, a model for calculating the number of ways in which a given action program can be implemented in an environment with a specified geographic and temporal structure. The aim, using PESASP as a probe, was to be able to compare the degrees of freedom in the everyday life of households in different types of residential settings. Solveig Mårtensson and Tommy Carlstein had simultaneously collected empirical material on interdependencies in the temporal organization of society.

During the same period, Sture Öberg devised a model for calculating distance-related variations in access to services in Sweden, i.e. access to offerings with limited capacity, assuming that everyone achieved the national, average level of consumption. Öberg also led work on the development of GEDAP, a program for computerized cartography without which we would have been unable to process chorological variables for Sweden as a whole.

Modeling work was supported by a large number of empirical studies. Most were small-scale case studies. But several large studies merit mention. Maj Ohre-Aldskogius's "*Folkmängds-förändringar och stadstillväxt. En studie av stora och medelstora stadsregioner*" (Population change and urban growth. An investigation of big and middle-sized urban regions) was published in Uppsala in 1968. The following year, Gerd Enequist published her analysis of urban centers in Sweden, "*Tätorterna i Sverige 1960-65*" (Ymer 1969). In 1969, Sven Godlund et al. published "*Näringsliv och transportsystem*" (Economic activities and transport systems) (an appendix to SOU 1969:23). This study had both a historic and prospective perspective. Its main theme was the centralization of harbor activities and the attendant adaptation of road transportation of mass goods, adaptation with an unavoidable impact on the urban system.

In "*Rumsliga effekter av organisationsförändringar*" (Spatial effects of organizational change) (1970), Lennart Andersson pursued Wärneryd's and Nordström's ideas but placed the emphasis on how central decisions were modulated on their way down to local implementation as a result of divergent interests and territorial frames of competence on the levels traversed. Examples were taken from the ongoing reformation of the Swedish school system. The Göteborg group was particularly interested in the issue of Stockholm in its role of capital versus the rest of the Sweden.

Gunnar Törnqvist expanded on his previous observation that access to information was becoming an increasingly important locational factor, especially information requiring direct personal contacts. He organized a powerful program throwing light on the shape of the Swedish "contact landscape" in relation to the urban system as a whole.

His first step was, as was the case with Thorngren (1967) and Kristensson (1967), to reject the ability of traditional economic statistics to depict decisive features in structural changes. A breakdown of data in terms of work functions was considered to be far more illuminating. One such breakdown was achieved, at least in the form of approximate values, e.g. with the aid of statistics, collected by the Swedish Employers' Confederation and within branches of government.

In his thesis *"Regional arbetsfördelning"* (Regional division of labor) (1970), Mats-G. Engström showed that contact-dependent functions had become concentrated in the major cities, whereas people employed in manufacturing had been moved out. The shift was most apparent in the Stockholm region. Moreover, the thesis showed that employment in contact-dependent functions increased more than other groups. Multiplier effects on population development in the big cities were considerable.

The geographic patterns of personal contacts were examined in two theses: Bengt Sahlberg's *"Interregionala kontaktmönster. Personkontakter inom svenskt näringsliv – en flygpassage-*

*rarstudie"* (Inter-regional contact patterns. Personal contacts in Swedish economic life – a study of airline passengers) (1970) and Björn Hedberg's *"Kontaktsystem inom svenskt näringsliv. En studie av organisationers externa personkontakter"* (Contact systems in Swedish economic life. A study of external personal contacts in organizations) (1970). The former was based on 13 360 questionnaires filled by about 17 000 travellers, and the latter on replies from 1 760 white-collar workers at 14 companies throughout the country.

On the basis of all this material, Törnqvist (1972) calculated that moving out contact-dependent functions from Stockholm to regional centers without any changes in the existing transportation system would reinforce the capital's role as a meeting-place. However, if direct transportation links were established between regional centers, contact potential would be about equally distributed between southern and central Sweden, as well as greatly improved in the north. Even with the existing transportation system, the northern part of the country was found to be in a good position for day trips to the south but generally out of reach as a destination for day trips from the south of the country.

Another sub-project, led by Lennart Améen and Ulf Erlandsson, whose final report was incorporated in the latter's thesis, *"Företagsutveckling och utrymmesbehov"* (Company development and space acquisition) (1975), addressed the empirically difficult problem of the rapidity with which expanding enterprises are able to satisfy their needs for premises within the framework of existing urban spaces whose turnover is naturally sluggish for physical and planning reasons. The space consumption history of 32 companies in Stockholm and Malmö was documented. Among other things, it was shown that office-oriented businesses found it easier to make do with various provisional measures than manufacturing enterprises, especially since the latter prefer single-story buildings nowadays. This difference may be one of the explanations for the migration of manufacturing industries out of the big cities. Another may be the extensive urban renewal projects that obliterate old, inexpensive quarters in central locations. These proved to be the normal starting environment for budding enterprises, industrial incubators of a sort.

Erlandsson's unique material has been undervalued in the industrial location debate, probably because of the inability of social science research to connect micro and macro perspectives. This can also be said of Lennart Andersson's study of the filtration of central decisions on their way to implementation.

The projects begun in 1966/67 were rounded off in the book *"Regioner att leva i"* (Regions to live in) (1972). Here, experience gained in Erik Bylund's program for the sparsely populated areas in the north, pursued since 1966, was also given a prominent place. The book preceded a major Government bill in which regional policies and national planning of the use of land and water were coordinated (1972:111). This occurred in a way that would have been unlikely without the studies monitored by the ERU and mainly financed by the Foundation. A more technical account was published in 1970 in *"Urbaniseringen i Sverige"* (Urbanization in Sweden) (SOU 1970:14), an appendix to the ERU's first report *"Balanserad regional utveckling"* (Balanced regional development) (SOU 1970:3).

However, the 1966 program had not been fully completed by 1970. But two years later, most of the ground work in producing a picture of ongoing regional processes in Sweden had been finished. Among the reports published that year, I can mention Erik Wallin's *"Yrkesvalsprocessen och den regionala strukturen"* (Urbaniseringsprocessen 51, 1972) (Choice of occupation and regional structure) and the Göteborg group's *"Funktioner och kontakter"* (Gothia no. 11, 1972) (Functions and contacts). The task thereafter became to address certain issues in greater depth. The beginning of this phase is best illustrated by the appendices to the ERU's *"Orter i regional samverkan"* (Places in regional cooperation) (SOU 1974:1), viz. *"Ortsbundna lev-*

*nadsvillkor"* (Place-bound living conditions) (SOU 1974:2) and *"Regionala prognoser i planeringens tjänst"* (Regional forecasts in the service of planning) (SOU 1974:4).

The ERU's role as an intermediary between research and politics was, at least around 1970, a unique arrangement in an international perspective. In some quarters, this may have been regarded as improper influence on academic research. But this has not been my experience. No directives were issued, as is otherwise the case with Government commissions. Under Ingvar Ohlsson's leadership, the ERU was careful to avoid involvement in research work as such. Instead, it supported that work by means of seminars and uncensored publications. Communication channels were bidirectional. Academics met with leading politicians and administrators, thereby acquiring perspectives different to those usually available at university departments.

The practical importance of the research is quite a different matter. This question in itself could be the subject of studies. However, even when viewed superficially, the material from the "urbanization process" program and other parallel programs is clearly discernible in political texts and in certain decisions. The "Regional Structure Plan" enacted by the Riksdag in 1972 showed that the idea of the country's various urban centers as an interdependent system had been accepted. The physical infrastructure was seen to be one of the Government's most effective regional policy instruments. The aim was, without detailed controls, to coordinate locational decisions and to provide the business community with signals on intentions regarding regional structure. After a few years with a non-Social-Democratic government in power, the concepts "system of cities" and "alternatives to big cities" fell out of favor. But the concepts still clearly play a role in the taken-for-granted perception of Sweden.

One critical comment might concern the timing of publications. They were naturally adapted to the times at which regional policy bills were to be submitted. But research projects could not always be completed at that pace.

Participants in the "urbanization process" program established early contacts with foreign colleagues. This was rather natural, since people were working with the same problems in different parts of the world. Invitations to foreign university departments and conferences were frequent occurrences. These contacts have become lasting and been expanded. Swedish ideas and experiences were utilized in EFTA's *"National Settlement Strategies. A framework for regional development"* (Geneva 1973). The secretary of the working party, John Goddard from the London School of Economics, performed a large part of the actual writing work in Sweden. Torgny Segerstedt (chairman of both the Foundation and the Swedish Council for Social Science Research at the time) established contacts with the European Cultural Foundation's *"Europe 2000"* program. Allan R. Pred's long review article, *"Urbanisation, domestic planning problems and Swedish geographic research"*, published in Progress in Geography (Vol. 5, 1973), was one of the publications meriting special mention as far as international communications are concerned.

The concentration on the "urbanization process" program was a highly valued challenge. The program served as an educational background for many people who are now university teachers or employed in administration or business. It served as the seedbed of new lines of development subsequently supported by the Foundation, the Swedish Council for Social Science Research and other funding agencies.

However, any attempt to summarize experience from the point of view of the discipline cannot avoid noting that the concentration on just one problem area also represented a limitation by making heavy demands on the research capacity of the involved university departments. Other problems were left uncultivated. This development cannot be blamed on project financiers. It was due to the circumstance that universities only have limited resources for studies their established scholars can pursue without seeking outside funding. This situation can be illustrated with the circumstances of geographic research.

Within the framework of the main theme of mankind's terrestrial home, three problem strands have become intertwined in the course of time. One of the historians of geographic thought, Anne Buttimer (1990), refers to them with the three key words *identity, order* and *niche*.

"Identity" concerns the humanistic study of rural and urban landscapes as emotionally and socially binding phenomena. Home area studies in Swedish schools once reflected this tradition. "Order" refers to the functional organization in space of physical infrastructure, activities and dwelling. Finally, "niche" refers to society's appropriation of natural resources.

The "urbanization process" program concentrated almost exclusively on "order", even though regional policy problems arose to a great extent from the tension between local and regional identity and national order. Moreover, it was apparent as early as the 1960's that corresponding tension would develop between "order" and "niche", i.e. the environmental and conservation problems in which we are currently enmeshed.

Viewed in retrospect, we should have attempted to create preparedness for the present by joining together all three perspectives with the support of humanistic and ecological disciplines. If this idea had been proposed twenty-five years ago, however, the universities would not have had the resources needed. Nor would there have been any sector body offering support. In the same way as regional policy research needed an intermediary, viz. the ERU, a broader approach would have required something of that nature although with less of an economistic emphasis. However, the Foundation would not have had any impeding internal boundaries similar to those to which sector-controlled research must adjust. It does not need to bind the projects it supports to any particular sector or not even to academic disciplines. It will remain an invaluable asset for this very reason.

*Bo Gustafsson*

# Causes of the expansion of the public sector

In May 1973, the then dean of Social Sciences at Uppsala University, Gunnar Arpi, called to let me know that I had been awarded a grant from the Bank of Sweden Tercentenary Foundation for an economic history project on the causes of the public sector's expansion in the 20th century. This was my first project, and it indeed had a rather grandiose design. It was conducted by five doctoral candidates: Anders Forsman, Christer Florman, Enrique Rodriguez, Lennart Waara and Kurt Wickman (with Peter Gårestad subsequently joining the group) in addition to myself, a recently appointed associate professor of economic history. It became one of the biggest economic history projects conducted in the 1970's and ultimately resulted in eleven books and numerous papers.

## Background

By the time the project was launched in 1973, it had already been preceded by several years of preparations. One factor contributing to our special interest in the growth of the public sector was the discussions being conducted at the time in Marxist circles on how to explain the state's growing economic role in modern, capitalistic society. There were many schools of thought in international Marxism in this period. In the lively West German debate on Marxism, ideas from Marx's view of production conditions, put forward in "Grundrisse", were suggested. In the fifth volume of "Grundrisse", Marx noted that it was by no means certain that the private sector would be capable of achieving the production conditions necessary for capitalism. For a capitalist to build a road, for example, the capitalist had to raise sufficient capital, there had to be an adequate return on the investment, the traffic volume had to be sufficiently large and the people who demanded the road services needed incomes high enough to support this demand. Marx's conclusion was that capitalism presumed certain general production conditions that capitalism might not be able to create on its own. This created scope and a demand for intervention by the state. These ideas were expanded by West German "capital logicians" into a speculative system that attracted considerable attention at the time.

The public sector had indeed expanded in societies whose very foundation and development were based on capitalistic relations of production. But it was perfectly obvious that large parts of the growing public sector satisfied needs and demands emanating from interests other than the capitalists themselves. As a result of observations such as these we began searching for clues for our project studies by reviewing sources such as Gunnar Myrdal who had described his views as early as 1961 in the book "Planhushållning i välfärdsstaten" (views whose essential features had already been advocated by Myrdal in a lecture at his professorial inauguration in 1934). Myrdal cited three main causes for the growth of the public sector in the 20th century: 1. spontaneous forces in the form of accumulated, accidental measures taken by the state in solving specific crises and satisfying special needs but that were subsequently made permanent; 2. the increasing organization of markets as a consequence of large-scale operations, large-scale technology and the emergence and demands of different special interest organizations; and 3. increasing demands, arising after democracy's breakthrough, for economic equality. Myrdal referred to the fact that "effective protection of the interests of the poor is more likely when private services become public".

The first cause cited by Myrdal played a major role in a book published the same year as Myrdal's, viz. Alan T. Peacock's and Jack Wiseman's "The Growth of Public Expenditure in the United Kingdom". The book underlined the "displacement effect", i.e. the tendency for the demand for public spending to increase by leaps and bounds in times of crisis and war, and, instead of reverting to pre-war/pre-crisis level, "stick" on a somewhat higher level after the war or crisis, simply because the new spending leads to programs with new interested parties who defend their interests. This was clearly *one* important factor. The problem was that it was only capable of explaining the rises in levels immediately after the two world wars and the crisis in the 1930's but not the steady, progressive rise after 1950.

When we reviewed the econometric literature and found that there was rather close correlation between the level of economic development (measured in GNP per capita), on the one hand, and the level of public spending (measured as a percent of the GNP), on the other hand, our conviction that the public sector's expansion, despite inter-country variations, was probably due to several, very general structural factors related to modernization and economic growth, was strengthened. However, we were unable to find any major explanatory value in very generally formulated neoclassical theories (such as Pigou's and Samuelson's) because their models contained too few arguments to permit the building of any bridges between models and historical reality. On the other hand, some other, less general but more testable theories struck us as being too narrow. The Peacock-Wiseman theory on displacement effects belongs to this category, as well as Baumol's theory on productivity lag in the production of services and Niskanen's theory on production-maximizing bureaucrats. The problem with Baumol's theory was (and is) that it, although containing features important to a general explanation, is only relevant to the part of public sector activities which affect the production of services. We also found

Niskanen's theory too one-sided and (as is often the case in social science models) too dependent on American institutional conditions. In Sweden, the political process, rather than the administrative process, seemed to be the driving force in developments. Another problem was that the hypothesis on strong and virtually autocratic bureaucracies should have resulted in a particularly rapid increase in administrative costs. But we quickly found that this was not the case.

We also found elements for a general theory in less spectacular sub-theories, such as those claiming that public sector production of services could be induced by private production or consumption, as when the increase in automobile usage caused an increase in road building. Erik Höök's striking observations on the public sector's production of services as an outcome of the social division of labor also belong to this category. This was obviously the case for a large proportion of the production of care services, e.g. when the care of children and the elderly was transferred from the home to public institutions. Höök called this a "transfer of the production of services" and it was no more remarkable than the corresponding phenomenon in the private sector's production, as when the production of milk, butter and meat in the closed peasant households of yesteryear was transferred to specialized dairies and meat processing plants. But no matter how we analyzed the different transfer phenomena, they still failed to explain the public sector's expansion as a whole.

In this respect we perhaps should have done what many others before us had done, viz. grind to a halt and tell ourselves that finding an explanation for the growth of phenomena as diverse as defense, police protection, education, public health, road building, ice breaker services and income transfers was probably impossible. But developments still displayed some common denominators, such as the fact they were all shaped by government (national, regional and municipal) as the principal agent, and the development profile was fairly similar over time in different countries: expansion began slowly at the start of the 20th century, accelerated during the world wars and the crises of the 1930's and then rose sharply in most countries after World War II. Any explanation for this development would obviously have to be in terms related to basic features of the 20th century's modernization process: rapid technical and economic growth, urbanization, a rapid change in the specialization and the distribution of labor, the rise of democracy and the breakthrough of welfare and equality ideologies. This is what Myrdal had in mind, and this is what Marx should have had in mind, in our view. So we began doing some thinking of our own. We felt that it would be better to work according to a model which was approximate but relevant instead of a model that was precise but irrelevant.

## Preparations

Since the public sector encompasses so many different activities and operational forms, the project members held discussions for the purpose of identifying the main activities. Our conclusion was that we should address four main aspects: state-owned enterprises, public spending, public revenue and social planning (long-term planning). In the 1960's, state-ownership of enterprises had acquired considerable scope, due in part to the labor movement's economic offensive, and it was obvious that the driving forces behind the emergence and development of state-owned enterprises differed to a large extent from those in privately owned companies. The question also arose whether the growth in public income merely reflected developments in public spending or whether the scope and development of taxation was governed by other, independent factors, such as the role of taxes in economic policies. For many of the economists with whom we were in touch, the latter alternative was more or less self-evident: taxes are used for controlling demand. But older economists held a broader view. When Gunnar Myrdal conducted his major investigation (within the framework of the governmental unemployment commission, SOU 1934:1) into the effects of financial policies, he assumed not only that the main purpose of taxes was to finance public expenditures but that taxes were a definitive characteristic of public finance whose aim was to satisfy needs rather than provide revenue. Revenue is the end and spending is the means in the private sector, whereas the reverse applies to the public sector, i.e. spending (for the direct satisfaction of need) is the end and revenue only a means thereto. (A similar view was advanced by Kalecki when he contrasted the economic objectives of capitalists and wage-earners: capitalists spend to earn, whereas wage-earners earn to spend.) Could it be, as Myrdal intimated, that public management of the economy had introduced a new principle that was in conflict with private, capitalistic economic management? When comparing the liberal taxation freeze ideology of the 1920's with the policies in vogue in the 1930's when Myrdal (and others) began viewing public spending as investments in health, education and, thus, human capital, instead of as costs for non-productive consumption, we found that the view of the role of taxation tended to vary over time. Similarly, public income expansion was conditioned by the tax system's organization, governed in turn by both political circumstances (such as the tax system's degree of progressivity or regressivity) and purely transient and unforeseeable factors (such as economic growth and inflation). This implied that the driving forces in the expansion of public income were well worth special study.

But the 1900's had also witnessed a gradual increase in the degree of social planning and government control, a hitherto uninvestigated factor of presumably considerable importance to social development. Regulatory measures of different kinds, planning and building legislation, long-term planning etc. were major components. We decided to concentrate on one such component, viz. state long-term planning and its governing factors. What caused its emergence and development?

I also performed one pilot study in a sensitive area. This study lasted for two-three years. It was called "Perspektiv på den offentliga sektorn under 1930-talet" and was submitted as an interim report to the Scandinavian Conference of Historians in Uppsala in the autumn of 1974 (Gustafsson 1974). The "sensitive" aspect of the subject concerned the question of whether the 1930's really deserved to be viewed as a "watershed" in the public sector's expansion, the preceding era regarded as a kind of ancien régime and the subsequent era as a nouveau régime. Our intuitive view after studying empirical material was that the "watershed" was more likely to be found at the beginning of the century. If we were able to prove that this was the case, the public sector's expansion could not then be primarily ascribed to *specific* political objectives. Instead, it would be seen to be indicative of a more profound structural phenomenon with a governing effect on policy content, if not on pace or specific features. If e.g. the breakthrough of democracy and efforts to attain equality were important driving forces, the political "color" of specific governments was not necessarily a decisive factor (although the electorate's social composition would be). As my report shows, I found a number of circumstances that justified the view of the decisive importance of the 1930's. The rate of growth in real, public expenditures in the 1930's did not differ from the rate of growth in the 1920's, reform efforts were evolutionary rather than revolutionary, the change in unemployment policies (with a genuine pre-history dating from the late 1920's) differed in reality from objectives and the aims and results of the "new economic policy" were rather modest (it had been pursued periodically before and with greater effect without attracting much attention and without the actors themselves being fully aware of what they were doing). The 1930's were rather the starting point for *general* welfare policies that, however, were only *implemented after* World War II.

In 1976, with support from the Council for Social Science Research and the Foundation, we held a 3-day conference in Uppsala on the subject "Den offentliga sektorns expansion. Teori och metodproblem" attended by scholars active in the field at the time and leading representatives of the Foundation, the research council and Uppsala University. The conference resulted in a book edited by me with the same title as the conference. The following year, I held another conference, this time on an international basis, attended by distinguished scholars in the field such as Alan Peacock, Leif Johansen, W. Brus, Alec Nove, Ragnar Bentzel, Lars Werin and Poul Nörregaard Rasmussen. The conference contributions were published in a book edited by me, "Post-industrial society" (Gustafsson 1979).

## Results

Five of the six doctoral candidates in the project completed their project assignments in the form of doctoral dissertations. The sixth candidate would undoubtedly have produced a dissertation if he had not been stricken by a tragic personal loss. His task had been to describe and analyze the relationship between the state and special-interest organizations. However, he only completed a long paper on the conditions underlying the founding of the Swedish Standards Association (Florman 1976). Despite the limited scope of the subject, the paper's principal orientation was important. He showed that the Swedish Standards Association's tasks were performed by different, separate industrial associations prior to World War I. As a result of internal conflicts, however, the associations were unable to reach agreement on general Swedish standards. The actors involved were simultaneously convinced that common standards would be beneficial to all. They ultimately asked the government to found a public standards commission. Only a public organization would be able to protect private interests in the best way. One fascinating aspect of this analysis was that it showed that a public authority was founded as a consequence of the business community's internationalization, making necessary more uniform products as well as the long series required to be competitive. So there was a general correlation between big industry's growth and development, on the one hand, and public intervention, on the other hand. Public intervention was also undertaken in order to protect the interests of the (private) business sector. This all occurred because parties in the private sector were unable, owing to internal competition, to reach mutually binding agreements. In this study, the state was seen as a body emerging from and serving private interests, on the one hand, and capable of performing this task by virtue of the fact that it was not a private party but independent of all private interests, on the other hand.

Thus after a single case study, the doctoral candidate in question arrived at the same view of the state as had been presented 50 years earlier by the Russian jurist, Evgeny Pasjukanis in "Allgemeine Rechtslehre und Marxismus" (1928) and who, in turn, had been inspired by both Marxism and, in particular, by the leading 19th century jurists Hanatou and Gierke; they had shown that the perception of a specifically public sphere of society, in contrast to a private sphere, did not develop before the emergence of market-oriented urban societies in Western Europe in the 12th and 13th centuries. This was the problem: how can there be a special public sphere which is separate from but still based on private interests? Why is the state not a *direct* extension of private interests in a capitalist society? The explanation is to be found in the internal rivalry of the private interests. But this circumstance gives rise to interesting implications. Even if the state, especially in less well developed countries, is virtually autonomous in relation to the population at large (the Soviet Union and the states in eastern Europe are examples; predatory military dictatorships in Africa and Latin America are others), these countries cannot be viewed as "states" in the same sense as typical western countries. They are entities in which certain private interests have taken over the reins of government for their own benefit, not to serve private interests collectively. The "state" in the western sense of the word is a different device altogether. Its purpose is to serve private interests, but it can do so only by being detached from every private interest. This separation simultaneously creates conditions enabling the public sector (the state) to acquire its own interests supported by the public bureaucracy, and no perfect agreement could ever be expected between private interests and public interests. Another consequence is that the state can occasionally be expected to act *contrary to private interests in their own best interest,* viz. when it is important for the common interest to be at the fore or when there is a conflict between short-term and long-term private interests.

However, this paper only served as a promising gateway to an analysis of the public sphere's conditions of existence. So the more general analysis of the public sphere was approached somewhat differently, viz. in the monograph "En teori om staten och de offentliga utgifterna" (Forsman 1989). It was found that public spending's share of the GNP grew slowly from the turn of the century to 1950. It grew at a faster rate thereafter. The fastest growing components in public spending were (in the following order) expenditures on social insurance, social welfare and public health. On the other hand, expenditures on defense and administration declined, whereas the percentage spent on education remained relatively constant.

Neither Peacock-Wiseman's theory on displacement effects during crises and war nor Baumol's theory on a lag in the growth of public service productivity proved to have any major explanatory merit. (Less than of the total growth in spending can be explained by lagging productivity gains, even on the strong assumption that there is no increase in the productivity of public services.) According to the general theory presented in the monograph, the growth in public sector spending must be explained in terms of a *general social theory* with scope for factors related both to economic growth and to political conflicts. The state can then be viewed as an entity whose dual role is to satisfy the social system's stability while simultaneously expressing the interests of the most important social classes. The public sector's expansion occurs under developed capitalism. The two main social classes are assumed to be capitalists and wage-earners. The behavior of capitalists is assumed to be governed by profit maximization (surplus value production), whereas wage-earners are assumed to maximize welfare (maximize conditions for reproduction and the satisfaction of needs). This is a parallel to Kalecki's ideas (see above), viz. that capitalists spend (invest) to earn, while wage-earners earn to spend. The manifest function of the public sector then becomes to stabilize capitalistic production in a broad sense and to create the general economic and cultural conditions necessary to its reproduction (general conditions of reproduction). This activity of the public sector corresponds to the need of private capitalists to be able to pursue profitable production. But since the system also encompasses a second class, wage-earners, with another goal orientation than capitalists, viz. maximized welfare, this class also makes somewhat different demands on the tasks to be performed by the public sector. This means that the public sector has a latent function and, as we shall see, a latent function that expands over time. The relationship between the public system's manifest functions and its latent functions should be understood to imply that identical tasks may have different functions and that different tasks may be associated with different functions. The capitalist class is interested in having an efficient public educational system in order to ensure productive labor, whereas the working class, while also making similar demands on the educational system, is also interested in having the educational system supply other services catering to its specific needs, e.g. knowledge about society, culture or politics. In a similar manner, the public health system is expected to reproduce labor while enhancing the individual's welfare. Public functions do not have this clearly dualistic nature in other instances. Direct subsidy of private enterprise is of direct interest to the capital-owner class, whereas a high level of health insurance compensation is of direct interest to the working class. Since these functions are performed within one and the same system in which certain forces stabilize the system while other forces seek to change it, and long-term effects sometimes differ from short-term effects, making clear distinctions between functions may well be difficult. But in principle, distinctions can indeed be made.

Over time, the relationship between the public sector's manifest and latent functions changes. The changes are induced by the system's basic economic motive force: surplus value production. Surplus value production is the engine in economic growth, and economic growth gives rise to a number of phenomena that promote expanding public production to satisfy direct needs: a growing working class that organizes itself in trade unions and political parties, rising real incomes that increase the demand for education, public health and insurance, urbanization and increased participation by women in the work force etc. The increased expenditures for services and transfers tend to be public because the working class has no control over the means of production. But, thanks to political democracy and the large, growing working class, this class does have access to political power with which it can compensate for its lack of economic power and partially influence the shaping of the public sector. Naturally, the theory assumes some degree of conscious intent and political attitudes that are not subordinate to capitalist production's systemic properties and that are often capable of explaining differences in the public sector's structure and rate of development. In Sweden, considerable emphasis has been placed on the public production of services. In countries like Denmark, on the other hand, emphasis has been on public transfers.

The public sector, whose development is, thus, governed by two main driving forces acting both in symbiosis and in conflict while simultaneously representing system-inherent and system-altering factors, can therefore be viewed as a new system of production within the framework of the capitalist system of production. The only prediction the theory can make about the public sector's structure and growth is that direct production catering for the needs of the working class as well as redistributive measures depend on the scope, strength and values of the working class. Several scenarios are possible for the future orientation of the public sector. On the one hand, the public sector's expansion has hitherto tended to undermine the private business sector's most important resource base, i.e. access to labor, and even deprived that sector of a growing, potential market for the output of services for consumption. On the other hand, the public sector's output has mainly been restricted to health and education, and the private sector's growth has been favored by the growing demand for goods and services from the public sector and by the public provision of an educated, well-cared for and socially well-adapted labor force, the costs of which are paid by the wage-earner collective itself. There is nothing to stop us from assuming that the two production systems (or, more accurately, production and allocation systems) will continue to exist in contradictory symbiosis. The private, market-oriented business community has proved to be efficient at supplying society with mass-consumption necessities of different kinds, and the public sector has proved to be uniquely efficient at the equitable distribution of certain services important to the citizenry's social solidarity and presumably to its long-term social efficacy. At the same time, the social insurance system has probably resulted in lower transaction costs than private insurance schemes.

The causes of the growth in public income were studied in a separate monograph, "Offentlig inkomstexpansion. En analys av drivkrafterna bakom de offentliga inkomsternas utveckling i Sverige under 1900-talet" (Rodriguez 1980). This dissertation documented for the first time the long-term development of public income in Sweden in the present century. As was the case for public spending, the growth in public income was caused by multiple factors on various levels of social reality. The tax system was assigned new functions over time. At the beginning of the century, taxes and fees were only intended for financing necessary costs (the expenditure function). From the 1930's, when Sweden began pursuing comprehensive economic policies, the tax system was also assigned a stabilizing function. As the labor movement grew in strength, taxes were also intentionally used for redistributing and equalizing incomes (the allocation function). And as taxation's contribution to income grew rapidly from the 1970's, at the same time as the rate of economic growth was lowered, the growth function of taxes also became important.

This means that the expansion of public income was not governed solely by the growth in real income but even by political objectives, economic policy and the tax system's own inherent complexity. Even transient factors, such as the rate of inflation, have been important to the rate at which progressive income tax has generated tax revenue, as well as factors such as war and economic crises that actually had displacement effects on the volume of income, since tax rates were then raised and temporary taxes made permanent. Another distinguishing trend is the fact that as tax rates and the tax volume increased, governments were forced to search for more broadly based sources of taxes. Progressive income tax was introduced by a Conservative government as early as 1902 in order to meet growing demands caused by the military defense system and new social reforms. As the importance of wage-earners and mass consumption increased, consumption taxes, social insurance fees and payroll taxes became new foundations of the tax system. The tax system was also made increasingly "invisible" to the individual taxpayer.

This study was supplemented with a separate monograph, "Industrialisering och beskattning i Sverige 1861-1914" (Gårestad 1987). It proved to be as much of a pioneering investigation as the aforementioned dissertation. During the industrial breakthrough, Sweden was dramatically transformed in economic, social and political respects. Industry expanded at the expense of agriculture, a barter economy was superseded by a money economy to an increasing degree and imports and exports increased in absolute and relative terms. In political respects, property-owners, well-to-do farmers and industrialists predominated. These changes in Sweden's social structure were also reflected in the tax system's structure and development. Agrarian interests succeeded in forcing the abolition of the old land taxes and the old system for military recruitment. Instead, revenue from customs duty on rapidly growing imports increased, automatically to some extent and as the result of increased tariffs on both industrial and agricultural products. When industrialization deepened in the 1890's and wages and salaries became a mass phenomenon, the progressive income tax introduced in 1902 became the fastest growing source of income. The actual tax share (taxes as a percentage of the GNP) had remained virtually constant throughout the half century from 1860 to 1914 when it amounted to 7-8% of the GNP. The major structural changes in Sweden's tax system were found to agree quite closely with H. Hinrich's general theory of tax structure during the industrial breakthrough. Hinrich found that direct, fixed taxes on land and individuals predominated prior to this era. During the industrial breakthrough, the economy's degree of openness increased and, thus, indirect taxes (customs duty in particular) grew in relative importance. When an industrial structure generating wages and salaries had emerged – a circumstance that also changed the social and political structure with increased resistance to regressive, indirect taxation – the relative importance of direct taxation increased once again. As we have seen, a new structural change with an increased emphasis on indirect taxation occurred at a later stage when mass consumption became the most broadly based and "invisible" source of taxation. Compensation for regressivity in the tax system was provided by an intricate system of transfers.

When the project started at the beginning of the 1970's, the state had recently begun operating enterprises on a rather large scale, both in Sweden and elsewhere. So it was natural for us to examine the state's business activities as a parallel to the production of public services in municipalities and county councils. Frederick Pryor had recently published a major study ("Property and industrial organization in communist and capitalist countries" 1973) according to which the existence of state-owned enterprises had nothing to do with any underlying economic forces. Our study, "Den statliga företagssektorns expansion. Orsaker till förstatliganden i ett historiskt och internationellt perspektiv" (Waara 1980), found evidence suggesting that the state industrial sector had de facto expanded in absolute and relative terms throughout the western world after the Industrial Revolution. State-owned enterprises were established in the 19th century primarily within the economic infrastructure (what Marx would have called "capital's general conditions of production"), viz. the railways, postal, telegraph and telephone services. Here, state enterprises had often started as private companies before being nationalized, either because they were profitable or because they were unprofitable but essential to the business community. During the first half of the 20th century, especially during and immediately after the two world wars and the crisis years of the 1930's, a new wave of nationalization commenced, this time encompassing basic industrial sectors such as energy production, mining, forestry and steel-making. A third expansion of the public business sector occurred from 1950 to 1980 when state-owned companies were even established in manufacturing (shipyards, the automotive industry, textile and clothing industry) and banking fields.

Developments in Sweden followed this general international

trend, even if (contrary to expectations) interest in nationalization has been relatively weak in our country and mainly flour-
ished in periods of structural crisis, as in the early 1920's, the
late 1960's and in the 1970's. The state industrial sector's share
of total, gross investments grew in Sweden until it peaked at
about 10%, whereas the figure rose to 10-20% in countries such
as Austria, France and Italy. No direct party-political conditions
of nationalizations were found, since nationalizations occurred
both under bourgeois and socialist governments. (The extensive
nationalizations in Sweden during the bourgeois Swedish governments in the 1970's are one example.) However, the project
was able to discern general political pressure behind certain
nationalization moves, pressure related to demands for employ-
ment-enhancing measures in dealing with structural crises in
certain sectors or regions. But it was also obvious here that state-
owned enterprises even began to be established in growth
sectors when requisite investments were extremely large, attendant risks were commensurately great and anticipated profitability was uncertain. In both these respects, expansion of the
public industrial sector could be traced to market failures in
private business in combination with socio-political mobilization and more ambitious economic and political goals. In other
words, we found the same complex causal picture as in the
studies of the expansion of public spending and income. The
expansion of state-owned enterprises could therefore be interpreted as one aspect of the modern welfare state's emergence
and development.

Our decision to study the reasons for certain planning trends
in the welfare state (in the dissertation "Makroekonomisk
planering – orsaker och utveckling" by Wickman in 1980) can
be viewed as an attempt to address more qualitative aspects of
the public sector's expansion.The concept "planning" is inherently ambiguous. We decided to limit the study to the kind of
indicative macro-economic planning arising from government
decisions on long-term or intermediate term economic policy

for the purpose of reproducing and expanding the economic system, i.e. proper economic long-term planning. In this sense, economic planning in western countries, including Sweden, started in the 1930's, expanded immensely during the second world war to encompass virtually the entire economy and was systematized after World War II. Long-term planning has concentrated primarily on increasing the flow of information within the business community and between that community and the state, influencing the supply of labor and investments for stabilization purposes and, at least in Sweden, facilitating the implementation of a full employment policy. Here, it is interesting to note that planning of the national economy can be viewed as an extension of the increased planning predilection initiated by major companies in the inter-war years for the purpose of reducing uncertainty and compensating for the growing limitations displayed by the price system, as a carrier of information, in an increasingly organized business sector. But even in this area of the public sector's growth, demands for public intervention were found to arise from the new social and political contexts created by the breakthrough of democracy and the political and trade union mobilization of wage-earners with a corresponding growth in the demand for security and equality.

Several conclusions seemed natural on the basis of these studies. First of all, public sector growth in different respects has been more or less continuous throughout the 20th century, but three phases can still be distinguished:

1. A period from the turn of the century to the 1930's when expansion was initiated in the form of the first nationalizations of private companies, the first modern social welfare legislation on child care, restrictions on working hours and social insurance legislation.

2. A period from the 1930's to the 1950's when the labor movement's newly acquired hegemony and the new social stances adopted by the Liberals on social issues paved the way

for the first attempts at redistributing income, long-term planning and greatly expanded municipal responsibilities.

3. A period from the 1960's when the increasingly expansive social insurance system came into force, public health and care of the children and the elderly were expanded, the educational system was reformed and public transfers to households and companies were extended – all on the basis of an exceptionally high degree of economic growth and new, broadly based sources of taxes. Public planning and comprehensive nationalization were instituted at the same time. Governments were stable, and the concept of a welfare state became generally accepted.

These are the contours of developments in Sweden. They differ from developments elsewhere, primarily in their scope, consistency and radicalism. Thus, the Swedish model was often viewed as a forerunner reflecting future trends in other countries. There are good reasons for attempting to identify the governing factors common to public sector expansion in the Western world, on the one hand, and factors that operated with particular intensity in Sweden, on the other hand. Two basic circumstances immediately suggest themselves. Firstly, capitalism in Sweden displayed the fastest rate of growth in the western world during this period. This created resources more rapidly than in other countries. Secondly, the labor movement was stronger, better organized and more extensively mobilized, both in terms of political and trade union activity, in Sweden than elsewhere. This obviously meant that the movement was able to frame policies and gain support for those policies while finding easier access to resources in achieving social security and equality reforms. Here, Sweden's comprehensive welfare policies had an enormous moral impact, since all citizens thereby acquired a stake in public welfare.

## *Aftermath*

At a conference in London on the Foundation's research projects in the field of public finances, I contributed a lecture summarizing our project's results. My lecture was expanded into a small booklet, "The causes of the expansion of the public sector in Sweden during the 20th century" (1983).

Since project members had previously worked on the causes of the public sector's expansion in very general, explanatory terms, I felt the need to examine the problem in greater depth by selecting a small sub-topic. Public roads struck me as being a fruitful subject. The Swedish rural road network had been nationalized in 1944, after previously being the responsibility of road districts and financed by a special municipal road tax. Prior to this period, roads had been a responsibility of the peasantry, and a large proportion of roads were privately owned. The study's most interesting finding was that the gradual transition from private to cooperative and, finally, to public ownership of roads had a special historical background. The decisive change here occurred with industrialization and the attendant regional division of economic activity. This made road utilization increasingly collective and anonymous, thereby severing the link between road maintenance and road usage and led to the municipalization of road maintenance (road maintenance districts from 1891). After the breakthrough of motoring in the 1920's and the expansion of the national highway system, a district organization became too restrictive, as reflected in very poor roads in interdistrict border areas. However, the question is whether the correlation between public maintenance of the road network and nationalization in 1944 really was all that simple. In the first place, no effort was made to try the alternative involving a new subsidy system (whose control costs *could* have been considerable, although this was never verified). In the second place, the world was at war, and the military was clearly in favor of nationalization for purely military reasons. In the third place, and most important of all, the nationalization decision in parliament was the outcome of an agreement reached in the municipal tax committee at the time. The committee was anxious to reduce municipal taxes; payments to the poor and road maintenance expenses were the two main municipal cost items. Aid to the poor could not be nationalized to advantage. That left road maintenance. So this political agreement on reduced and equalized municipal taxes may well have been the most important reason for nationalization! The study confirmed previous observations that the public sector's expansion was powered by a complicated interplay between profound social and economic changes, on the one hand, and politics, on the other hand.

But we had still not reached the "heart of the matter". The project was conceived during the early 1970's and influenced by positivistic and Marxist thinking. By the beginning of the 1980's, I started to become interested also in the *effects* of the public sector's expansion and its concrete impact on people.

I completed a study "Den tysta revolutionen. Det lokala välfärdssamhällets framväxt. Exemplet Örebro 1945-1982" (Gustafsson 1988). This book described the revolutionary change that occurred in the city of Örebro in the post-war era and the impact of that change on Örebro's inhabitants from the cradle to the grave:

"The entire nature of public services was transformed from being primarily a commanding, order-creating, conservative force into a service-oriented, radical, progressive factor. Policemen and tax officials as the main representatives of government were replaced by service suppliers (mainly women, even if they were not in leading positions). Children were no longer browbeaten into future roles but allowed to develop to the best of their ability, and mothers were simultaneously given opportunities to attain greater freedom with the aid of jobs and income outside the home. A completely new school was introduced with 9 years of compulsory schooling plus upper-secondary schools open for all. Despite this school system's shortcomings and problems, it still represented the abolition of an important class privilege. Sports facilities, recreation centers and municipally supported club activities were set up for young people. Extensive municipal building programs enabled many people to move into decent, modern homes for the first time in their lives, although on terms that seem limited and defective when viewed with the benefit of hindsight. Many people gained access to books and music, also for the first time, thanks to the opening of people's libraries and music schools. The elderly and disabled were offered greater security and dignity in daily lives they could lead as individuals instead of as barely tolerated "inmates". This new, public sector with all its collective services was remarkable in the extent to which it supported individuals, supplied increased opportunities for the preservation of personal integrity for people in distressed straits and offered freedom-of-choice instead of control, invasion of privacy and an arrogant exercise of its power, as was often the case in the old authoritarian public sector."

## Experiences and influences

The project on the causes of the public sector's expansion was naturally a product of its time and can tell us something about the conditions of research. In the 1970's, the public sector was not viewed as a "millstone" around the neck of society but as a popular, democratic facility for increasing welfare, equality and security. Taxes were not seen as non-productive fees to be kept as low as possible but as income needed for productive investments in education and public health.

The project was also performed at the right point in time. In any case, it enjoyed the generous supports of sponsors. Here, I would like to make special mention of the role played by the Foundation's director, Nils-Eric Svensson, in encouraging and assisting us. This assistance was by no means unconditional, and we received our share of gentle but justified, objective criticism. Still, our work was the subject of unfailing, cheerful generosity. This was of immense psychological importance to the mobilization of research energy.

Naturally, many things would have been done differently if we had been more experienced. Project members would then undoubtedly have interacted with one another more systematically than was the case. In fact, we would have agreed on a stricter delineation of tasks and imposed time limits on completing assignments, thereby enabling us to penetrate issues more deeply and move forward more rapidly. But the humanistic and social science subjects were and are still burdened by a long-standing academic tradition in which a doctoral thesis is a small, personal enterprise devoted as much (or to an even greater degree) to personality development as to research findings. As a result, doctoral candidates are often bogged down with incomprehensible and unsolvable tasks for long periods of time.

In respect to the project's impact, it was certainly of major importance to the project members' own education and future occupational efforts. Two of the candidates became division heads at the Swedish National Audit Bureau. One became an energy planner at the National Institute for Building Research, one became a researcher in the Central Organization of Salaried Employees (TCO) and one found work with the County Labor Board in Dalarna, i.e. almost all ended up with jobs in the public sector! Their acquisition of general know-how in the project naturally played a major role here. The project also generated a number of papers by undergraduate students. Since the project organized a number of activities in conjunction with the research, it also generated external impulses affecting other scholars. Two textbooks for basic university education saw the light of day, one on the public sector's development and the other on the history of taxes in Sweden. The project members devoted a great deal of time to research information at and, especially, outside universities at public agencies, for organizations and in debates.

Some might accuse us of overreach when we, a relatively inexperienced associate professor plus five doctoral candidates, attempted to explain the general reasons for the public sector's expansion in the 20th century. But I do not feel that our work was a failure. We also learned incredibly much along the way. And, I must confess to missing a devil-may-care audacity, of the kind that powered the project, in much pre-doctoral research of today.

*Assar Lindbeck*

# Internationalization process and national economic policies

The Institute for International Economic Studies lives a "double life". It is both an independent research institute with its own board of directors and a department at Stockholm University. The research proficiency acquired at the institute would not have been possible without a series of research grants from the Bank of Sweden Tercentenary Fund. The first grant (in 1973) was for the project "Internationaliseringsprocessen och den nationella ekonomiska politiken" (The internationalization process and national economic policies). A number of subsequent grants from the Foundation can be viewed a logical follow-up of the initial grant (1).

Generally speaking, these studies put the institute on the international research map in the field of international economics, especially in "open economy macro theory", after the change in the direction of the institute's activities in conjunction with Gunnar Myrdal's 1970 retirement from his position as head of the institute and his completion of "Asian Drama".

The purpose of this paper is to provide a brief report on some of the problems in and results of the first of our projects to be financed by the Foundation and to shed some light on the importance of the project to the institute's later work.

The project's design and organization reflect the institute's character at the beginning of the 1970's as an institute of doctoral candidates, except for the institute director who also headed the project on internationalization. The institute at that time was primarily an *institute for the training of researchers*. But even at this time, one feature is apparent which was subsequently to become characteristic of the institute's work approach, viz. the active involvement of distinguished visiting scholars from abroad. As a result, know-how began to be imported from the international research frontier.

The project was inspired, of course, by fact that the ongoing internationalization process was rapidly altering prerequisites for independent economic policies in individual countries. On the one hand, the process contributed to increased efficiency and, accordingly, an enhanced standard of living. On the other hand, it led to increased dependency on other countries and increased demands for adjustments to changes in the outside world.

The research project consisted of three parts: (i) The driving forces in the internationalization process and its general impact on the ability of countries to conduct economic policy on a national level; (ii) its impact on national stabilization policies; and (iii) its impact on national allocation (industrial) policies.

## The internationalization process

The first sub-project (mainly performed by the project leader, i.e. the author of this paper, and by Sven Grassman, Michael Michaeli and Per Magnus Wijkman) showed how the internationalization process is fueled by technical, economic and political factors. As a result of rapid developments in communications technology, the cost of transporting goods, services, technology, capital and information tends to fall more rapidly than the cost of production. This stimulates an increased volume of international transactions in these sectors (Lindbeck 1973 and 1975). Falling information costs in particular also make it possible to coordinate and lead global organizations at far lower costs and with less time lost than hitherto, a circumstance promoting the growth of multinational companies (Lundgren 1974 and 1975). To an increasing degree, markets have become international instead of national, and to an increasing degree, companies are becoming international rather than national enterprises. Exceptions in this process are mainly to be found in the public sector, housing sector and, as a result of protectionistic measures, agriculture.

"Economic" and not solely "technical" factors also contribute to these developments. When incomes rise, people do not respond by merely increasing their demand for a larger quantity of goods and services they already consume. They also demand more *varieties* of different kinds of consumer products. In other word, the demand for goods and services becomes more heterogenous and fragmented because of great income elasticity for product differentiation. But if companies are to be able to satisfy demands for more heterogenous products, without sacrificing the cost-saving advantages of large-scale operations, companies must specialize on narrow segments in different product categories. So there is a powerful expansion of trade *within* various product sectors, i.e. intrasector trade, instead of *between* sectors, i.e. intersector trade (Lindbeck 1973 and 1975). This means that aspects other than those serving as the basis of traditional foreign trade (the Heckscher-Ohlin theory) apply, at least in part, especially factors such as imperfect competition, product heterogeneity and the advantages of large-scale operations.

The biggest expansion of foreign trade in the postwar period did in fact take place in intrasector trade. This also meant that the expansion in trade mainly occurred between countries on about the same level of development rather than between rich and poor countries. But it should also be noted that the greatly increasing degree of internationalization after World War II reflected at least *in part* a recovery of the strongly growing autarchy in the 1930's and 1940's (Grassman 1980).

As several sub-studies have shown, political decisions have

also contributed to the internationalization process. This especially applies to decisions on the convertibility of currencies during the latter half of the 1950's and the successive liberalization of foreign trade and, subsequently, of capital movements. Markets and market-oriented organizations, such as businesses, are spreading beyond the jurisdiction of national governments to an increasing degree. As a result, national governments are becoming increasingly ineffective economic and political decision-making units in sector after sector. When politicians facilitated the economic internationalization process as a result of their own decisions, they released forces, like the "Sorcerer's Apprentice", they were unable to control (Lindbeck 1973 and 1975).

In the long term, economic openness in countries is governed by ongoing technical and economic internationalization and by political conditions which may have integrative or disintegrative effects. These governing factors have interacted after World War II, resulting in rapid internationalization developments during this particular period (Grassman 1980).

The result of these developments is not merely that trade and capital movements are taking over an increasing proportion of domestic production and domestic capital markets. International product and capital flows are also becoming increasingly *sensitive* to changes in incomes and price relationships ("relative prices"), both on the world market and in individual countries. The income and price elasticity of international flows is increasing. As several sub-studies have shown, this makes individual countries increasingly sensitive to disruptions from abroad. This could lead to increased economic instability in some of those countries where disruptions are mainly imported from the world market. But this development could also lead to the "export" beyond their national boundaries of disruptions occurring *in* individual countries, a process damping the impact of these disruptions on their domestic economies. However, this means that the effects instead appear in the form of variations in the balance of trade (Lindbeck 1978). This then implies that increased economic integration tends to reduce economic instability in countries where various economic disruptions are produced "at home".

One basic dilemma, a main topic in the "internationalization project", is the fact that the economic system is becoming increasingly international in nature, whereas the political system continues to be largely national. If the consolidation of the national state in the 1700's and 1800's can be described as a logical adaptation of the political system to the economic system's geographic expansion, the national state today is encountering difficulties because the economic system, in contrast to the political system, is expanding beyond existing national boundaries. Many of the present national and international problems can be viewed to advantage in the light of the tension between an increasingly internationalized economic system and political systems which remain predominantly national. What we are currently observing is increasing difficulty in accommodating the new, international, economic forces, as created by modern technical and economic developments, within traditional political concepts and institutions based on the idea of sovereign national states (Lindbeck 1973 and 1985). Contemporary trends towards economic integration and "supranational" entities, such as the EC, can be viewed as an attempt to stimulate economic internationalization, especially on the regional (world area) level, as well as an attempt to adapt the political system to the increasing international orientation of the economic system.

## Stabilization policies

These complicated economic and political developments have interesting consequences for economic policies, stabilization policies not the least. Traditional Keynsian demand policies become a less efficient way of influencing domestic production and employment, since a significant part of demand "leaks out" via the balance of trade in the form of increased imports instead of stimulating domestic production and employment. But economic and political measures changing the price ratio between the domestic economy and foreign economies are simultaneously becoming *more* effective than hitherto. Altered exchange rates and production taxes, such as wage taxes, will be affecting domestic production and employment to a greater degree than was previously the case. In an analogous manner, wage "explosions" will have a more adverse effect than before on domestic production and employment.

The emphasis in the institute's project was on stabilization policy problems. Some of its most important results were included in the doctoral theses of Lars Calmfors, Johan Myhrman, Lars Nyberg, Staffan Viotti and Claes Wihlborg (all published in the institute's "monograph series"). Other results can be found in a large number of papers published both by the institute's permanent staff and by visiting scholars. Important parts of the results were summarized in a book jointly published in 1979 by the institute's scholars: "Inflation and Employment in Open Economies".

Among other things, the book contained an empirical analysis of the relative importance of domestic and foreign factors to domestic price rises (Lars Calmfors and Jan Herin) and the relationship between inflation and domestic economic activity (Johan Myhrman). One conclusion made by the former study was that the prices of both domestically produced export products and of import-competing products could deviate considerably from prices in competing countries, at least in the short and medium term. Domestic wages and prices for input goods proved to be of major importance to price-setting in domestic enterprises and in the sectors subject to the most intense competition (although more so in import-competing sectors than in export-oriented sectors). But the study also found that the importance of domestic conditions, such as domestic economic policies, to domestic price developments was declining as international inflation increased (Myhrman).

Other articles dealt with the *mechanisms* by which domestic factors and inflation "imported" from abroad affect the general, national rate of inflation and the way national economic policies may be able to counteract the effects of these inflation impulses without any major increase in unemployment (Lars Calmfors and Assar Lindbeck). Four interlinked inflation mechanisms were schematically identified: international inflation, changes in exchange rates, domestic productivity developments and variations in the pressure of domestic demand (or unemployment). One special methodological contribution was to elucidate the relationship between Phillips curve analysis and the Scandinavian inflation model (Calmfors). Another contribution was to elucidate the role played by increased real wages for increased unemployment in the "tradable" sector, i.e. the export sector and the import-competing sector (Calmfors).

Another article in this book (Hans Tson Söderström and Staffan Viotti) shows how domestic (exogenous) wage disruptions tend to reduce production and employment in the sector exposed to competition and the way such disruptions can "induce" expansion of the public sector when there is a wish to keep unemployment from rising without any change in the exchange rate.

The book also contained a dynamic analysis of the three-dimensional problem of a trade-off between employment, inflation and the balance of payment (or, more accurately, foreign exchange holdings) in an open economy (Lars Nyberg and Staffan Viotti) and an analysis of the way investment and devaluation cycles can arise in an open economy with inflationary wage formation in conjunction with variations in corporate profitability (Pentti Kouri).

Other papers analyzed the importance of the choice of an exchange rate system on the rate of domestic inflation (Lars

Nyberg) and the relationship between exchange risks and integration of capital markets (Claes Wihlborg). Whereas the "fixed" exchange rate systems used from 1944 to 1971, like a system based on the gold standard, made great uniformity in the development of national economies with respect to business fluctuations and the rate of inflation, monetary policies in a system with floating exchange rates can concentrate on national objectives to some extent, especially in respect to price trends which may then be relatively independent of developments abroad. Stability on the currency market and its importance to foreign trade and domestic wage formation were studied in other articles (by William Branson and Douglas D. Purvis). One conclusion was that there is a tendency for the rate of exchange to "overshoot" in systems with floating rates of exchange in conjunction with monetary and financial disruptions, whereas there is a corresponding tendency for it to "undershoot" in conjunction with disruptions occurring in the economy's real sectors (such as the production sector or the choice between consumption, saving and real investments).

The book also contained a theoretical and empirical analysis of the importance of the mix between monetary and fiscal policies in the context of various exchange rate systems (Stanley Black). Whereas earlier theoretical studies showed how the linking of monetary policies to the foreign trade balance and fiscal policies to the domestic balance may be appropriate, under certain conditions, according to principle of the "relative efficiency" of the various instruments, the paper showed that the relative distribution of power between the central bank, ministry of finance and trade unions in the society is also a decisive factor in practice.

Ever since the first research project financed by the Foundation, the institute has strived to confirm its position as a leading research institute in the field of "open economy macro analysis". Several projects were subsequently conducted, and these have renewed the know-how acquired by the institute in conjunction with this "debut project" in macro analysis. Continued research in macro analysis concentrated on e.g. the relationship between wage formation and unemployment in open economies and the theory of economic policy, including the importance of household and corporate expectations and confidence in future economic policies. The institute's international reputation is based to a large degree on its competence in the field of macro analysis and stabilization policy.

## Allocation policies

The part of the "Internationalization Project" dealing with problems related to resource allocation mainly examined the effect of the internationalization process on resource allocation in an individual country and that country's ability to conduct an independent national economic policy. The internationalization of national economies means that foreign and domestic changes in production possibilities and the demand for goods and services are having an increasingly powerful impact on the competitiveness of different production sectors, thereby making necessary constant reallocations of productive resources.

One component in this part of the project was an analysis of the increased importance of multinational companies (performed mainly by Nils Lundgren). In respect to the forces fueling this development, it was noted that the cost of geographic information transfer in the postwar period fell more rapidly than the cost of transporting goods. Some studies (Lundgren, and Hamilton and Söderström) also noted that technical and organizational conditions on the company level have a major effect on the way world production in various sectors is allocated *between companies* and the way differences in factor proportions, the level of development, market share and economic policy contribute to an explanation of the *national economies* in which these companies locate their production. Moreover, they discussed ways of achieving various economic and political objectives in respect to economic efficiency and income distribution in societies in which entrepreneurship has become highly internationalized. Generally speaking, the conclusions in this part of the project scarcely supplied any support for widely advocated hypotheses which claim that international corporate groups do not behave the same way as large national companies. However, several studies (Lundgren 1974 and 1975, Hamilton and Söderström 1981) identified the important role international corporate groups can play in contributing to an efficient allocation of resources in the world economy. International corporations also play a major role as regards the international dissemination of technology, since effective transfer of production technology and organizational skills often occurs *inside* the corporate framework.

*Input (intermediary) goods* now represent a major part of the value of world trade. As a result, processing chains are being extended to many countries. This aspect of the internationalization process was examined in a study of the internationalization of technology (Carl B. Hamilton and Hans Tson Söderström). It described the circumstances in which technology can be regarded as a produced input item, the countries which will then lead the spread of technology, and the impact this spread of technology can be expected to have. In this study, the issue of international technology transfer was examined within the framework of traditional foreign trade according to the Heckscher-Ohlin approach.

Other sub-projects dealt with the proportions between direct corporate investments and portfolio investment in previous periods (Peter Svedberg), the impact of the internationalization process on the trade in services (such as shipping and financial services) and on factor mobility (Melvin Krauss and Per Magnus Wijkman) and the internationalization of "externalities" such as overfishing and fishing conflicts between different countries (Per Magnus Wijkman and Claes Wihlborg).

## Final remarks

In retrospect, it is amazing to note how about ten doctoral candidates, plus a small group of foreign visiting scholars, were able to achieve such impressive results with their work in the course of only a few years. The most important explanation, apart from sheer talent, was probably the presence of visiting scholars from abroad and the powerful interaction which developed between the young scientists who met on a daily basis and commented on one another's work at seminars and in intense informal discussions. In conjunction with this project, the institute evolved from being a unit for the training of scientists into a research institute, which ultimately even began training doctoral candidates at the Department of Economics at Stockholm University. To an increasing degree, it also began contributing to education in economics and international economics at almost all levels at the university. Several of these doctoral candidates subsequently acquired doctorates and took up positions as assistant professors and professors at the institute. But most became professors at other universities, entered the civil service or found employment with private companies and organizations.

Thanks to a large extent to this project, a new generation of researchers in international economics emerged at the institute. In conjunction with the project, institute scholars also began developing a wide network of contacts with distinguished scholars in other countries. This circumstance, in combination with the desire to publish research results abroad (primarily in foreign journals), contributed to the development of an *international level of research aspiration* among institute scholars. This has been a great help in the increasingly comprehensive teaching programs undertaken by members of the institute in the Department of Economics at Stockholm University.

*Sten Carlsson*

# Emigration and family history

## Migration Project

Some time in 1962, the Vice-Chancellor of Uppsala University, Torgny Segerstedt, invited me to a meeting attended by university representatives and the head of the American Council of Learned Societies, Richard Downar. This well-endowed research council, backed by the Ford Foundation, wished to award some major grants to European seats of learning, including Uppsala University which enjoys a solid international reputation. One important result was the establishment of a chair in American literature on July 1, 1962. I proposed that an assistant professorship in history also be created. This came about on the same date and carried with it a grant for the purchase of literature on American history. The grant was awarded for five years and was subsequently extended to a sixth year. The idea was for the programs to continue thereafter with Swedish funding, which in fact occurred.

The decision made it possible to establish a unit for American History at the Department of History plus an attendant American history library stocked with purchased literature and books on long-term loan from the university library. The first to fill the newly created post was Håkan Berggren, currently the Swedish ambassador in Ottawa. During his tenure, which lasted until 1966, he wrote a survey of United States history (*Förenta staternas historia* 1966). Under my supervision he was also responsible for day-to-day work in the project, "Sverige och Amerika efter 1860: utvandring, återinvandring, social och politisk debatt" (Sweden and America after 1860: Emigration, remigration, social and political debate), launched in 1962 and commonly referred to as the "Migration Project". The university financed some equipment for it. The initial funding was then followed by extensive grants from the Swedish Council for Research in the Humanities (1964-76) and the Bank of Sweden Tercentenary Foundation (1968-75). As a result, we were able to finance the salaries of other scholars, hire office staff, buy various material, produce excerpts, carry out various statistical investigations, make transcripts, make research trips and arrange conferences. There was no shortage of licentiate candidates, and even undergraduate students participated. Berggren was succeeded first by Sune Åkerman (1966-73), currently a professor in Umeå, and, in turn, by Harald Runblom (1973-76), currently the head of the university's Center for Multiethnic Research. I had the overall responsibility for the project and, as did the associate professors, led special seminars within the project framework and supervised graduate students. Our offices were in a building next door to the Department of History. When more spacious accommodations became necessary, the project moved to St. Johannesgatan 21 in 1973, still the location of an American history library.

The project was started at a favorable time for this type of project research and became one of the first and largest in a series of flourishing, large-scale projects in the field of humanities. A 1976 list of project scholars includes 41 names, including the supervisors. Eighteen project members ultimately received doctorates (as late as 1986 in one instance) within the project framework while five others produced licentiate theses. In addition six scholars received their doctorates after 1976 within the framework of the Family History Project, which adopted part of the Migration Project's research traditions. A summarizing volume, *From Sweden to America: A History of the Migration* (1976), edited by Harald Runblom and Hans Norman, constituted the project's formal completion. This volume, and all the doctoral dissertations, were published in the

*Studia Historica Upsaliensia* series. Moreover, a popular anthology, published in 1973 and edited by Ann-Sofie Kälvemark (Ohlander), and a significant number of reports and articles published elsewhere are worthy of note.

The mass emigration from Sweden to North America, which comprised one and a quarter million people in the period from 1845 to 1930 (one million of whom remained in the U.S. or Canada throughout their lives), was long the subject of only sporadic interest by professional historians. The major work *Sveriges historia till våra dagar* dismissed this highly traumatic development in our history in only a few pages. However, the statistician Gustav Sundbärg and the geographer Helge Nelson did extensive pioneering work, the former as a *primus motor* in the large investigating commission on emigration (*Emigrationsutredningen*) that resulted in a series of publications (1908-13), the latter through studies in the field and of the literature that culminated in the invaluable work *The Swedes and Swedish Settlements in North America* (1943). The ethnologist Albin Widén may also be counted among the pioneers on both the scholarly and literary levels. In the latter respect, he was overshadowed, somewhat unfairly, by Vilhelm Moberg, whose emigration, immigration and pioneer epics (1949-59) really aroused the book-reading public's interest in the vast emigration adventure.

Vilhelm Moberg is often regarded as the spiritual father of emigration research and enjoyed being viewed as such. However, this historiographic interpretation is incorrect. Instead, two parallel developments are involved. Emigration research was a natural consequence of the great interest in quantitatively oriented social history which developed in Sweden and other countries in the postwar years and culminated in the 1970's (for my own part, I was conducting emigration research on a small scale as early as the 1940's). It is important to note in this context that the research councils and the Foundation supported this research with funds whose magnitude seemed fabulous to a somewhat older generation of humanists. Vilhelm Moberg's novels undoubtedly contributed to the goodwill emigration research enjoyed. Nor could historians fail to be influenced by his depictive powers, even though their overall view differed considerably from his. His view of mass-emigration was influenced both by his own distaste for the old authoritarian society and by his romantic view of the American pioneer culture. Using the author's poetic license Moberg overemphasized the rebellious elements in the emigrant's feelings about departure. More than historical reality warranted he also put too much stress on the role of Swedish immigrants as farmers in the midwest.

A primary task for the project was to elucidate the background of emigration in various Swedish regions, especially those with high rates of emigration. Thus, there were studies of Stockholm (Fred Nilsson 1970), northern Östergötland province (Ulf Ebbeson 1968, unpublished), Småland province (Sten Carlsson 1966-67), Öland island province (Margot Höjfors Hong 1986), Halland province (Bo Kronborg and Thomas Nilsson 1975), the Göteborg region (Eric De Geer 1977), Dalsland province (Paul Noreen 1967, originally unpublished but posthumously printed in 1987), Örebro county (Hans Norman 1974), southern Hälsingland province (Björn Rondahl 1972), Västernorrland county (Lars-Göran Tedebrand 1972) and the Åland Islands (Frank Blomfelt 1968, unpublished).

These reports describe distinctive local features. At the same time, they convey a clear, integrated picture of the emigration's social background. The upper social strata, i.e. people with a good education and relatively good economic resources, were clearly underrepresented, except during the "pioneer phase" (1845-54). This also applied to impoverished people: agricultural laborers, the landless unemployed, workhouse inmates etc. For these people, the shortage of cash, plus family circumstances and age inhibited emigration. Employment on an annual basis did give agricultural laborers some security, albeit short-term and on a low level. Public servants with modest incomes, such as soldiers, postmen and railway station hands, also remained in Sweden. The state's bounty was modest but dependable.

Most of the emigrants were younger practitioners of agricultural and industrial trades. Family emigration – encompassing a father, mother and children in a group, sometimes accompanied by farm-hands and servant girls – was rather common during the pioneer period and even during the famine years (1868-69) but became less frequent thereafter (Sten Carlsson 1968). Peasants and crofters did not emigrate to any great extent, but their sons, daughters, farm-hands and servant girls did. Female servants outside the agricultural sector also comprised a large group. In trade and industry owners of enterprises were underrepresented. However, apprentices, blacksmiths, carpenters, tailors and seamstresses were numerous. There were more men than women, but conditions for women changed most (Ann-Sofie Ohlander 1986). Mass-emigration was a product of the surplus vitality that had long had difficulty in finding an outlet in the traditional Swedish society.

Since Sweden was still an agrarian society, most of the emigrants were from the agricultural population, but industry displayed about the same rate of emigration as agriculture. The distribution between rural and urban areas was about equal. However, there were considerable regional differences. The drain was greatest in regions with small-holders and in southern and western Sweden (Halland, Jönköping, Värmland, Kronoberg and Kalmar counties), whereas the lowest figures were recorded for the Lake Mälar district with its large estates and agricultural laborers (Uppsala, Stockholm, Södermanland and Västmanland counties). Upper Norrland (Västerbotten and Norrbotten counties) was a kind of America in Sweden with rather limited emigration, but the rate increased after the turn of the century.

A rather common factor was "urban spheres of influence": the inhabitants of parishes close to large or medium-sized towns often migrated to the latter instead of to America, whereas emigration was more extensive in peripheral areas (Eric De Geer and others). Similar trends were apparent in the areas around Copenhagen, Kristiania (Oslo), Bergen, Helsinki, Åbo (Turku) and Budapest.

The "stock effect" was another important factor. This meant that the tendency to emigrate often remained considerable in areas affected by emigration at an early stage and stimulated by information from relatives and former neighbors who had settled in America (Hans Norman and others). In many regions, an "agrarian-industrial barrier" was also significant: peasant sons and farm-hands often preferred America to nearby factory towns (Björn Rondahl and others).

The major cities usually had a rather high rate of emigration, but many of these emigrants from urban areas were born in rural areas. As far as Stockholm was concerned, they were often migrants from areas with heavy emigration, such as Kalmar county. As a rule, their step-by-step emigration was affected by urban conditions, such as overcrowding (especially for female servants) and seasonal unemployment. These erstwhile country-people had usually spent quite a few years in Stockholm before departing for America (Fred Nilsson).

Generally speaking, the intense research has led to a decline in the credence attached to some of the psychological explanations previously in vogue. For example, it was found that aversion to conscription was usually only of secondary importance to decisions to emigrate (Ann-Sofie Kälvemark 1972). Opposition to the Church of Sweden also played a subordinate role, except for Baptists, Mormons, the followers of Erik Jansson and other minority groups. Districts affected by the religious revival usually did not display a greater rate of emigration than those loyal to the Church of Sweden (Sten Carlsson 1967). Discontent with party politics and labor unions was an important factor in some instances, especially at the beginning of the 20th century (Björn Rondahl). In the broader perspective, however, this driving force only had marginal impact.

For many years, the tendency in Sweden, especially among public officials, was to view emigrants as less law-abiding, less responsible and less patriotic than people who remained at home. However, emigrants and their descendants usually regarded emigration as a step reflecting personal courage, dynamism and a desire for freedom. Research has failed to confirm the presence of any such general discrepancy between the personal characteristics of emigrants and Swedes who remained at home.

Emigration agents played a major role in emigration by helping emigrants travel to the New World. The extensive archives of one of the emigration agencies, Bröderna Larsson in Västergötland, have survived and enable scholars to make a number of observations and draw conclusions. Useful source material is also available for Kalmar county. It was found that the agents did not steer and encourage emigration with extravagant advertising, as has sometimes been claimed. Instead, the agents functioned about the same way as present-day travel agents. A large number of people consulted them, many more than those who actually went to America. A large segment of the population thus consisted of potential emigrants (Berit Brattne 1973, cf. Margot Höjfors Hong 1986).

One of the scholars who studied emigration's Swedish background also studied the fate of emigrants, especially in western Wisconsin (Hans Norman). Another combined emigration and remigration and arrived at certain conclusions about developments on American soil (Lars-Göran Tedebrand). Three doctoral candidates (Ulf Beijbom 1971, Sture Lindmark 1971, Richard Lucas 1974) concentrated entirely on North America. Some smaller-scale reports were also devoted to North America. The most important metropolis for Swedish immigrants to the U.S. was Chicago. Until the end of the 19th century, a large percentage of the Swedes in this city (primarily craftsmen and factory workers) settled mainly in one neighborhood, the provincial and rather proletarian *Svenska Bondegatan*. One important exception was the many young women who accepted employment in American households and were accordingly dispersed throughout the growing metropolis, a circumstance that often led to rapid Americanization. Cultural activities were rather lively right from the start. However, they were, in principle, of two wholly different types: those enjoyed by the long dominant conservative and religious group with a rather solid peasant background, and those enjoyed by a more worldly, more upper echelon minority interested in the theater, literature and other profane cultural endeavors (Ulf Beijbom).

The Swedish population in agricultural communities of the midwest had a completely different structure. Here, farmers with relatively stable settlements predominated, but there were also railway workers and other highly mobile occupational categories. Sex distribution was uneven; young men predominated. Women of marriageable age who emigrated from Sweden, from Örebro county to Wisconsin for example, quickly attracted attention on the nuptials market. People married early, stayed married a long time and often had many children. There were virtually no illegitimate births. Lutheran pastors and Baptist preachers had a strong hold on their parishioners' minds (Hans Norman).

Americanization was unavoidable but did not occur with unusual haste and was hardly faster than among Norwegians and Germans, for example. Swedish immigrants long continued to marry mainly other Swedes or Norwegians. World War I with its patriotic fervor accelerated Americanization, a process which became even more intense in the 1920's. During the depression years (1929-32), however, the immigrants tended to stick together and support one another. "Ethnicity" in Illinois and Minnesota remained strong for many years (Sture Lindmark). Canada is an example of an area with very weak Swedish ethnicity (Harald Runblom 1977).

The Swedish immigrants were politically rather passive for many years. They found it hard to assert themselves in a city as big as Chicago (Ulf Beijbom). They did constitute a rather large proportion of the electorate in Minnesota but were long regarded as "voting cattle"; they voted for the Republicans without demanding anything in return. But after the Democrats began adding Scandinavian candidates to their election slates in the 1880's, this party began to attract marginal voters, and both Norwegians and Swedes soon acquired strong positions in both parties. Many of the Scandinavian immigrants were more interested in the ethnic background of candidates than in the party which the candidates represented. From the 1890's onwards, most governors of Minnesota and many other politicians have had a Scandinavian background (Sten Carlsson 1971, 1973).

One leading American figure was the Swedish-born Charles A. Lindbergh, the son of a former member of the Peasants' Estate in the *Riksdag*. Lindbergh acquired a great reputation in Minnesota where he represented the Republican Party's progressive, "populist" wing that catered to the widespread dissatisfaction among Scandinavian and German farmers with capitalistic, big city interests, as represented by the large railway companies (Richard Lucas). Lindbergh subsequently became a spokesperson for the rather large number of Scandinavians and Germans who were opposed to U.S. involvement in the First World War.

There was a definite correlation between occupational background in Sweden and the sites at which immigrants settled in North America. Smiths from small iron-making communities in northern Östergötland (including towns such as Finspång) made their way to the metal-working districts in Connecticut (Ulf Ebbeson). Farmers' sons from Ångermanland preferred agricultural communities in the midwest, whereas forest and sawmill workers from the Sundsvall district and Ådalen emigrated to the forests of Michigan and Canada. I might add that emigration to Canada has been underestimated in the official Swedish statistics. Farmers were an important group among the Swedish-Americans who remigrated to Sweden. After a generally brief period of time on farms and building sites or in forestry or factory work, they returned primarily to their own farms, villages or parishes. Despite their stay in a foreign country, they proved to be a rather conservative element in their old homeland (Lars-Göran Tedebrand). The numerous remigrants to Öland island displayed a similar structure (Margot Höjfors Hong).

Several studies examined the social and political debate in Sweden. During the American Civil War political developments in the U.S. began to attract Swedish interest to a greater extent than before. Sympathies varied considerably with shifts in war developments and were not as pro-Union as might be imagined. In Swedish textile centers such as Borås, people sided with the cotton-growing Confederacy for economic reasons (Kjell Bondestad 1968 on the basis of an unpublished licentiate thesis). The Swedish government and Riksdag long displayed rather sporadic interest in emigration, despite its enormous magnitude. There was no serious political debate on the issue until around the turn of the century. Demands to halt emigration were then raised mainly by the military and farm owners, who feared a shortage of soldiers and farm workers, respectively. Agriculture's shortage of labor was due more to industrialization than to emigration, but blaming emigration was more convenient and more popular. The creation of new, small farms (*egnahem*) was believed to be the answer to the problem, whereas people on the left demanded more sweeping social reforms (Ann-Sofie Kälvemark 1972). This debate resulted in the appointment of an investigating commission on emigration (*Emigrationsutredningen*) in 1907. However, this measure came too late, and its orientation was too agrarian to have any effect on actual developments.

Emigration to Latin America was never very great but

contains numerous, interesting aspects. Two of the project scholars worked in this field. Emigration to Brazil, which initially culminated in 1891 and mainly comprised emigrants from the Stockholm and Sundsvall areas, was the subject of a special study. This emigration was more proletarian than emigration to North America and encountered greater difficulties than the latter (Karin Stenbeck 1973, unpublished). The occasional emigration of businessmen and engineers to countries such as Mexico, Argentina and Chile was different in nature. It has also been investigated in a study which concentrated on a number of major Swedish companies: Bofors, Tändsticksbolaget (Swedish Match Co.), Aga, SKF (Swedish Ballbearing Co.) and L.M. Ericsson (Harald Runblom 1971). The numerous political upheavals in these countries created major problems for Swedish export companies and frequently led to the loss of valuable, carefully nurtured contacts. The payment of bribes often proved to be a prerequisite for success.

Scholars whose work did not primarily concern relations between Sweden and North America were also associated with the Migration Project and were able to benefit from the methodological experience gained there. Four doctoral theses are worthy of note here: Jan Sundin's on foreign students at Uppsala University (1973), Mike Samson's on Dutch migration (1977), Jan Larsson's on Swedish diplomatic and military activities in China (1977) and Viveca Halldin Norberg's on Swedes in Ethiopia (1977).

During its 14-year life, the Migration Project acquired a large number of contacts in Sweden and abroad. This was to a large extent due to Sune Åkerman's initiatives and resulted in conferences in Uppsala. The Emigrant Register of Värmland in Karlstad, which under the leadership of Sigurd Gustafson established links with the U.S. before research in Uppsala got started, was an important contact, as well as the Swedish Emigrant Institute started by Gunnar Helén (inspired by Vilhelm Moberg) in Växjö in 1966. Its director, Ulf Beijbom, now a professor, was an early member of the Uppsala group. Continuous links were maintained with emigration scholars in Norway, Denmark, Finland and Iceland (*Nordisk emigrationsatlas* 1980). Nordic collaboration continued in the 1980's with Hans Norman and Harald Runblom (1980, 1988) as the most important contributors. Sune Åkerman submitted research papers at the 1971 congress of Nordic historians in Copenhagen and at the International Congress of Historical Sciences in San Francisco in 1975. Many activities were pursued on American soil. One highlight was the conference held in Duluth, Minnesota, in 1976 with many participants from Uppsala (Nils Hasselmo 1978). Contacts with the U.S. were revitalized in many ways during the commemoration of New Sweden in 1988, contributions being made by scholars from Uppsala at conferences in the Delaware area and in the midwest (Stellan Dahlgren and Hans Norman 1988).

After initially concentrating on the population exchange with North America, the project ultimately began working on internal migration to an increasing degree, both the long-standing "circular moves" (Åkerman's term), transfers from one community to another or from rural to urban areas within the same region, as well as "effective" population movements from Värmland and Dalarna to the sawmill districts in Västernorrland county, for example. One of the dissertations mentioned earlier (by Bo Kronborg and Thomas Nilsson 1975) devoted most of its attention to internal rather than external migration. One of its main tasks was to elucidate the way in which expanding Halmstad attracted male and female labor from rural areas in southern Halland and southwestern Småland. This dissertation was unusual since it was defended by two respondents, an opportunity not previously used for a historical subject. This example was followed in 1978 by Ingrid Eriksson and John Rogers in the Family History Project. Quite a number of the papers and articles within the framework of both projects were by more than one author.

## The Family History Project

When our Migration Project was about to end, we had the feeling that the collective knowledge and experience we had acquired should not go to waste. So we decided to launch a new project, also with a demographic slant but without continuing to address the issue of migration. The project was called "The Family in the Swedish Demographic and Social Transformation after 1800" (*Familjen inom den svenska demografiska och sociala omvandlingen efter 1800*). The Swedish Council for Research in the Humanities and Social Sciences and the Foundation provided support, making it possible for us to employ Hans Norman as a research leader as well as other staff. The offices on St. Johannesgatan were still at our disposal. Seminars and the supervision of graduate students continued. The grants ended in 1983, but research has continued, intertwined with new, smaller-scale projects. In 1980, a publication series was launched, edited by John Rogers and Hans Norman, ten issues of which having appeared to date.

While the Migration Project evolved in a gradual process, the Family History Project got off to a flying start with participation by post-doctoral scholars and active doctoral candidates. The project has encompassed more than 20 scholars above the undergraduate level. Eleven have received doctorates with 10 dissertations, all published in the series *Studia Historica Upsaliensia*. Project output also included three works by post-doctoral scholars (Sten Carlsson 1977, Ann-Sofie Kälvemark Ohlander 1980, Ulla-Britt Lithell 1988), the anthology *Den utsatta familjen* (The vulnerable family) edited by Hans Norman (1983), and a number of reports and journal articles. The large percentage of female scholars is striking; 8 of 14 dissertations were written by women (in one instance in collaboration with a man). The history of women occupies a prominent place in the cited research.

Regional studies dominated family history to an even greater degree than was the case for the migration material. Norrland was represented with five works, Ostrobothnia with one, and two combined observations from Ostrobothnia, Karelia and Jämtland. Five studies (by six authors) either concerned the Lake Mälar region or obtained exemplification from it. Göta-land was not represented, a consequence of the location of the provincial archives.

One of the studies concerned the families of peasants and agricultural laborers (*statare*) in 19th century western Uppland. The number of peasants declined somewhat, whereas the prole-tariat increased. The number of children per peasant family was small; utilizing some form of birth control, peasants sought to protect their children against future proletarianization. The number of genuine "extended" families, i.e. with two married couples in the same household, was insignificant. This kind of family never occurred among agricultural laborers (*statare*) who often moved from estate to estate with their wives and many children, not aimlessly but in a conscious effort to successively improve their lot (Ingrid Eriksson and John Rogers 1978).

Two other works related birth control to breast-feeding hab-its. In Ostrobothnia, where women only breast-fed their child-ren to a limited degree (a consequence of their husbands' long absences at sea), infant mortality was high, and confinements occurred at frequent intervals. In Jämtland, where women nursed their children for a long period of time, infant mortality was low, and intervals between pregnancies were long. Feudal conditions and widespread poverty prevailed in Karelia, a province that had belonged to the Russian Empire from 1721 to 1812 before being incorporated into the Grand Duchy of Fin-land. There, infant mortality was high, even though women breast-fed their children to a considerable degree (Ulla-Britt Lithell 1981, 1988).

The rate of marriage was an important demographic factor. In the 19th century, the "European marriage pattern" became increasingly prevalent in Sweden. This pattern entailed a low incidence of marriage and a rising age at marriage. The upper social classes took the lead here, followed by the poor, whereas the peasantry whose productivity was based to a great degree on traditional sex roles had the highest, although declining rate. The large number of spinsters (nearly 50% in certain groups) necessitated the introduction of reforms in the labor market and educational opportunities for women. Spinsters in the nobility took the lead, followed by "mamselles" (daughters of clergymen), not-titled persons of standing and prosperous burghers. "Maids" and "female servants" from the large mass of common folk were the last groups to be reached by women's emancipation. Differences between social classes and between rural and urban areas were considerable in respect to the rate of marriage, the age at which people left their parental homes for good, illegitimate births, pre-marital pregnancies, mortality etc. (Sten Carlsson 1977, 1978). Before the 1930's, the government, heavily influenced by the Myrdals' book *Kris i befolkningsfrågan* (1934), made an attempt to stimulate the falling birth rate by instituting a number of family policy measures. However, demographic studies have shown that the measures, in the form of housing loans, maternity assistance and maternity grants, failed to produce any increase in the birth rate. Young couples were generally more interested in improving their housing standard than in having more children. On the other hand, investments in houses for large families, a form of housing much criticized in some quarters, did have the intended effect (Ann-Sofie Kälvemark 1980).

## Summary

Both the projects mentioned here can be described as an entity; virtually the same scholars and work methods were used in both. Project activities covered a rather long period of time, 1962-84, and research is still in progress, both in Uppsala and in Umeå which received a research chair in historical demography in 1980. This chair can be seen as a spin-off effect of both Uppsala projects. The professorship is held by Lars-Göran Tedebrand, who is himself a product of the Uppsala group.

The projects produced 27 doctoral dissertations (by 29 authors), more than ten other books, five licentiate theses which did not result in doctoral dissertations plus a large number of reports and journal articles. The quantitative, social history emphasis has been striking. The papers have generally been based on statistically processed mass-observations and, in several instances, on cohort studies in which a large number of people of more or less the same age (e.g. 25) and same place of birth have been followed for a quarter of a century or for life with the aid of parish records. This is a time-consuming method, but it does permit definite conclusions, especially when different cohorts are compared.

Teamwork played a major role in this research. When the large-scale history projects commenced in the 1960's, a strong tradition of solo research prevailed within this discipline. Graduate students and associate professors tended to stake out early claims on broad fields of research and were not pleased when other scholars encroached upon these fields. This kind of attitude was uncommon in project research. There, it was natural for team members to help and complement one another. Candor and mutual generosity were often extended (although not invariably) to scholars outside the team. The research environment featured continuous, sometimes daily contacts; this also applied to conferences or more festive settings.

Part of this special atmosphere still prevails, but the heyday of large-scale projects is probably over, in part because of the new climate on the academic labor market. The decades from 1960 to the middle of the 1980's can now be seen as a unique period in Swedish historiography. It witnessed a powerful shift away from the dominance of political history, but only the

ignorant have felt called upon to dismiss the preceding generations. Viewing the work performed during these decades with
condescension from the supposedly exalted ideological plat-
forms (such tendencies have not been lacking) would be equally
improper. All research occurs in waves, and the generations
should learn from one another, without arrogance and without
false generalizations.

It cannot be denied that quantitatively oriented research is
sometimes too preoccupied with measurable factors, the result
being that developments on individual levels are occasionally
obscured by all the diagrams and tables. On the whole, however,
the situation can be described as a fruitful interplay of a general
pattern and a number of concrete, observable details. The
transition from an agrarian to an industrial society was a rather
late but uncommonly sweeping process in Sweden, although
always within a peaceful framework and without any violent
upheavals. The generations involved in this process were affected geographically, socially and ideologically. Their relations
with parents, spouses, children, other relatives and with different public authorities changed considerably. One general impression is that the slow, ongoing social and economic dis-
placements were of far greater significance than apparently
more dramatic changes with a more limited psychological
impact.

Scholars have experienced considerable satisfaction during
this investigation of numerous interwoven human destinies.
Their research has required the use of extensive material resources. So we feel a great debt of gratitude to our generous
sponsors, not the least to the Bank of Sweden Tercentenary
Foundation.

When Sten Carlsson passed away, this article was nearly complete.
Judging by the manuscript pagination, however, he had apparently intended to include several pages on the Family History Project's research
results. After consulting Sten Carlsson's son, Carl Henrik Carlsson, we

made a few minor changes in the text and prepared the list of references. It should be noted that Sten Carlsson was working on emigration research and demographic studies right up to the end. For the New Sweden commemoration in 1988, he published *Swedes in North America 1638-1988* (1988). In March of this anniversary year, he attended a symposium in Newark, New Jersey (near Wilmington, Delaware) and gave a lecture entitled "The colonists in New Sweden 1638-1655. Their geographical and social origins". In the autumn of the same year, he held a lecture on Swedish engineers at North Park College, Chicago, at a conference on "Swedish American Life in Chicago 1838-1988". Both lectures are to be published in the U.S.

Uppsala in January 1990
*Hans Norman and Harald Runblom*

*Birgitta Odén*

# Studying the elderly in society

The aim of this article is to describe an interdisciplinary project's creation, activities and results with a special view to relationships with grant-giving agencies. A historical perspective on aging will be accorded particular attention. Finally, it will describe the project's "further development" in new studies.

## *Background*

In June 1971, the Prime Minister at the time, Olof Palme, appointed a committee, at the suggestion of the Swedish Government Research Advisory Board, to study the position of *future studies* in the scientific community and the organization that should be established to support these activities. The Committee, headed by Alva Myrdal, submitted its report "Att välja framtid" (To choose a future) (SOU 1972:59) in 1972. The report identified a number of problems in the society of the future whose contours were already discernible, primarily with the aid of population forecasts. One of these problems was known as early as the 1950's: the increasing proportion of elderly people in the future.

The Committee's recommendations on reinforcement of future studies resulted in the establishment of two new, research-initiating bodies: The Secretariat for Future Studies and the Coordinating Committee for Long-term Research (SALFO). Both these organizations addressed the problems of the elderly but with differing emphasis and ambitions.

Under Mårten Lagergren's leadership, the Secretariat conducted the project "Omsorgen i samhället" (Care services in society) that, in its report "Tid för omsorg" (Time for caring), exposed the confrontation between increasing care needs and increasing costs. At the same time, it submitted concrete proposals on solving the problem. SALFO initiated the interdisciplinary project "De äldre i samhället – förr, nu och i framtiden" (The elderly in society – in the past, present and future) whose express purpose was to analyze the elderly as a resource, not a problem.

In the first half of the 1970's, another commission was launched, "Forskningsrådsutredningen" (Research council commission). It submitted its report (SOU 1975:26) in 1975. Its task was primarily to identify the opportunities available for organizing large-scale projects and distributing research results in society.

A supplementary directive in 1974, also gave the commission the task of considering an appropriate organization for long-range basic research. A new body was established, the Swedish Council for Planning and Coordination of Research (FRN), with responsibility for developing interdisciplinary research and for research addressing special social problems. Both the Secretariat for Future Studies and the Coordinating Committee for Long-term Research (SALFO) were ultimately attached to this Council. The Council also had the special task of facilitating collaboration between the various research fields in areas of interdisciplinary interest. Thus, the problem of the elderly in the society of the future was a natural issue within the Council's sphere of responsibility.

## Planning a project

As a member of the working committee for future studies, I had become interested in the social problems that became discernible when demographic forecasts from the past were extended to the future: over-population in developing countries and the growing proportion of elderly people in industrialized societies. At the same time, it was apparent that my own subject, history, encompassed a growing interest in inter-generation relationships. One of the persons who gave voice to this interest was the leading Nordic social historian Edvard Bull. In an address held in January 1970, he predicted that historical research in the 1970's would concentrate on small, local communities and on studies of relationships between the generations. There was also international interest in this topic. In 1965 Peter Laslett published "The World We Have Lost" (England's family history in a long-term perspective). It was widely read and the subject of lively discussion at international conferences. Historical demography began leaning towards family history, most obviously in the U.S. and France but even in Sweden, especially in Uppsala where papers by Sune Åkerman (1977), Ann-Sofie Kälvemark (1977, 1978) and David Gaunt (1976) approached family history. But the Odense historian Hans Chr. Johansen (1976) provided the greatest inspiration. A demographic probability calculation he made showed the great unlikelihood of adult children ever living with aged parents in earlier historical periods.

The exciting position of historical research in respect to family and the problem's relevance to the future convinced me that this was a field of major interest to a historian. It was obvious that other historians also found the field worthy of consideration. Several important books were published at the end of the 1970's, such as Peter Stearn's "Old Age in European Society" and David Fischer's "Growing Old in America". ("Der Alte Mensch in der Geschichte", published by H. Konrad in 1982, supplies a historiographic description of historical research on ageing.)

After a request to the SALFO, this Committee decided to hold a conference to which scholars in research on the elderly from all parts of the country were invited. The purpose of the conference was to take stock of ongoing research and opportunities for continued collaboration. After the end of the conference, it was apparent that three different research groups had found one another: H 70 in Göteborg with a geriatric emphasis, the gerontologists in Uppsala and the historians in Lund. The SALFO awarded a 2-year planning grant and appointed Alvar Svanborg in Göteborg, Lars Tornstam in Uppsala and Birgitta Odén in Lund as the planning supervisors.

During the planning years, the members from the three centers met to "show their hands". It was important for the individual scholars to frame their own problems. But it was up to the planning supervisors to arrive at a common objective and a common theoretical design. The planning supervisors' expert, Joseph Zitomersky, employed on a part-time basis, made valiant efforts to array the various ideas within a theoretically consistent framework. I made an attempt, with the aid of a matrix, to determine where we should initiate research in order to fill in the knowledge gaps we successively discovered (Odén 1978).

We never did achieve total agreement on the design of our research, but we did identify a research field and had listened to the views and problem descriptions of our co-scholars. So we felt optimistic about the prospects of collaboration when we submitted an application to the FRN on a longer and more interdisciplinary research project than the three-year programs of most projects.

Work during the planning years was subsequently documented in two volumes: "Äldre i samhället – förr, nu och i framtiden" (The elderly in society - in the past, present and future). Part I: "Teorier och forskningsansatser" (Theories and research approaches) (1982); Part II: "Probleminventeringar (Problem inventory) (1983).

The project's supervisory group agreed on, briefly, the following common approach:

"The elderly are to be viewed primarily as a *resource* in society, not as dependent people.

"Elderly people in society are to be studied from both a *long-term* and a *short-term* perspective.

"Measures – *intervention* – are to be introduced in order to delay the ageing process and give elderly people a good life. The intervention is to be instituted on an experimental basis, as operative, interdisciplinary action in which theory and practice approach one another.

"The studies are to be conducted on three different levels, i.e. an individual level, a group level and a national level, or in other terms on micro, intermediate and macro levels. The point of this design is to facilitate clarification of the *interplay* between the various levels".

The supervisory group's grant application was submitted to the FRN which assumed the main responsibility for project financing. But the Council also started negotiations with other research-granting organizations. The medical Göteborg project received some financing from the Swedish Medical Research Council, and the sociological project in Uppsala received some financing from the Delegation for Social Research. The historical project was awarded a grant by the Bank of Sweden Tercentenary Foundation to cover the full cost of a project on elderly industrial workers. The ethnological study of the housing conditions of elderly people was fully financed by the Swedish Council for Research in the Humanities and Social Sciences. The Council for Building Research, which expressed an interest in financing the ethnological part of the project, instead made a generous grant to the entire project without specifying any particular recipient part. Finally, the FRN assumed full responsibility for project administration and for expenses, books and travel costs. This greatly eased the scholars' workload. So we were not afflicted by the usual fate of jointly financed projects: different grant-giving agencies ruling in different ways or at different times.

It should also be noted that the three sub-projects developed along somewhat different lines with respect to the establishment of interdisciplinary collaboration in the local environment. The

IVÄG project in Göteborg, where an interdisciplinary reference group and an interdisciplinary research group were founded and remained intact throughout the work, was most successful. Interdisciplinary contacts were more loosely organized in Uppsala and Lund.

In retrospect, I must admit that siting the sub-projects in three different university towns was not successful. Once the empirical work began, time was in short supply, and joint conferences became increasingly rare. So our report series turned out to be more important to our unity than personal meetings and direct collaboration.

## *The elderly in society – in the past*

During the planning phase, the project was in touch with two historians who had already made contributions to the field: Sune Åkerman and David Gaunt. This got us off to a flying start.

The first year, Sune Åkerman published the report "De stackars pensionärerna" (Poor pensioners!") (1981). With the aid of previously conducted interviews in an oral history project on a thinly populated district in Jämtland County, he was able to conclude that pensioners in their 80's had a large, frequently utilized contact network. Children who had moved away from home maintained regular contact with their parents by telephone or through visits. Only childless or single pensioners constituted a potentially isolated group.

At the end of the 1970's, David Gaunt had made important contributions to our understanding of the relationship between family form, family size and the agrarian structure. He now studied the "undantag" system (an obsolete system dealing with the beneficial rights of retired farmers) in a European perspective and propounded the view that this retirement system actually contained the seed of inter-generation conflict, since the productive and reproductive generation was obliged to set aside a large part of its production to the ageing generation. If Åkerman's work was mainly of importance to sociologists by emphasizing the integration of the elderly into social activities, Gaunt's various contributions were an important starting point for the subsequent work of the Lund historians. So there is every reason for me to revert to Gaunt's results.

Every sub-project was to strive to achieve the central objectives upon which the project was based: intervention, the release of resources and a long-range approach taking levels into account. For the historians, this was not achieved without difficulties and internal conflicts.

*Intervention* in the lives of living people is obviously an unfamiliar activity for historians. But there was at least one trend in cultural life of the 1970's to which scholars could relate: the "Gräv-där-du-står" (Dig where you're standing) movement. Sven Lindqvist's ideas about historical research as a popular movement had been well-received. A large number of working groups, often with pensioners as members, examined the conditions of work. Interest among older people in investigative activities was also expressed in the growing number of amateur genealogists who began descending on county archives. Historians witnessed a genuine interest in historical research among older people. As a result of our contacts with geriatricians and gerontologists we gained new insights into the importance of "cultural intervention". Geriatricians and psychiatrists were able to report positive results for intellectual stimulation in the treatment and care of very old and/or senile patients. Sociologists reported that past experiences were important to elderly people's perception of the present. The American anthropologist Barbara G. Myerhoff's reports on the importance of reconstructed live histories to existential conditions in ageing were particularly inspiring. Methodological interest in studies of life destinies began growing in different disciplines at the same time (Odén 1985). So intervention was combined with new forms of data acquisition supplying historians and the elderly with new knowledge and experience. This new knowledge was particularly important in a class perspective (Andreasson 1983). If Simone de Beauvoir was right, the cultural gap between the privileged and ordinary people is greatest in the final phase of life.

Activities with an interventionist and resource-liberating objective were started in all three projects. If these experiments were to correspond to the aims of intervention, the projects would have to reach people who had not previously been motivated for participation in activities of this type. The projects would also have to activate participants thereby freeing the latter's resources. Neither of these objectives were achieved in Uppsala or Lund, and the projects were concluded without attainment of the desired results (1). But this did not mean that the concept was abandoned, only that we had to try a different approach.

My assessment of the lack of results in Lund is that we did not have any adequate pedagogic methodology for investigative efforts by the elderly. These people tend to adopt a passive, student role and to glean information straight from the teacher/instructor. Role allocation was based on the elderly people's experiences in the cramming school of yesteryear (2). A new dilemma arises when investigative activities are combined with the oral history method: the questioner unconsciously influences the answers, and respondents may easily feel manipulated. These problems were discussed mainly in the Göteborg group (Glimstedt 1984). The enthusiastic emphasis on studies of life destinies has begun to be discussed in terms of ethical and moral objectives even in more recent research. There is a risk here that the pursuit of knowledge by the scholars could overshadow responsibility for elderly people's need for knowledge.

The problems in the *long-term* historical studies were related to the "resource" concept. One of the project leaders published a critical overview of the results attained to date by the historical project (Olsson 1984). Was it possible in past societies to identify the elderly as a resource, in the politics, in conveying traditions, in work distribution and in the care of children in societies of the past? Joseph Zitomersky (1983) employed the sociological theory of exchange in devising a future-oriented model for mutual, inter-generational care, a model assumed to have worked in past societies. The model maximized family care of the elderly in a social class which was neither destitute nor affluent but in which families, by collecting labor resources, received increased economic return and opportunities for supporting the elderly.

However, empirical testing of the historical material did not prove to be a completely uncomplicated matter. The source material did not permit any long-term analyses except in respect to cohabitation or proximity residency, where mutual exchange could be assumed to have functioned within the framework of the household or farm. In other respects the scholar was referred to scattered, mainly ethnological information.

## Micro level

It was to be the task of the ethnologist Gunilla Kjellman to analyze the patterns of cohabitation that could be identified in rural areas. She utilized historical and demographic material from the Demographic Database in Umeå, the archives of Statistics Sweden and ethnological interview material. Four "typical parishes" were studied: a coastal parish in Bohuslän County, an Uppland County parish with a typical farm laborer culture, a rural parish in Småland County and a Medelpad County parish in the sawmill district of northern Sweden (Kjellman 1984). She found that the cohabitation of ageing parents and *unmarried*, adult children was relatively commonplace. However, it was relatively unusual for families to live together. Kjellman attempted to explain the geographic variations found for the period from 1880 to 1940 with social and economic changes. But she also suggested a more long-term process of change in family patterns: from being a family-oriented cultural patterns to an individually *and* collectively oriented pattern. Here, she concurred with a research tradition strongly represented by the ethnologist Börje Hanssen and the church historian Hilding Pleijel. Kjellman adopted a particularly interesting analysis approach by comparing the cohabitation of the elderly and adult children at four different periods in life. A common pattern then found was that parent-child cohabitation had not dissolved by the 60-year phase, had dissolved in the 70-year phase but recurred in the 80-year phase, when the 80-year olds lived mainly with married children. Her observation that cohabitation with siblings or nieces/nephews was uncommon was important. Her historical findings were linked to Gerdt Sundström's "Caring for the aged in welfare society" (1982).

Kjellman's study was augmented and supplemented with smaller-scale studies whose intention was to analyze certain issues and test new source material. Kerstin Nilsson (3) examined Blentarp with the aid of church records, population registers and diocesan records and was thereby able to increase the volume of qualitative information. Lifeline methodology was tested and the influence of moves to other places on family dynamics was identified. Monika Edgren (4) studied moves between a small town and its rural surrounding in order to detect the effect on the residential patterns of elderly people and found that the circular nature of moves reduced pressure on the elderly people left behind.

Joseph Zitomersky performed a critical analysis (1987) of the various interpretation frameworks for family patterns. Zitomersky described Gaunt's interpretation framework as "ecological", Kjellman's as "culturalistic" and his own as "socioeconomic and structural", a historiographically interesting distinction that should be studied further in the light of the disciplines' varying scientific approach. (An analysis of ethnology's and history's different scientific approaches can be found in Winberg 1988).

Since Sweden was an agrarian society in the middle of the 19th century (the project's far limit), attention was first directed to rural conditions. At an early stage, however, Zitomersky claimed, with the support of English and American research findings, that there was an urban pattern in the working class with a high degree of inter-generation cohabitation in which work tasks and economic responsibility were shared. So a special study to determine whether this urban pattern was identifiable even in Sweden was of interest. An initial, preliminary examination suggested that this was not the case (Odén 1983 a). Swedish working class families lived in overcrowded conditions and had rent-paying lodgers, not elderly parents who shared responsibilities.

Additional studies of family structure in the cities were performed: C.G. Stenkula's study (1983) of Lund from 1900 to 1920, Gunilla Kjellman's study (1987) of Lund in the 1940's and Monika Edgren's study (4) of Falkenberg in the 1850's and 1870's. None of these works was able to confirm a general, urban pattern with a high degree of inter-generation cohabitation in the Swedish industrial working class. International research also questioned the general aspects of the hypothesis and regarded the patterns as being specific to textile worker towns in anglo-saxon countries. A study commenced by Monika Edgren of the family pattern in a Swedish textile worker town, Norrköping, should be able to shed further light on the issue.

If the homes, households and family relationships of the elderly represented one line in the historical sub-project, the second line concentrated on the *labor market*. What happened when the industrialized and capitalistic society superseded the patriarchal structure of the pre-industrial society? Lars Olsson was the main person responsible for studies of the labor market and the elderly.

Lars Edgren (1982, 1983) examined the transitional period between handicrafts and industry. As we know, handicrafts had developed special forms for work and household relationships. How then did the various social strata in handicrafts view ageing? In a series of lifeline studies, Edgren was able to show that elderly craftsmen and the widows of craftsmen did not normally live with their children. Instead, craftsmen in various social strata became residents of poorhouses - if they did not die before the age of 50.

Lars Olsson's studies of the departure of older industrial workers from working life were naturally linked to the introduction of the pension system, i.e to the macro level (Olsson 1983 a). But his work mainly concentrated on the micro level, i.e. on industrial workers' experience of ageing. He selected typographers for empirical investigation, an industrial aristocracy who were organized in unions at an early date and, thus, had excellent opportunities for arranging things for older workers. The results of Olsson's work were surprising (Olsson 1983 b, 1986, 1988 a, 1988 b). At the end of the 19th century there just were no elderly workers in the printing industry. The work environment was so trying that workers were "old" by the time they reached 35. Almost all died before the age of 60, mainly from pulmonary disease. In the light of these findings, trade union activity was more interesting than the social arrangements for retirement from working life. Olsson's results, in combination with the Göteborg physicians' interest in mortality patterns, shifted the focus in subsequent work from the social situation of workers to the work environment, health hazards and class differences in mortality (Berggren and Olsson 1988, Olsson 1989). Two new research fields opened up as a result of these unexpected research results: research on the historical work environment and on health hazards.

In the planning of the project, we had neglected to pay particular attention to the position of women. We had been what feminists call gender-blind. But as the work progressed we began to realize that ageing women constituted a particular problem. This realization was later confirmed by Kerstin Abukhanfusa's 1986 book "Piskan och moroten" (Stick and carrot), funded in part by a grant from the Foundation. So we became interested in performing a supplementary study of the old age and retirement of female industrial workers. The History Department's specialist in female industrial workers, Christina Carlsson Wetterberg, decided to tackle the subject and received generous support from the Foundation. The project is still in progress, but several preliminary reports have been published. Wetterberg (1988, 1989) attempted to capture three dimensions in her theoretical frame of reference: gender, age and class. The women's reproductive function linked them less rigidly to working life and to a less standardized "retirement age". They often abandoned the work place in their 40's. She was also able to show that elderly female industrial workers constituted a small group and were completely surpassed in size by the groups comprising menial servants, housemaids, cleaning ladies and washer-women loosely associated with some employer.

## Intermediate level

The work of the historians concentrated primarily on the micro level. But during the course of the work, the intermediate level emerged as being relevant to the life situation of ageing people: in Lars Olsson's examination of the work of trade unions and Lars Edgren's observation of the contributions made by guilds. But the collective intermediate level was addressed most systematically by Gunilla Kjellman. With the aid of official statistics, Kjellman (1981) studied the housing conditions of the elderly in 1887 and found major, local variations among different municipalities. The variations formed a pattern. In northern Sweden, institutions for the poor were uncommon and lodgings in households commonplace. In central and southern Sweden, however, housing for the elderly was mainly arranged through the provision of cottages for the destitute, subsequently transformed into poorhouses and old-age homes (5). Kjellman found the explanation for the differences in different mentalities in the north, where people had a more collectivistic outlook and did not hesitate to look after old, destitute people within the framework of the household, and in the south, where a more individualistic outlook relegated marginalized groups to controlled, public institutions. The dividing line was set at *Limes Norrlandicus*, as is so often apparent in ethnological material.

It is possible that this explanation will not stand the test of time. Local studies by other scholars outside the project – Sven-Anders Söderpalm (6) and Ulla Johansson (1984) – have pointed to other factors, primarily the interest by municipal authorities in solutions capable of reducing their responsibilities and costs. Differences in social structure between northern Sweden's peasant farmers and the huge estates in Sweden's southernmost province, Skåne, would then be due to social and economic conditions in relation to the municipalities' economic strength.

This view is close to Lars Olsson's hypothesis that peasant acceptance in the Riksdag of pension legislation at the turn of the century was due to the fact that this legislation was designed so municipal expenditures on the poor would be greatly reduced if the system were implemented as envisaged.

Finally, another Uppsala project merits mention: Torkel Jansson's association project (1985, 1986). It has provided new and valuable insights into the alternative strategies available in the 19th century as the need for a general pension reform painfully emerged, viz. private or local benevolent funds, consumer cooperative enterprises etc. The results of this project, and of other ongoing projects dealing with municipal self-government, will fill in some gaps in our knowledge on the intermediate level. But it is already apparent that the elderly appear as a resource only to an insignificant degree on the intermediate level.

## Macro level

In the project, "macro level" was defined as the "social level on which macrosociologists, historians and politicians seek social structures and social change processes of relevance to the environment of elderly people".

The first task completed on the macro level was the paper "Pensionärspolitik" (Policies on pensioners) (1982) by the political scientist Nils Elvander. Elvander found that the elderly had generally become a non-political issue by the 1950's and 1960's, with the exception of the big pension battle from 1956 to 1959. When these matters again became political issues at the end of the 1970's, it was because of economically harder times. The political parties devised policies for the aged according to a right-left scale in which standpoints on the right centered on privatization, family responsibility and old-age homes, whereas standpoints on the left emphasized municipal home service, collective responsibility and apartment hotels for the elderly. In the political debate, the elderly were viewed as a group in need, not as a resource, apart from self-care which in reality is a form of resource mobilization. Only the Communist Party actively advocated the *right* of old people to work, not so much because that work was a resource but because work would enable them to maintain their social identity as long as possible.

A link between the political macro level and the intermediate level was achieved by a study of the actual implementation of central government's intentions in municipal reality. This empirical work was conducted in Lund, a university town that had previously been studied on the micro level by other project scholars (7). Observations could then be made about the freedom-of-action available to municipal self-government in a field with powerful central controls – exercised through legislation, recommendations and subsidies. Here, the historical project could be linked to modern political science studies of the service offered by municipalities.

The introduction of legislation on pensions is one of the most important political measures in respect to the aged. In the initial phase of the project, Lars Olsson (1983 a) propounded the hypothesis that the famous 1913 pension reform was not mainly motivated by humanitarian concern about the elderly but was a vital prerequisite for the introduction of more efficient operations in Swedish industry.

Another policy matter was analyzed on the macro level: research policies in relation to the elderly. International studies by geriatricians had disclosed that physicians and the scientific community held a highly restrictive view of geriatrics and gerontology. This was usually interpreted as an expression of a negative attitude to the elderly as a patient (or client) category. A study of the Swedish Riksdag's handling of proposals on professorships in geriatrics and gerontology also exposed other circumstances (8). The demands for chairs dealing with the elderly were mainly raised by the public health sector and channeled through individual members of the Riksdag. The universities' – and thus the Government's – opposition can be ascribed to the unclear position of geriatrics in terms of scientific theory. By definition, it was a vague subject that cut across established disciplinary boundaries. In addition, it comprised pronounced interdisciplinary aspects and links with social science. So the subject did not correspond to the scientific community's view of *how* a discipline should be set up.

Attitudes to the elderly were a field which attracted the special interest of sociologists right from the start. A number of sociological studies were performed on the basis of current questionnaire material (Tornstam 1978, 1984, 1985). International historical studies were also largely preoccupied with attitudes towards the elderly. A study of attitudes to the elderly from 1830 to 1950 was started in Lund by Conny Blom. He decided to scrutinize the latent image of elderly people in children's books and found that elderly people at the beginning of the 19th century were viewed as a poor, resource-weak group in need of children's support. By the turn of the century, however, they were instead regarded as a resource-strong category and children's allies in conflicts with the parental generation. But by the middle of the 20th century, the elderly had almost completely disappeared from the social staffage in children's books. The children were the sole heros. Blom continued his studies of attitudes towards the elderly as reflected in public ordinances and proclamations (1987) (9).

In international respects, historical studies of attitudes towards elderly people have concentrated on the power and influence of the elderly. Views about past ages with a clear gerontocracy have been legion. An overview of the power and influence of the elderly in Swedish politics and administration produced somewhat different results. Generally speaking, upper middle-aged men have been the real power brokers in Sweden, as was previously found to be the case in England (Thomas 1976). When older people remained in positions of power until advanced old age during certain periods, this was not primarily a matter of attitude, i.e. any express *desire* to be ruled by the elderly, but a consequence of the circumstance that there was no regulated retirement from working life. The pensioning of civil servants emerged early as one way of avoiding any decline in the proficiency available in important posts (Odén 1988 a).

Legislation is obviously one of the most important interlevel control mechanisms. Legislation can be viewed as a reflection of the ruling class' normative plaintext (Odén 1988 c). Legislation in Sweden on relationships between the elderly and their adult children can be followed from laws in the Middle ages down to modern family law and the Social Services Act. However, the way laws are applied is more important than the laws themselves if the interplay between central government and individuals via the local collective's interpretations is to be understood. Ongoing studies of inter-generation relationships, as reflected in law court rolls, shed light on a virtually unknown field (Odén 1987) (10). They found that the courts heard cases of assault against aged parents and that this was a far more common charge than assaulting master or someone in authority. This crime was eliminated from statistics by the revision of the penal code in the 1860's. Inter-generation violence was relegated to the closed world of family life but subsequently reappeared as the subject of modern sociological studies, mainly performed in Sweden by the project leader Lars Tornstam (1989).

The macro level was defined in the project without any ethnic dimensions. But during the course of the work we became increasingly aware of the importance of an ethnic variable to the interpretation of an elderly person's situation in life and of the problems encountered by ageing, early immigrants with poor or declining proficiency in Swedish. We also became curious about developments in the lives of the Lapp people when their physical mobility became impaired. We wondered about the strong family bonds among Jews and whether the Jewish culture's pronounced concentration on intellectual development created special patterns for the final phase of life. Our contacts with specialists increased our curiosity, but did not lead to any new sub-projects (Odén 1983 b, 1983 c).

As a result of our contacts with e.g. Japanese and Chinese guest lecturers, we even became cognizant of the far-reaching change processes occurring in non-Swedish cultural spheres. The project's administrative assistant, Monica Udvardy (1983), happened to be a well-trained anthropologist, and she started a project on ageing women among East African Bantu people. Her work resulted in African field studies lasting many years and ultimately brought her to the Department of Cultural Anthropology at Uppsala University.

The historical part of the project had concentrated on the theme of the elderly, their relatives and the state (Odén 1986, 1988 c). So it was natural for the Lund group to assume responsibility for this theme in a future prospective. Pia Pikwer, who studies social work, and two statisticians, Ingvar Holmberg and Arne Arvidsson (1984, 1986) analyzed the present and the future from the point of view of clarifying the possibility of supplying home medical care in the future. Their most important contribution was to initiate the development of a demographic simulation model for evaluating future possibilities for relatives to care for aged relatives.

## Moth-balling the project?

A project has – and should have – a limited life. Grants and financing opportunities are limited. The various participants in the historical part of our project have all gone on to new duties, more or less closely linked to impulses and ideas emerging within the project framework.

The reports published to date by individual project members are obviously based on each sub-project's particular premises. These reports also reflect each scholar's scientific outlook. But an interdisciplinary approach demands a synthesis, an evaluation of results on the basis of scientific traditions *other* than one's own. So a synthesis must be critically analyzed according to other principles, not merely structured according to reports from individual sub-projects. This synthesis is still in progress and will be documented in a final volume on the project: "Äldre i samhället 3 – ett långsiktigt perspektiv" (The elderly in society 3 – a long-term perspective).

But even if no final synthesis has yet been produced, the individual reports published to date have aroused interest and been evaluated positively on several occasions. The report series inspired the Nordic Research Policy Council to initiate a Nordic comparative project that has hitherto addressed medical and social psychology aspects. Further development has also continued through international contacts. This especially applies to Alvar Svanborg who now works in the U.S. Lars

Tornstam's new projects are mainly Nordic. The historical perspective here has aimed at comparative studies of the shifting social policy measures in different countries from the early 19th century to the present time.

A project limited in time has a special life cycle: a visionary and ambitious planning phase, an exciting but resigned implementation phase and a pressing concluding phase. But is it then moth-balled and forgotten?

One fairly common experience is that an interdisciplinary project is by no means moth-balled when it comes to its natural end but continues on in other forms by capturing new issues and changes in perspective. The project team does break up for natural reasons, but the seed of new research is planted in other teams and in new projects.

# Lars Furuland

# Swedish sociology of literature

Comprehensive research on the functions of popular movements (such as the temperance and trade union movements) and their importance to democratization processes in Sweden from the 1850's to the 1950's began at Uppsala University in 1965. This was one of the very first interdisciplinary research programs supported with funds from the Swedish Council for Research in the Humanities. A number of doctoral candidates in history, under the leadership of Carl Göran Andræ and Sven Lundkvist, worked in the program, collaborating with both social scientists and representatives of the esthetic sciences.

In order to participate in this research program, literary historians in Uppsala set up a new section, with the author of this paper as its head, at their department. Collaboration with doctoral candidates and teachers at other universities, Stockholm University in particular but also at the universities in Lund and Göteborg, started as early as in 1965. The project network is represented in the research bulletin *Litteratur och samhälle* (Literature and society), launched in 1965, and in the publication of several Stockholm theses in the Uppsala section's publication series (1).

Comparative literature studies within the program naturally concentrated on Swedish proletarian authors and the popular movements. Through their meetings, periodic publications, publishing companies and libraries, they became cultural and literary institutions. Some studies were already in progress at Uppsala University or were initiated by the new project. These studies expanded into research such as the social backgrounds and education of authors, their ability to earn a living, their social position and their roles as intellectuals. Other fields were the expansion of the market economy and mass literature in Swedish book production plus the reading public's growth. Interest in other, virtually unresearched fields, such as children's literature and popular literature, soon followed.

This represented an expansion of the traditional fields for comparative literary research and made new theoretical and methodological demands on the program's scholars. Their attempts to exceed the boundaries for the popular movements project's basic research tasks can be discerned in the name selected for the new research facility: *Avdelningen för litteratursociologi* (Sociology of Literature Section).

However, it was the unit's next program, supported from 1967-71 by the Bank of Sweden Tercentenary Foundation, plus a research appointment established at the Swedish Council for Research in the Humanities and Social Sciences (HSFR) in the 1970's, that supplied the basic resources enabling the growth of the new line of research in comparative literature. The popular movements project had featured a broad design, time-consuming supervision of graduate students and committed scholars ranging from associate professors to students struggling to produce their first scientific papers. But the new program, called the "Swedish sociology of literature program", was based on work by advanced scholars.

The Swedish sociology of literature program comprised three independent scholars collaborating with one another. In one of these projects, Kurt Johannesson continued his analysis of literature during Caroline absolutism and concluded a study of considerable sociological interest (Johannesson 1968). Here, the emergence and content of Swedish baroque culture was not viewed merely as a consequence of the influence of continental countries but even as the product of structures and economic and social conditions in 17th century Swedish society. In the 17th century, the Swedish Court and aristocracy acquired a position of power they attempted to crown with an ethical and metaphysical superstructure demonstrating the aristocratic social stratum's concordance with Nature and the order of things. Johannesson performed a detailed study of Nature symbols in particular and was able to show how the north star, as a central symbol of the Caroline dynasty's absolute power, gradually began to supersede the sun symbol of the French autocracy. Through the use of the pastoral symbology, the happy, pious shepherd was also made into a symbol of the ideal Swedish subject (2).

Bo Bennich-Björkman was responsible for a project on the career of authors in Sweden up to the middle of the 19th century. He examined the economic circumstances and social status of Swedish authors. A hypothesis confirmed by his study was that the predominant production form in this period consisted of writings produced as an official duty or as qualifications for an office. At the end of the studied period, however, this system collapsed. The importance of market forces gradually increased: authors in Sweden began to earn their livings from the sale of their work on an open market. The writers became more and more specialized, and "fiction" grew into an independent literary category with several subdivisions. This pioneering study, based on a comprehensive examination of old records, was submitted, like Johannesson's study, in the form of a doctoral thesis (Bennich-Björkman 1970a) (3).

In a semantic investigation that was part of a special study in the program financed by the Foundation, Bennich-Björkman also conducted a detailed examination of terminological developments in respect to the production of literature. Here, he showed how important shifts in the meaning of the concept "literature" occurred in the period from 1750-1850. From being a very broad term comprising even texts published for schools and universities, "literature" became a term used for material for the new book and newspaper market. In this development, *fiction* acquired increasing importance as a central, intellectual field. Thus, the investigation showed how reorganization of the cultural elite's functions and regroupings into intellectual ranks had a decisive impact on language usage and terminology in the period from 1750-1850 (Bennich-Björkman 1970b).

For my part, I was in charge of research administration for the entire "Swedish sociology of literature" program but was still able to work in a project dedicated to the interplay between public debate and literature, a subject I examined by charting the "farm laborer" motif in Swedish literature. My examination resulted in a book on the Swedish author Ivar Lo-Johansson as a simultaneous literary depicter of farm laborers and a representative of literature among farm workers, especially those who were trade-unionists (Furuland 1976). I also studied the way new educational pathways opened up outside secondary schools and universities from 1880 to 1960. For at least three-quarters of a century, the new pathways for autodidacts could lead to professional writing careers (Furuland 1970a, 1989b).

During these years, however, my most important task as a research leader was to prepare a problematized overview of the new discipline and identify urgent research tasks (4). The scholars in the program had to introduce methods and perspectives from the international debate – only newly aroused at the time and still sporadic – on the sociology of literature.

But we also continued to make the most of the experience gleaned by Swedish and Nordic scholars interested in the history of learning and social history. We could build on a rather strong Uppsala tradition in literary research and art studies. This tradition can be said to have started around 1900 with Henrik Schück. It was continued to some extent (as is often overlooked) by Anton Blanck, Schück's successor in the chair of literature, through his studies of political occasions as mirrored in literature (Blanck 1935). Blanck's disciple, Gunnar Tideström, well-known for his interest in basic esthetic issues, held a broad-based post-graduate seminar where several of Uppsala's sociology of literature theses were discussed (5). But the research trend was mainly developed through Victor Svanberg's seminars and his own sociology of literature work, mainly conducted in the 1940's (Svanberg 1943-46, 1980), and through Gregor Paulsson's sociology of art tutoring and research. While the three young literary historians (Bennich-Björkman, Furuland and Johannesson) were working on their "Swedish sociology of literature" research program, they were able to derive further inspiration from advanced seminars led by Sten Lindroth, history of learning, Sten Carlsson, social history, and Karl-Gustaf Hildebrand, economic history, as well as from Svanberg and Paulsson, all of them in the productive environment of Uppsala University. The younger scholars' manuscripts and ideas were the subject of lively discussion with Svanberg or Tideström and at relevant seminars outside the Department of Literature.

In the light of history, I think it is now safe to say that the Uppsala section of the sociology of literature is a good example of the importance of strong roots within a discipline and of the stubbornness a local center needs to display. These are basic prerequisites for a creative research environment. Drastic administrative decisions from the top down, without local and regional consensus, may result in wasteful, ineffective use of resources.

The scholars involved in the Foundation's "Swedish sociology of literature" program subsequently continued working in the Uppsala department. Over the years, Bennich-Björkman has worked here as a tutor and researcher in the sociology of literature. Among other things, he has led a project, supported by the Foundation, on popular fiction in Sweden and started a special history of books seminar attached to the sociology of literature unit. At present, he is working on the Foundation project "The spread of books in Sweden 1750-1829".

I have served as the head of the sociology of literature unit and, as the discipline's professor, conducted several projects in collaboration with individual young scholars or groups of doctoral candidates: e.g. on the literature of non-conformist (Revivalist) churches and on the 1970's book crisis in Sweden. At present, a historical and sociological project on Swedish-American literature is in progress. The biggest effort after the "Swedish sociology of literature" program was a project developing long-neglected Swedish research on children's literature (Edström and Furuland 1976). The project was financed from 1974-76 by the Foundation and conducted in collaboration with Vivi Edström and the Department of Comparative Literature in Stockholm.

In recent years, Kurt Johannesson has concentrated on reviving rhetorical analysis based on philology and communication theory, work with early roots in his study of literature and its functions during Sweden's era as a major power. For the past few years, a rhetoric unit has been attached to the Department of Comparative Literature, headed by Johannesson as a professor of rhetoric at the HSFR. This unit collaborates with sociology of literature scholars, most recently through a series of studies of Swedish politicians who appeared as folk tribunes during the 19th century (*Heroer på offentlighetens scen*, 1987).

## What is the sociology of literature?

Sociology of literature research is now being conducted at every department of comparative literature at Swedish universities. (But the very name of this specialty on the rise is probably being cited more often than is objectively warranted.) Cultural sociology research has been conducted in Sweden for decades under the sociology heading. Even if we keep strictly to literature, scholars with a base in sociology have been active in the sociology of literature field at least at two universities (Karl-Erik Rosengren in Lund and Peder Hård af Segerstad in Uppsala).

Comparative literature scholars, interested in the sociology of literature, in Uppsala largely agree on what the "sociology of literature" is or should be. Fortunately, this does not prevent authors of papers or debate commentators in our seminar from expounding varying views on the subject or on where the interdisciplinary line should be drawn.

If the first part of my paper comprised a description of the Uppsala unit's origin and the external contours of its activities, the following description will be more personal in nature and influenced by current developments in my work as a scholar and tutor (6). Among other things, I would like to show that self-understanding in comparative literature, the discipline that is my mother subject, could be enhanced if scholars considered certain sociology of literature aspects in their work.

The sociology of literature, as I see it, is the science that attempts to pursue systematic study of literature as a social phenomenon, a system and an institution in society. It does not represent any particular research methodology but is a collective designation for a field of interest employing different methods and theories in various contexts.

During the first phase of this subject's evolution, the influence of sociology was considerable. The choice of the designation "sociology of literature", an international term (the French and German equivalents are "sociologie de la littérature" and "Literatursoziologie"), reflects the discipline's debt of gratitude to sociology. However, scholarly contacts with ethnology, folkloric, sociology of language, rhetoric, social and mental history and social anthropology are equally important to the discipline's future.

Sociology of literature scholars (sometimes with direct links to the mentioned subjects or disciplines in the social and behavioral science fields) can make important contributions to the analysis of different literary sub-institutions: authors, publishers, book trade, critics, the public and public agencies. But as my opening remarks show, sociology of literature scholars in Uppsala have also found it important to follow research traditions in humanities subjects, i.e. preserving their links to disciplines dealing with text interpretation.

I would also like to emphasize that the sociology of literature should retain a historical perspective on objects of research, even if sources of material for historical studies may be hard to come by. The Uppsala unit conducts considerable research that could be described as *the history of books*, an internationally lively field of research in recent years. But the difference between our field of interest and the history of books, as research in the latter is usually conducted, is that sociology of literature also attempts to interconnect observations about book production and dissemination with analyses of texts and their message, often even of their structure and form. So the sociology of literature, as conducted in Uppsala, does not concentrate solely on the study of literature as an institution or communication system. (This delineation is sometimes made in other countries.) One example of the way the sociology of literature can be successfully linked to advanced narratological research is a new thesis elucidating the Swedish author Almqvist's varying narrative strategies for different reader categories on the book market (Svedjedal 1987).

## Literary research and literary pedagogics as a national priority

In the 19th century, comparative literature, that evolved from bibliography and esthetics, gradually became more firmly established as a university discipline. Professors and associate professors in the new subjects sought the roots of national literature in past centuries. This was a task that could induce some people to produce anachronistic depictions of characters from the past. The major authors were often perceived as bearers of patriotic ideals similar to those of the 19th century, even when these authors were active long before the birth of modern, national awareness. Demonstrating literature's patriotic ancestry by describing the country's literary history became an important task for history of literature scholars in Sweden. Similar developments, in respect to the pursuit of national tasks in research, university teaching and folk education, were expected of philology, ethnology and, of course, history in an age in that national awareness was spread to the "people".

For the subject ultimately called "litteraturhistoria" (history of literature), dealing with both esthetics and history, an important task was also to interpret and evaluate texts and authors. Works and authors would be assigned appropriate niches in the literary system constructed in the 19th century. Since the beginning of the 19th century, literary criticism in Sweden had served as an increasingly effective separator attempting to extract the most valuable products from the rapidly growing flood of literature. Thus, critics and reviewers selected a literary *canon* of elite work. By its very nature, this body of recognized literature is very small in relation to the growing volume of fiction.

Most comparative literature scholars have kept to this national canon in their research. On the basis of the selections made by critics – in an interplay between critics and scholars – even fewer works and authors subsequently attained the position as classics. Many representatives of the history of literature/comparative literature have been active both as scholars and historians and as critics.

Originality esthetics, emerging in pre-Romanticism, has remained a determining factor in literary criticism and to a large degree also in history of literature selection. Most scholars have concentrated on the birth and uniqueness of literary works, i.e. their "originality" at the time of conception. Before the introduction of the sociology of literature, however, there were seldom any studies of the post-publication life of literary works and their subsequent death in various public strata (7). Here, the sociology of literature can contribute research ultimately leading to changes in the conditions of comparative literature so that this discipline will be in a better position to comment on a work's rise and fall in the reading public's favor and not merely generate a long cavalcade of various kinds of "modernisms".

## Neglected literary fields

Sub-cultures and counter-cultures have been the legitimate subjects of literary research only when they could be linked to new esthetic developments. This is one of the reasons why large sectors of literature, in which innovative literary forms and daring poetic expressions were not the main objective, long remained outside the interest of comparative literature. Examples are early proletarian literature and the revival movement fiction (in the form of religious songs, tracts and "true, real-life stories"), plus children's literature, popular fiction and numerous, innovative (in term of subject matter) literary works by female authors, who however remained traditionalists in esthetic and philosophical respects.

Women were highly active as authors in the 19th century. They dominated novel-writing, especially in popular literature, and were well-supported by the expanding novel-reading public. But the decisive change in the balance between men and women in "recognized" literature did not occur until our own time when women had become critics and scholars. This apparently affected evaluation processes and contributed to the fact that women, to a much greater extent than hitherto, can currently devote themselves to and win recognition in other literary fields than the novel, long regarded as an "inferior" form of literature.

A further example of the way unwritten institutional rules govern the boundaries of comparative literature is Swedish-American literature in North America. The almost 100 years of book and newspaper publication in Swedish by immigrants in the U.S. and Canada, has been forgotten in the literary history.

188 · *Lars Furuland*

On the other hand, innovative works, in terms of form and esthetics, often produced by Finnish-Swedish authors have been the subject of great interest in Swedish criticism and the history of literature with good reason. However, Swedish-American literature is scarcely even mentioned in handbooks before 1989 (8). This literature is of considerable cultural and sociological importance but is characterized by its traditional means of expression. The literature of linguistic minorities did not become the subject of study on both sides of the Atlantic until the emergence of the lively interest in "roots" over the past few decades, i.e. when various ethnic groups have sought their origin and identity. Uppsala scholars in sociology of literature are now belatedly trying to produce the equivalent of the basic work on the Swedish language in the U.S. performed by the philologists Folke Hedblom and Nils Hasselmo through collections and research.

These examples should suffice to show why the initial phase of the sociology of literature has concentrated on various neglected literary fields. In these fields, we find, as we have seen, fiction from the popular movements, such as early proletarian literature and the literary output of revival movements and non-conformist churches, not to mention the very widely read children's literature, neglected by research until the 1970's, plus popular literature as a whole. The latter literature represents an almost unimaginably vast research field. Here, Bo Bennich-Björkman and his students in Uppsala have conducted a number of strategically selected special studies (9).

## Fiction giving life to social history

The material available to the social historian interested in studying changes over time consists of physical objects, administrative documents and statistical information from different public agencies, industries and societies. In one special study, I attempted to show that fiction is an invaluable source of information in the study of social changes. The example I selected was the impact of electrification (Furuland 1984). The scholar must seek new source material when attempting to understand the way people respond to innovation and when wishing to explain the importance of innovation to everyday life.

For the most part, people's experiences and responses to major changes in everyday life are expressed orally, and memoirs in folk archives often constitute one of the most important sources of information for a social historian but are seldom utilized outside the field of ethnology. Other commentaries have generally been private in the form of e.g. notes, diaries and letters. Most of this material has disappeared in the course of time, and the remnants are often hard to trace.

Authors of novels and memoirs, who were also trained observers and skilled writers, are a truly neglected source of information meriting greater attention. My study of the impact of electrification on individual people and their life situations showed that fiction was the richest source of information, whereas ethnographic collections had surprisingly little to offer in this case.

The difficulties involved in obtaining adequate source material should not lead to the conclusion that fiction should be rejected as source material. Fiction depicting social conditions is neither more difficult nor easier to use than other legitimate sources but it does make it necessary for the researcher to possess certain special knowledge and proficiency, in addition to a social history perspective, i.e. she/he should primarily be familiar with the genre, be widely read and familiar with biographical research. Tests of the legitimacy of source material cannot be made according to any fixed pattern but must be individualized from case to case.

The author of a novel is often highly pedagogic in her/his depiction, seeking to highlight key aspects in a course of events and contrasting developments with one another. But is coming to grips with e.g. a politician's diaries and letters really any easier? In any event, fiction is often able to supply invaluable, concrete examples of historical events that are also documented in statistics and other material. Hard data can obviously be generalized to a completely different degree than literature's often episodic glimpses of people's lives. But without the observant eye of authors we would know infinitely less about psychological responses, attitudes, mentality, habits and conventions in various social strata. This especially applies to the time preceding modern sociology, Gallup polls etc. but also to the period thereafter.

Attaining analyses based both on traditional historical sources and more ethnological and literary material is a desirable ideal for many important research tasks in social history.

## Closing remarks

Most Swedish scholars in comparative literature now use the concept "sociology of literature" as a broad, collective designation for scientific efforts whose aim is to shed light on the entire problem complex and the interplay between literature and society. The fact that the literary institution, its various sub-institutions and the entire literary system exercise a powerful influence on texts is quite obvious. So the sociology of literature scholar should also be able, on the basis of her/his special field of interest and competence, to contribute to the analysis and interpretation of the text itself.

Sociology of literature research is often conducted in the borderland between comparative literature and other disciplines, and theory formation and methodology in the social sciences and behavioral sciences are important to the scholar interested in studying literature in society. In any event, interdisciplinary collaboration is of major importance to the further development of the sociology of literature, irrespective of whether new approaches to the study of literature and its social context originate in esthetic and philological disciplines or the social sciences.

Swedish sociology of literature is well-known in the Nordic countries, and Uppsala scholars are frequently invited to serve as experts, lecturers at seminars and reviewers of manuscripts from other universities. Uppsala has had a special chair in comparative literature with emphasis on the sociology of literature since 1978. Another Nordic chair in literature, following the Uppsala model, was established in Copenhagen a few years later.

Outside the Nordic countries, Swedish sociology of literature with roots in the humanities has not been equally successful in spreading its approach. This is primarily because we work, for obvious reasons, with Swedish source material and study Swedish or Nordic conditions and because we (like many other institutions in the humanities) have extremely limited staff resources for activities over and above tutoring and teaching.

There are international examples of the way humanists, such as the well-known French literature scholar and comparatist Robert Escarpit, specialize in the sociology of literature. But this is still uncommon outside Sweden. When the sociology of literature is pursued, it is usually within the framework of a department of sociology or in mass communication research. Swedish sociology of literature has a different tradition. It was not only inspired by sociology (a young subject at the time) and other social sciences. It is also strongly linked (as already shown) to Swedish social history and history of learning, as well as to our older, broadly based literary overviews and studies (Schück, Svanberg et al.). In the U.S., for example, scholars and university teachers working professionally with literature have generally kept to a text-oriented tradition. Complementary approaches, very familiar to Swedish comparative literature and sociology of literature scholars, are most often encountered in social history, ethnology, social anthropology and, not the least, ethnicity and immigration research.

The Uppsala group was offered a guest professorship at a major U.S. university, an offer subsequently taken up in 1988 (10). There was a special reason for the offer. Humanists (philologists, historians, literature and art scholars) were to collaborate in a large department with social science colleagues (cultural and physical geographers, sociologists etc.) for the purpose of broadening and deepening studies in the Scandinavian region by means of interdisciplinary collaboration in teaching and research. The Swedish model for the sociology of literature then acquired sudden interest.

*Erik Dahmén & Karl-Göran Mäler*

# Environment, natural resources and society

## Background

The middle of the 60's witnessed the first precursors of the environmental debate that has left its mark on the western world ever since. Rachel Carson's book *Silent Spring*, in which the effect of biocides and pollutants on nature were dramatically depicted, made a significant contribution to international developments in this area. In Sweden, Hans Palmstierna's book *Plundring, svält, förgiftning* had a similar impact. Awareness of growing environmental problems induced many groups to become involved in the debate on man's environment.

## The first economic research

Economics deals with the management of scarce resources. After the sudden realization that environmental resources, such as clean air, clean water, birds, vegetation etc., are finite, these resources also became the subject of economists' interest. But it would be an error to believe that economic research commenced from some abysmal depth. The theory of external effects, i.e. the effects on production and consumption of decisions outside the normal price framework, had played a central role in Marshall's and Pigou's work at the beginning of this century. Pigou (1932) identified situations in which the invisible hand was inoperable and even suggested a solution. One external effect, e.g. a negative effect, means one or more people in a society being subjected to impairment of welfare and the instigator of that impairment has no reason to take the impairment into account, since the effect has not been priced on any market. As a result, resource utilization is poorer than would otherwise be the case. But if the market is unable to put a price on negative effects, the State could intervene, according to Pigou, and *tax* the impairment. If the tax is set so it is equivalent to the welfare loss caused by the impairment, decision-makers will find it to be in their best interests to take the external effect into account. This internalizes that external effect.

This Pigou idea was commonplace in textbooks on resource allocation theory, but the presence of external effects was generally believed to be the exception rather than the rule. Only after environmental problems became acute in the 1960's did people discover that the Pigou analysis could be used in practical efforts to improve understanding of environmental issues and devising practical recommendations on environmental policies. The first person in Sweden to adopt this approach was Erik Dahmén who as early as 1965 in *Planerar vi för den ekonomiska utveckling på längre sikt som vi verkligen vill ha?* discussed the possibility of utilizing fees in environmental policies. This paper was published in "Svensk ekonomisk tillväxt", a collection of papers published in connection with the Government's long-term planning. Dahmén's paper was the first analysis in conjunction with long-term evaluations to address environmental matters. His starting point was the Pigouvian tradition discussed above, and Dahmén strongly maintained, on the basis of this tradition, that long-term planning be performed in such a way that externalities in the form of environmental impact are internalized so decision-makers do not solely take into account the consequences for their own enterprises but also environmental impacts on others.

One way to achieve this internalization, according to Dahmén, was to charge fees for the discharge of pollutants. The magnitude of the fees should reflect the impairment inflicted by

the discharge on valuable environment. Here, Dahmén emphasized that the internalization of external effects did not result
only in better management of existing, limited resources, as
noted in established theory, but even stimulated the development of new, environmentally superior technology. This argumentation was deepened and reinforced in Dahmén's *Sätt pris
på miljön* (1968). The book evoked a powerful response in the
public debate and can be said to represent the beginning of the
fees versus regulations discussion pursued by economists for
more than a decade after Dahmén's book.

Even if most "established" conservationists responded nega-
tively to the idea of fees, viewing them in the same light as
indulgences of yesteryear, they did listen attentively to the
economic arguments, and the importance of economic analysis
was ultimately acknowledged. So Dahmén and Assar Lindbeck
decided to seek funding for a research project on environmental
economics and received a grant from the Bank of Sweden
Tercentenary Foundation. This marked the start of the research
program *Miljö, Naturresurser och Samhälle* (Environment,
Natural Resources and Society) at the Stockholm School of
Economics (HHS). The program was launched in 1969 with a
small grant for a pilot study. A large grant was awarded in 1971
for Sweden's first comprehensive study of environmental economics. This investment in research proved to have considerable long-term consequences, since the program is still thriving
twenty years after its inception.

## The program's initial years

The program was initially planned as a major social science
study of environmental issues with contributions made also by
scholars other than economists. For a few years, it collaborated
with other disciplines, e.g. in the form of a regularly convened
seminar attended by ecologists, meteorologists and historians.

But this organized, interdisciplinary collaboration ultimately terminated. However, a broad contact network encompassing other disciplines was utilized during the whole program.

In 1969 Dahmén recruited Karl-Göran Mäler to the project. He held a licentiate degree from Stockholm University and had a background in abstract, mathematical economics. He was also a recipient of a fellowship from the Ford Foundation for one year of study at American universities. He was at the Massachusetts Institute of Technology (M.I.T.) in the autumn 1969 term and at Stanford University in the spring 1970 term. His work at Stanford was financed to some extent by a research grant from the Foundation. His stay at M.I.T. proved to be of decisive importance to both Mäler's and the research program's future. Thanks especially to Peter Diamond's course in Public Economics at M.I.T., Mäler acquired a firm, rigorous foundation for advanced work on environmental economics, something that became a feature of large parts of the program's research (in contrast to the position in environmental economics research in many other countries). The contacts Mäler established with Resources for the Future (RfF) in Washington, D.C., especially with Allen Kneese, the director of the RfF's program on the Quality of Environment, was also decisive to the program's subsequent activities. At the time, the RfF was the world's foremost center for research on environmental economics. It is probably no exaggeration to claim that modern environmental economics research was born at the RfF in the 1960's and that a large part of current research in this field can be traced back to RfF activities at the end of the 60's and beginning of the 70's. In December 1969, Mäler visited the RfF. There, he met the young scholars Charles Chichetti, Myrrick Freeman III and Clifford Russel, in addition to Kneese, contacts that were to prove very useful to the research program's subsequent work.

Environmental economics research at the RfF at this time placed particular emphasis on the development of practical methods, with a solid theoretical foundation, for the planning and management of environmental resources. Kneese and Robert Ayres had published an article (in 1969) in which they introduced the first law of thermodynamics into economic theory. Subsequently, the importance of the second law was also stressed, especially by Nicholas Georgescu-Roegen (1971). The first law states that energy cannot be destroyed but merely change form. Since mass and energy are interchangeable in a ratio laid down in Einstein's special theory of relativity, it follows that mass is also conserved. Kneese's and Ayres's contribution was that they were the first economists to attempt an analysis of the consequences of the conservation of mass. Their conclusion, briefly expressed, was that the utilization of natural resources, such as ore, gravel, air, crops etc., measured as the total mass of these resources in tons, increases during periods of economic growth. But mass is not destroyed in the economic process. It must either be stored in the form of long-life capital goods or returned to nature in the form of residuals, i.e. substances with no economic use (at current prices). The amount of residuals that must be returned to nature therefore increases when natural resource utilization increases, and since residuals generally cause changes in the environment, it follows that economic growth involves potential environmental problems. The term "potential environmental problems" is used because not all residuals give rise to environmental damage. Impact on the environment can be reduced by the utilization of raw materials generating less harmful residuals, by utilizing less harmful production methods and by modifying the residuals.

With this approach it becomes necessary to follow the entire chain of economic activities from the harvesting of raw materials to the discharge of residuals for any consistent economic analysis to be possible. So the RfF (with B. Bower as a *primus motor* and C. Russel and W. Spofford as active researchers) attempted to design operations analysis models for the entire chain of economic activities in a region. This part of the RfF's research program was subsequently incorporated into the research program financed by the Foundation.

Another theoretical research branch at the RfF concerned the possibility of achieving lasting growth when natural resources are limited and economic activity inevitably leads to an impact on the environment. In current terminology, we would call this the possibility of attaining sustainable development.

The RfF also conducted an active analysis of different environmental policy instruments, something that became important to the research program at the HHS.

All these research issues left their mark on the Foundation-financed research program at the HHS. They were discussed at the RfF at a conference in Washington, D.C., held in the spring of 1970, to which Mäler was invited in order to read a paper on economic growth and the environment. This also provided him with an opportunity for informal discussions about two other papers written at Stanford.

At a 1970 symposium held by the International Social Science Council (ISSC) in Tokyo, Dahmén presented a paper on environmental and economic systems (Dahmén 1971).

## The research program's first year

In 1970, Dahmén applied for funds for a major research program in the field of environmental economics. The application was drawn up after discussions with Mäler and Johan Facht. At that time, Facht was a licentiate in economics at the HHS and employed by the Swedish Industrial Institute for Economic and Social Research (IUI). He had documented his interest in environmental economics in his licentiate thesis that contained, among other things, a review of various issues and models in environmental economics.

Dahmén's application concerned a research program encompassing three different parts. In an empirical study, Johan Facht was to analyze the cost of emission-reducing measures in industry, based on information on the system for environmental conservation subsidies in force at the time. This part was financed both by the Foundation and by the Marianne and Marcus Wallenberg Foundation. In a more theoretical part, Mäler was to conclude the theoretical work commenced during his stay in the U.S. In a third section, he was to study the possibility of applying the operations analysis models developed at the RfF to Swedish conditions.

## Theoretical studies

During his studies at Stanford University, Mäler had written several papers on environmental economic subjects. The idea was to complete these papers in a doctoral thesis. One of these papers concerned a method for estimating the demand for a better environment on the basis of data on people's individual behavior. The starting point was an article by J. Stevens (1966) in which he estimated the recreational value of improved water quality by studying the different consumers' surpluses before and after the improvement. However, Stevens did not mention any theoretical justification for the procedure. And there was some doubt about whether the concept "consumers' surplus" could be used in this context. It was soon clear that Stevens' approach had to be based on the assumption that changes in water quality in an area were only important to people who used the area. But if people who did not use the area for fishing or some other form of recreation also felt that improved water quality had a positive value, the Stevens approach would obviously not work. So Mäler introduced the concept "weak complimentarity" to designate a situation in which there exists a product that can be freely bought or sold on a market and whose environmental quality is such that an individual only values the environmental quality positively when she/he consumes a positive quantity of the product. This immediately shows that weak complimentarity is a necessary condition for the Stevens approach to be correct. But is weak complimentarity an adequate condition? As a result of knowledge acquired in Diamond's course on public sector economics, Mäler was able to frame the problem of adequacy as a problem concerning the existence of a solution to the Slutsky equations in consumer theory. Mäler also showed that if classic integratability conditions were met, the Slutsky equations would have a unique solution. Weak complimentarity would then be sufficient for determining people's evaluation of certain types of environmental quality. This finding was published in the Swedish Journal of Economics (1971). It subsequently became the subject of numerous articles and was found to have considerable empirical value.

However, this study was only partial and only concerned one special method for estimating the demand for a better environment. But the aim was to incorporate this and other partial approaches into a more general study. As a result of this initial paper, Mäler was invited to the RfF as a guest scholar. There he wrote the first draft of a doctoral thesis subsequently published by the RfF (Mäler 1974).

The thesis employed a general equilibrium perspective. Kenneth Arrow and Gerhard Debreu had mathematically proved the existence of equilibrium in an economy with perfect competitive markets for all goods and services and that this equilibrium is economically effective. Mäler adopted their model but introduced environmental effects and the fact that the quantity of matter extracted from nature also had to be equal to the quantity of matter returned to nature. He showed that the result of market equilibria would be effective resource management, assuming that these environmental effects were priced in a given way. More exactly, Mäler showed that there were pseudo-prices for environmental effects in support of Pareto-effective resource allocations, that these prices reflect people's collective, marginal willingness to pay for a better environment and that for each Pareto-effective resource utilization there is a set of equilibrium prices for ordinary goods and services and a set of pseudo-prices for the environmental effects generating the given resource utilization. In principle, this means that the Pigouvian tradition was expanded from partial equilibrium to general equilibrium: there are emission fees which make resource utilization effective. Mäler subsequently refined and generalized this analysis (1985).

However, the magnitude of fees must correspond to the estimated damage inflicted by the pollutants. How can this damage be estimated and appraised? Mäler worked with two possible methods for appraising the cost of damage: by direct questions to consumers and by studying the behavior of consumers. The first approach was, and continues to be, criticized because consumers may have some strategic reason for hiding their true preferences. According to Mäler's analysis, however, it is possible to describe the problem in a way making truthful answers a "max-min strategy". This result was reached at the same time, but independently of Mäler, by other economists and on a far more general level.

The second approach is based on an *a priori* assumption on household preferences. By assuming complimentarity between environment and some market product or weak complimentarity or perfect substitutability, it is possible, Mäler showed, to reveal people's preferences for environmental improvements with the aid of empirical information on the way people behave. This analysis has been developed by many scholars, perhaps most prominently by Myrrick Freeman III (1979). A theoretical elaboration can be found in Mäler (1985).

Finally, the thesis addressed the choice of environmental policy controls. The analysis showed that a consequence of the general equilibrium analysis was that fees for emissions were effective control measures, provided the authorities had sufficient information on underlying factors to set fees at an appropriate level. However, when information is incomplete, the question of control measures is an open matter. Mäler analyzed the factors that should govern the choice of various control measures. This study had been preceded by a paper presented and discussed at the International Economic Association's 1972 conference on environmental economics. The main finding in this paper was that emission fees would require less information than other conceivable control measures when numerous companies are discharging some environmentally homogenous substances and when the objective is to reduce total discharges by a given quantity. However, the environmental objective is given here. The situation is different when the environmental objective is governed by individual evaluations of the environment and when these evaluations are unknown. This situation was analyzed by Weizman (1974) and utilized by Bergman, Mäler and Ståhl (1987) when they studied economic control measures for reducing hydrocarbon emissions in Göteborg. In a situation in which discharges cannot be monitored, Mäler showed that it is always possible to devise a combination of taxes and subsidies whose net effect is the same as an optimum discharge fee. It is interesting to note that Mäler utilized the material balance principle in order to show this.

The book contains a chapter in which various growth pathways are analyzed with respect to their sustainability. In the past five years, this analysis has become directly applicable to the issue of sustainable development. The book also contains a chapter outlining principles of environmental accounts, principles that have attained new currency in the past year.

The thesis attracted international attention and is still read, even though it is now greatly out-of-date. Mäler (1985) contains an update of the central theory sections. His thesis was followed up by a smaller-scale book by Mäler and Ron Wyzga (1976). Wyzga was a statistician with a Ph.D. from Harvard. At the beginning of the 1970's, he was working for the Environment Directorate of the OECD. This book contains a review of methods for estimating damage cost functions and empirical illustrations. The book only contains two new theoretical contributions: an analysis of the capitalization of environmental changes in real property values and a study of the valuation of changes in illness risks. Despite its limited scope, the book was widely read for several years, since it was the only book on the valuation of environmental effects that was directly based on established welfare economics. However, Freeman's book (1979) provided an even better treatment.

## Regional environmental management models

The material balance principle shows that
1) a reduction in the discharge of one residual (assuming the utilization of natural resources) leads to increased discharge of other residuals;
2) that the only way to reduce long-term total discharges is to reduce the utilization of natural resources;
3) that purification only represents a transformation of residuals of one kind into residuals of another kind;
4) that product technology and the selection of raw materials, like purification, are important to the degree of environmental impact.

In addition, the effect on the environment obviously depends on total emissions. So the control of individual effluents (the consequence of Swedish environmental legislation) is ineffective. For this reason, an attempt to design operation analytical models encompassing the entire process from natural resource utilization to final impact on the environment is a step that readily comes to mind. One such project was planned and implemented within the framework of the Foundation-financed Gavle River Project.

K.-G. Mäler was the project leader, and Henrik Delden, a B.Sc. in economics at Stockholm University, was employed as a project assistant. Delden was the one who collected the project's empirical information and was independently responsible for most of the project work. The project comprised a study of the Gavle River's catchment area. This area was selected in collaboration with staff at the National Environment Protection Board. The water in the Gavle River is affected primarily by two pulp mills, Hammarby and Mackmyra, in addition to municipal effluent and by the Sandviken factory. The objective was to devise a detailed model of the production technologies at these plants so as to permit calculation of the costs of achieving environmental improvements in the Gavle River's catchment area, including the costs of reducing emissions into the air.

Delden succeeded with the trick of learning the technology needed for the project and, after frequent contacts with representatives of the involved factories, designed linear programming models for some of the activities polluting the environment in the area. However, it was soon apparent that the research task was impossible because facility-specific knowledge was not available and because devising a model capable of satisfactorily depicting technical developments proved to be impossible. The essence in Dahmén's advocacy of the utilization of fees in environmental policies was that they would make a major contribution to technical developments. In the planning of the Gavle River Project, however, the project leader devoted far too little thought to dynamic conditions, so static efficiency acquired excessive scope. As a result, the Gavle River Project was a failure. But it simultaneously supplied valuable insights showing that the central planning philosophy characterizing the project (and many similar projects in other countries) was poorly substantiated. The project also supplied other practical information that was utilized in subsequent empirical and theoretical research. For example, the importance of temporary or stochastic emissions was studied. This type of emission was also the subject of special study in Mäler's thesis in conjunction with the analysis of various environmental policy control instruments.

The Gavle River project resulted in an unpublished report.

## The cost of emission controls

The aim of the Gavle River project was to create a detailed model of complete production processes, but Facht's project had more modest but realistic aims. Facht was interested in the actual, realized cost of the emission restrictions introduced from 1969-73 in the iron and steel and pulp and paper factories.

Facht's work was performed in close collaboration with the National Environment Protection Board (SNV), and the SNV supplied the empirical source material. Underlying his study was the financial subsidy program enacted by the Riksdag. It offered industries state subsidies for emission-reducing measures. These state subsidies were introduced at the same time as the Environment Protection Act and were intended to accelerate developments in the direction of a reduction in emissions. The subsidies were clearly violating the PPP (Polluter Pays Principle), i.e. the OECD's recommendation that polluters should defray all the costs, and was perceived in many countries as improper support for Swedish exports. However, these subsidies were mainly paid for old plants, so it is doubtful whether they were of any major importance to Swedish export.

Subsidy applications had to contain a description of the choice of technology, the impact of emissions and the cost of reducing emissions. This material constituted a rich source of information for empirical analyses of the cost of emission controls. Since subsidies were only paid for capital expenditures, Facht had to calculate operating costs from other material.

Facht's analysis of the available empirical material resulted in a doctoral thesis, *Emission control costs in Swedish industry* (1976). The thesis also comprised an analysis of the economic consequences of the subsidy program and a review of the central, environmental economics ideas, in addition to empirical calculations of actual costs. Facht's empirical studies suggest that the subsidy program led to a reduction in unemployment by nearly 20% and that the effect doubled when indirect costs were included.

It is interesting to note that Facht's empirical analysis was immediately utilized by the National Environment Protection Board, whereas Mäler's theoretical analysis scarcely evoked any response among practicians. This was due in part to the circumstance that the Board had an immediate need for empirical information for its everyday operations, and Facht's study was designed along lines that reflected Board thinking. Mäler's abstract arguments were generally rejected, although not by all. But fifteen years later, many of Mäler's arguments have been accepted by practicians, since his work provides a basis for useful empirical studies.

## Practical use

We have already noted that Johan Facht's empirical analysis of the cost of reducing emissions from iron and steel and pulp and paper factories was put to immediate use by the National Environment Protection Board. After receiving his doctorate, Facht moved to Paris to take a job with the OECD. Among other things, his task was to conduct international studies of the cost of reducing emissions.

Through Dahmén, Mäler was engaged for work on the Swedish case study for the 1972 UN conference and planned the economic analysis for this study. Since Mäler was abroad in the spring of 1971 to serve as a visiting scholar at the RfF, he was replaced by Margareta Johannesson at Stockholm University. She carried out the economic calculations. They mainly consisted of the determination of costs of reducing sulfur emissions in Sweden. The case study also included a discussion on the use of a sulfur emission fee for reducing national emissions. This was apparently the first time the idea of using fees in environmental policies was put forward in a public document in Sweden.

In 1971, the Government appointed the Environment Cost

Commission chaired by Valfrid Pålsson. The Commission's work concentrated on studies in various sub-fields. Economists generally played a major role in most of these studies. Karl Liedgren from Lund University was the main author of the concluding volume. One of the interim reports concerned sulfur emissions and acidification and the choice of environmental policy measures for reducing sulfur emissions. Mäler was the author of two chapters in this interim report and made substantial contributions to other chapters. The primary argument was based on results in Mäler's doctoral thesis and resulted in the view that the charging of a fee for sulfur emission was preferable to alternative control measures. However, the committee's political representatives adopted another line. In retrospect, we can see that the proposal finally drafted had a major influence on the proposal submitted by the Environment Fee Committee in 1989 on charging fees for sulfur and nitrogen emissions.

## Continued research

After the initial grant from the Foundation, interest at the HHS in continuing a research program on the environment, natural resources and society remained high. In 1975 Mäler was appointed to a chair in economics at the HHS, and the prospects of continuing the research program with alternative financing were good.

The Energy Forecast Study (EPU) asked the Economics Research Institute at the HHS to construct an "energy forecast model". As a result of this assignment, research for the next few years concentrated on energy economics. Lars Bergman, Anders Björklund and Claes Bergström were employed for work on the energy forecast model. Mäler was in charge of the project. The idea was to develop a numerically computable, general equilibrium model for the Swedish economy and to relate various kinds of energy utilization to this model. Björklund was responsible for econometric estimation of demand functions, Bergström for the design of a system model for refineries and Bergman for the central equilibrium model.The project resulted in a large number of reports, the most important of which Bergman's doctoral thesis (1977). While Mäler served as a visiting professor at the University of New Mexico in the 1975/76 academic year, Bergman took over project management and led the work to a successful conclusion.

After taking his doctorate, Bergman was offered an opportunity to conduct research at the International Institute of Applied System Analysis (IIASA) in Austria. During his stay at the IIASA, he met the Hungarian mathematician Andras Pohr with whom he developed a new type of solution algorithm for the processing of numerical, general equilibrium models. After his return to Sweden, Bergman made major contributions to the KRAN Project, a new project in the research program. KRAN, an acronym for the Swedish term meaning "crisis and adaptation in Swedish energy supplies", was a project initiated by the Energy Research Commission. Its object was to study the Swedish economy's reactions to future energy market shocks. The project had three "legs" – one at the IUI with B. Ch. Ysander as the project leader, one at the FFE with Alf Carling as the project leader and one at the HHS with Mäler as the project leader. Bergman's contributions to the development of a system for numerical general equilibrium models were at the heart of project work (Bergman et al. 1983). These models were also utilized in a number of major energy studies conducted from the end of the 1970's to the present day. Bergman subsequently showed how numerical general equilibrium models can be used in environment economic analyses.

Claes Bergström abandoned academic research for a few years but returned after a time to take a doctorate in economics in the middle of the 1980's with a thesis on oil preparedness (Bergström 1985). Stefan Lundgren, employed as a project assistant in energy research, took part in some of the environment research during this period, but his thesis addressed the possibility of integrating the type of equilibrium models developed by Bergman with more sector-specific models (Lundgren 1985). He took his doctorate at the same time as Bergman. Björklund also gained a doctorate with a thesis on issues in labor market economics.

During the 1980's research has returned to environmental problems to an increasing degree. This is largely because the Energy Research Commission and National Environment Protection Board jointly financed a professorship in environmental and energy economics for Lars Bergman and because the National Environment Protection Board offered to finance 50% of Mäler's professorship.

Ing-Marie Andreasson was the latest Swede to take a doctorate in the environmental economics field (1989). Her thesis deals with the choice of control instruments for controlling agriculture's use of nitrogenous fertilizers on the island of Gotland. Over the years, a number of licentiate theses in the Environment, Natural Resources and Society program have been defended at the HHS. Some of these theses concerned work on acidification issues whereas other analyzed matters dealing with radon, bio fuels, high country forests etc.

## Future developments

The program's staff currently ranges from 10 to 15 people, four of whom are Ph.D.'s. The program's thrust has expanded in recent years to include environmental issues in developing countries. A project whose aim is to achieve a system for evaluating land and water management projects in Lesotho and another studying policy failures leading to environmental damage are currently in progress. The concept "sustainable development" and links between such development and environmental destruction are being studied simultaneously, both with a theoretical starting point. An analysis of ownership rights should be particularly interesting. Interest in analyses of the acidification problem has persisted since the first studies in conjunction with the 1972 UN congress in Stockholm. The economic incentives for a country to participate in international collaboration on joint solutions to environmental problems have been the subject of special attention with the aid of modern game theory. Here, the original Pigouvian analysis was replaced with an alternative conceptual apparatus. Theoretical analysis of the models for general equilibrium played an important role during the project's initial years. Numerical versions of such models were developed in conjunction with energy ergonomic studies. In recent years, this type of approach has acquired increasing importance to studies of various environmental policy issues. For example, they have been used for empirical estimates of costs for reducing impact on the environment. Bergman recently used a numerical model for the Swedish economy in order to study conflicts between the goal of phasing out nuclear power, protecting the remaining, untouched rivers in Sweden's far north from hydroelectric power programs and avoiding any increase in carbon dioxide emissions.

Environmental economic research is undergoing rapid development outside Sweden. A special European organization, the "European Association for Environmental and Resource Economists", has been founded (its second annual congress will be held at the HHS in 1991) and several new international journals make their debut every year. At the same time, research-financing organizations all over the world have become increasingly aware of the importance of environmental economic research. One indication of this is the decision by the European Science Foundation to start a comprehensive European research program in the field. The research program has established close links with many foreign research centers, such as the RfF, IIASA, the Institute for Environmental Studies (Amsterdam), the London Environment Economic Centre,

WIDER (Helsinki) and with many eminent scholars at universities all over the world. So there is every reason to expect the Environment, Natural Resources and Society research program to survive and continue to expand. However, scholars in the program need thorough training in central economic theory. Without this training, the program will quickly degenerate into second-rate research. It is equally important for program scholars to maintain continuous contacts with the research frontier in established economic science. Without this contact, the program could easily degenerate for this reason as well.

The Environment, Natural Resources and Society program has had problems and pursued unsuccessful projects. But on the whole it has been a major success. From 1969 to the present, the program has succeeded in retaining a core of scholars with an interest both in environmental issues and in economic theory. This combined interest has been the source of the program's success.

*Anders Rapp*

# Soil conservation for survival and sustained development

*In memory of Dr. Paul H. Temple and Bunduki's green valleys*

My university discipline is physical geography. A physical geographer's research subject is the landscape, man's external environment. We study landscape environments and how they work and change through natural processes or the actions of man. Geomorphology (the science dealing with landforms), climatology and remote sensing are three important branches of physical geography in Lund, where I now work, and were important in Uppsala during my university training. Zoology, botany and physical geography were my subjects in Uppsala.

Professor Filip Hjulström founded the process school in geomorphology in Uppsala as a result of his research on the erosion and sedimentation of rivers. He was an inspiring teacher with many students who continued to investigate the action of rivers on the landscape. Hjulström suggested "recent erosion and its effects on mountain slopes" as the subject of my dissertation. Abisko Scientific Station and the Kärkvagge mountain valley in Lapland became my research field from 1952 to 1960. My 1961 doctoral dissertation addressed processes on slopes in a mountainous area relatively untouched by man. In comparative studies of erosion in the Alps, on Spitsbergen, in the Rocky Mountains and in Alaska, other geomorphologists and I took up practical matters concerning preparedness and protection against slope erosion. Rockfalls, earth-slides, snow avalanches and mudflows were an increasing threat to the population and facilities in the mountains. Ascertaining whether our method for studying and monitoring recent erosion in Scandinavian mountain terrain could be used for study of the scope and importance of erosion processes in environments heavily exploited by man in developing countries with a tropical climate was a natural step.

That is why a line of research led from my studies of erosion in Scandinavian mountains to erosion and erosion control in Africa.

A trip to Ethiopia and East Africa in the spring of 1966 for the Earth Science program in Uppsala increased my personal interest in erosion and erosion control in the badly damaged mountain and savanna areas we visited. The Earth Science program at Uppsala University and the University of Agricultural Sciences was financed by the Swedish International Development Agency (SIDA) and resulted in a Bachelor of Science degree in earth science for 60 scholarship holders from Ethiopia, Kenya, Tanzania and other countries in Africa. I was one of the teachers in the Earth Science program and was anxious to improve my knowledge about soil degradation and soil conservation in Africa. After consulting Filip Hjulström and Åke Sundborg, I submitted an application to the Bank of Sweden Tercentenary Foundation and was awarded a grant for a research project called "Jorderosion i Tanzanias och Kenyas torrområden" (Soil erosion in Tanzania's and Kenya's semi-arid areas). The study was to be performed from 1968 to 1971 in collaboration with the Bureau of Resource Assessment and Land Use Planning (BRALUP) at the newly established university in Dar es Salaam.

I received the requested Foundation grant after a decision in February 1968. The same year, Dr. Paul Temple and Dr. Len Berry in Dar es Salaam and I commenced field studies of heavily grazed or excessively cultivated land in Tanzania's

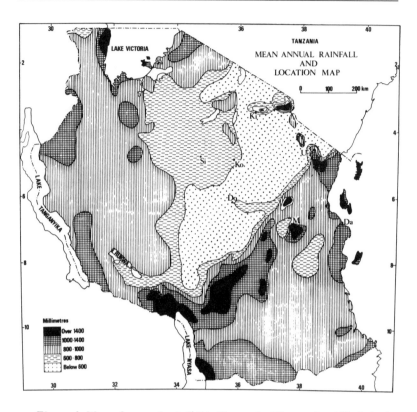

*Figure 1. Map of annual rainfall in Tanzania. The semi-arid belt in the interior has an average of 600 mm of rainfall a year and high evaporation. The mountains are important source areas for rivers as a result of high precipitation and low evaporation at high altitudes. Map according to Jackson in Geogr. Ann. A 3-4, 1972. Abbreviations: Da = Dar es Salaam, Do = Dodoma, Ki = Kisongo, Ko = Kondoa, M = Morogoro, U = Usambara Mountains, Si = Singida.*

savannas and heavily populated mountains (Fig. 1). We soon found that it would be appropriate for us to concentrate our major work on just a few areas in Tanzania and only to conduct small studies in the Kenya section. The subject was big enough as it was. We surveyed and quantified erosion and sedimentation through measurements in the field and by remote sensing using aerial photographs. This work resulted in numerous publications, including a volume with 15 scientific articles in the international journal "Geografiska annaler" (Rapp, Berry and Temple 1972). My BRALUP colleagues P. Temple, H. Murray-Rust, L. Berry, I. Jackson, J. Townshend and J. Watson plus the Swedes V. Axelsson, C. Christiansson, B. and L. Lundgren and Å. Sundborg, were some of the authors in the work group. All the contributors subsequently continued work as researchers and teachers in similar problem areas in Tanzania and other developing countries. C. Christiansson, L. Lundgren and B. Lundgren all took doctorates around 1980 on subsequent field work in Tanzania, the first two in physical geography and the latter in silvicultural soil science. L. Berry continued his research career as a professor of geography at Clark University in the U.S. P.H. Temple became a professor at Birmingham. He died prematurely in 1986. This article is dedicated to his memory.

Paul and we others were inspired in our work by a love for nature, respect for all life and solidarity with the poor of the world.

## History of soil erosion and soil conservation in Tanzania

As early as 1931, a special commission was appointed for the purpose of studying soil erosion and its relationship with cultivation, animal husbandry, afforestation, tse-tse flies, artificial irrigation, water resources, roads, railways and public health. This commission reached the conclusion "that we should concentrate on informational activities in the absence of sufficient economic resources for attacking the problems" (Harrison 1937, p. 4).

In 1945, a Soil Conservation Service was established for Tanganyika, and several soil conservation programs were launched. The reason for this move was a general increase in awareness of the scope of the erosion problem, as conveyed by e.g. Bennet (1939) in the U.S., Jacks and Whyte (1939) in

England and Gilman (1940 and subsequent) in work on conditions in Tanganyika.

In 1947, the infamous peanut scheme started in Tanganyika. This was a poorly prepared and ecologically unsuitable project that ultimately resulted in a loss of about SEK 500 million for the British Exchequer. In the 1950's, the colonial administration continued a number of soil conservation projects both in semi-arid areas and in the mountains, the two most eroded environments in Tanzania. One of the latter projects was the "Uluguru Land Usage Scheme" from 1950 to 1955. It ended in riots after about SEK 1 million had been expended on a program whose purpose was to induce smallholders to build terraces on strips of land in the Uluguru Mountains (Temple 1972, p. 116).

This and similar enterprises elsewhere in the country induced smallholders to start a resistance movement against the colonial power. Small holders in many parts of Tanzania viewed independence in 1961 as exemption from soil conservation regulations. They began cultivating the soil without terracing, protective hedging or any ban on grass burning. In the light of all this, it was not easy for the authorities to begin preaching the benefits of soil conservation.

## Recommendations from Tanzania's planning minister

We were honored when Tanzania's Minister for Economic Affairs and Development Planning, Dr. W.K. Chagula, contributed the foreword to our Tanzania volume. He had studied the book's 15 articles and selected eight practical recommendations quoted below:

> "... of even greater importance is the fact that some of the results of the DUSER Project could be widely applied in Tanzania, particularly as we are now in the process of implementing the Party's Guidelines of 1972 on modern agriculture, "SIASA NI KILIMO", in which the problem of

soil erosion is given due prominence. I shall mention only a few of these results:

"(i)    The importance of tree cover in minimizing landslides: the studies recommend *how* re-afforestation for the purpose should be done.

"(ii)    Soil conservation measures to be acceptable to the people must bring both a demonstrable advantage to the individual farmers in the short-run *and* long-term advantages to the whole community...

"(iii)In the semi-arid areas of Tanzania, losses of water and soil can be drastically reduced by an undisturbed vegetative cover and through the prevention of over-grazing.

"(iv)    The water reservoirs in the semi-arid central regions of Tanzania have high rates of sedimentation and their total useful "life" can be thirty years or even shorter. This should be very useful information to the national planners for rural water supplies.

"(v)    Construction of new dams and reservoirs should continue however, for even a short-lived reservoir may be economically justified in areas where the need for water is so pressing as in the semi-arid areas of central Tanzania.

"(vi)    Wind erosion can be as serious as water erosion in certain parts of Tanzania and both can be stopped or minimized by planting trees and by controlled grazing.

"(vii)    The lack of hydrological data for the Luwegu and Luhombero Rivers in the Rufiji Basin makes immediate development and flood control in the Rufiji Valley difficult.

"(viii))A full analysis of the probable sedimentation in the Stiegler's Gorge reservoir should be undertaken before the 600 MW Stiegler's Gorge hydropower station is built".

Dr. Chagula concluded by expressing the strong hope that the relevant state authorities in Tanzania pay consideration to the project's practical conclusions. He also hoped that the project could continue: "The results of the DUSER Project should therefore be regarded as only a "bench mark" in this complex research project on soil erosion and sedimentation which should be continued for a much longer period than the 3-4 years of the DUSER Project". ("DUSER" = Dar es Salaam/Uppsala Soil Erosion Research). The latter hope was realized e.g. through continuation studies by C. Christiansson (1981 and subsequently), B. Lundgren (1978), L. Lundgren (1980), A. Rapp (1976) and L. Strömquist (1976 and subsequently). Implementation of the aforementioned 8 points has been impeded in Tanzania by poor state finances and poor organization. (Also see the section "Comments on the DUSER project's consequences".)

## Two types of environments: mountainous areas and semi-arid areas

In our studies of erosion and water problems in Tanzania, we decided to monitor conditions in a number of small, typical areas, instead of attempting to institute a complete inventory of some major region or the entire country. The two critical areas are noted in the heading above.

1) Mountainous areas with steep, cultivated slopes, relatively heavy precipitation and strong exploitation pressure on land, water and remaining forest.
2) Semi-arid savannas with a long dry season, a shortage of water and erosion through over-grazing and over-cultivation.

The map (Figure 1) shows the extent of the two environmental types. On the map, mountains are designated as area with more than 1 400 mm of annual precipitation. Two of the investigated mountain areas are in the Uluguru Mountains (M on the map). Tanzania's semi-arid belt extends in a continuous zone across the country's middle section. The most arid zone receives less than 600 mm of rain a year. The semi-arid belt also covers large areas with 600-800 mm of annual rain southeast of Lake Victoria.

We conducted studies in the semi-arid belt in four drainage areas at Dodoma (Do) and one at Kisongo (Ki) near Arusha, Carl Christiansson also conducted studies at Kondoa (Ko) and Singida (Si) (Christiansson 1972).

The studies of erosion and sediment transport in the Uluguru Mountains showed the importance of three different processes:

1) Sheet erosion and splash erosion occurring each year, although with varying intensity, on cultivated slopes.
2) Numerous, small, approximately 1-2 m deep, 5-20 m wide earthslides and mudflows, triggered by extremely heavy, pelting rain occurring every one or two decades (the Mgeta example) (Figures 2, 3).
3) Occasional large earthslides, many meters deep, with a far

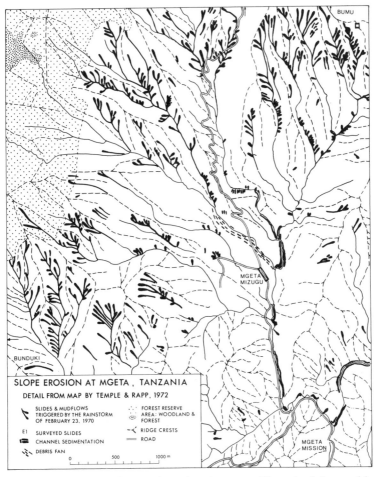

*Figure 2. Detailed map of erosion due to mudflows in deforested land in the Uluguru Mountains, Tanzania. According to Temple and Rapp (1972).*

lower prevalence than type 2, but they may still have a major impact, mainly due to flood and sedimentation damage, even far downstream in the river system (the Palu example). Only the first category can be studied in small test areas or in the laboratory. The other types must be studied in natural catchment basin because they are so large and occur relatively infrequently.

## Studies of erosion and soil conservation in semi-arid areas in Tanzania

From 1968 to 1972, our research team in Tanzania performed several studies of erosion, sedimentation and soil conservation in the country's semi-arid areas, such as Dodoma (Rapp, Murray-Rust, Christiansson and Berry 1972). Kondoa (Christiansson 1972) and Arusha (Murray-Rust 1972). These studies covered small catchment basins with an area of about 5 to 600 km and water reservoirs. In order to clarify the net effects of erosion and sedimentation in a major river area in a semi-arid climate, P. Temple and Å. Sundborg (1972) conducted a simultaneous study of the Rufiji River in southern Tanzania. It drains a river area 175 000 km in size and transports up to a million tons of sediment a day during high-water periods (Figure 1, Figure 4).

Detailed studies of the way in which water erosion begins with splash erosion, sheet erosion and rill erosion can be performed on test areas, several meters wide and long, on fields and pastureland, areas called runoff plots or erosion plots. These measurements were performed in Tanzania at several agricultural research stations in the 1930's. Data from one such series of experiments performed by Staples (1939) in Mpwapwa, Tanzania, were tabulated by us in a diagram shown in Figure 5. It shows that the annual loss of surface runoff water and flushed off topsoil increases dramatically when vegetation is weakened

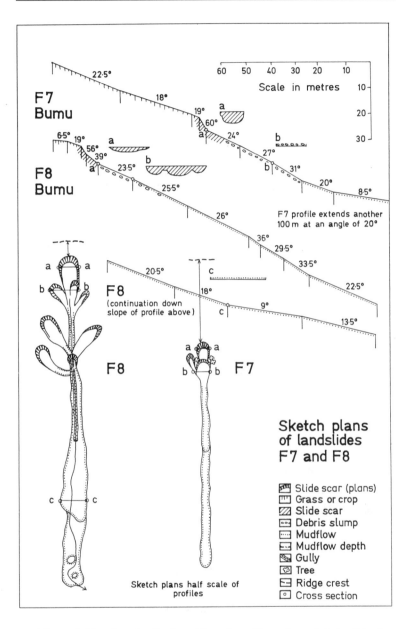

*Figure 3. Two longitudinal profiles of mudflows from debris slides in a tropical environment, Bumu, Uluguru, Tanzania. According to Temple and Rapp (1972).*

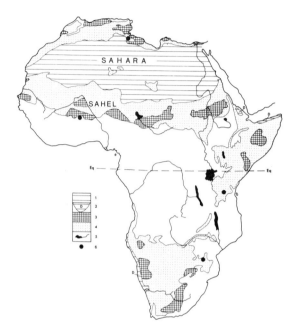

*Figure 4. Generalized map of desertification zones in Africa, simplified from UNCOD's world map (1977). 1-2 Hyper-arid zones (deserts); 3. Arid to subhumid zones with a very high risk of desertification; 4. Arid to subhumid zones with a moderate degree of desertification hazard; 5. Major lakes and rivers; 6. Location of case studies.*

in the savanna environment. The loss of surface water and soil is insignificant under a tight grass cover. On bare soil, without any vegetation cover, up to half of all rain water runs off. In addition, 80-150 tons of earth/hectare is flushed away with an unknown amount of humus, nutritive salts, fertilizer or toxins.

We selected four river reservoirs plus attendant catchment basins for a more detailed study of erosion and sedimentation. At the end of the dry season, these reservoirs are completely or partially dry, and the deposition of sediment can then be determined by the levelling or sounding of profiles right across the river bottoms from fixed points on land (Figure 6).

However, a general strategy for reducing the loss of soil and water, as well as improving land usage in these areas, would be

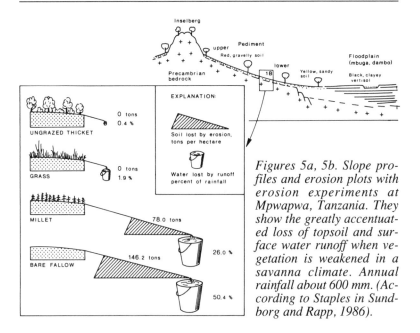

*Figures 5a, 5b. Slope profiles and erosion plots with erosion experiments at Mpwapwa, Tanzania. They show the greatly accentuated loss of topsoil and surface water runoff when vegetation is weakened in a savanna climate. Annual rainfall about 600 mm. (According to Staples in Sundborg and Rapp, 1986).*

to reduce pressure from grazing livestock, build runoff-collection ridges, use straw mulching and plant trees (agroforestry) on cultivated land. These measures should be combined with water harvesting (Figure 7).

During the colonial period, small and large surface water dams were generally regarded as a cure-all for the water shortage in Africa's arid areas. Many dams were built for irrigation, protection against flooding and as reservoirs for people and livestock. In the 1970's, our DUSER project and studies by others showed that many reservoirs were short-lived because of sedimentation. As a result of this shortcoming, plus the loss of large amounts of water through heavy evaporation, development aid began concentrating instead on drilling wells in order to provide water for the people. When SIDA and several other aid agencies subsequently began evaluating the many drill holes and water pumps, they found that almost none of the engine-powered pumps were operable. This was because of a shortage of fuel or the lack of spare parts needed for repairs.

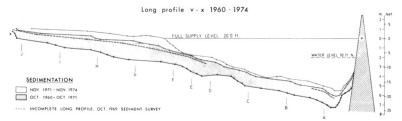

MATUMBULU DAM

Long profile v - x 1960 - 1974

*Figure 6. Matumbulu Dam, Tanzania. Accumulation of mainly sandy sediment in a small reservoir in the period from 1960-1974. (From Christiansson, 1981).*

About half of the simple hand-pumps installed were also out of action due to the lack of maintenance. But all the simple wells with ropes and buckets were functional. This was a painful experience underlining the importance of appropriate technology adaptation in developing countries (Andersson 1982).

*Figure 7. Simple device for the levelling of low ridges for water harvesting on gentle slopes in the western Sahel. (From J. Fries, 1988).*

## Some Swedish and international research measures in the field of soil and water conservation in Africa from 1973 to 1989

The DUSER project's final report was published in 1973. The preceding year, the U.N. held a major international conference in Stockholm on global environmental problems. This increased interest in environmental problems in developing countries and led to the establishment of UNEP, the UN's international environmental secretariat in Nairobi.

In Sweden, and for members of the DUSER project concluded in 1972, the increased international interest in environmental problems in Africa had e.g. the following results:

During part of the 1970's, the SIDA and the NFR had a joint group called the Secretariat for International Ecology (SIES). It was an advisory body for the SIDA in matters relating to the environmental impact of aid projects in Africa and for the NFR in matters concerning research (Rapp et al. 1977). Its role was taken over in part by SAREC when this body was established as SIDA's research council in 1977. The SIDA and the other Nordic development aid agencies, DANIDA, NORAD and FINNIDA, awarded substantial grants for soil and water conservation programs in developing countries in the 1980's. The Red Cross and other aid agencies also allocated large parts of their annual budgets for long-term soil and water conservation measures, all in the spirit of e.g. the Brundtland Commission's motto that the goal of development aid should be sustainable development, i.e. long-term development of land usage without environmental damage or overexploitation. In 1987, the SIDA adopted conservation as its fifth aid objective.

However, evaluations of and research on environmental damage in developing countries is a much neglected field in Sweden and in other countries. So reversals remain numerous in the 1980's, both in developing and developed countries. The pressure on environmental resources is increasing as a result of population growth, an increased hunger for land and increasing waste disposal problems. Research is in a difficult position and often accused of not producing results in time.

A lack of breadth is another criticized aspect of research. So e.g. Blaikie and Brookfield (1986) noted the following about our DUSER project (1972): "They carried out some excellent studies of processes both in general and at particular sites, placing special emphasis on varying climatic conditions ... The whole collection ends rather disappointingly on a mainly 'technofix' note".

Dr. Blaikie has recently declared that he regards the DUSER project as the first, major, integrated research project on land degradation and erosion control in Africa and that he had not had access to the recommendations subsequently issued by Minister Chagula (1972). They show that our project also encompassed useful information on man and society in the threatened environments of developing countries.

## Comments on the DUSER project's consequences

Twenty years down the line, what impact can the DUSER project and its final report be said to have had on subsequent research and practical applications of its results in developing countries in Africa and elsewhere.

When developments in Africa are viewed as a whole, the period from 1968 to 1989 will be seen to have been especially dramatic and tragic, characterized by disasters such as widespread drought, increasing soil degradation, reduced food output per capita, starvation, mass flight and war, especially in the Sahel region and Ethiopia, 1972-74 and 1983-85 in particular. This has led to a general increase in the understanding by the rich world and by leaders in developing countries of the need for more action for improving population survival and achieving the sustained development of agriculture by means of soil and water conservation (W.C.E.D. 1987). But research and its results have not been put into practice to a sufficient degree at the grass roots, especially not in Tanzania and Ethiopia, although to a much greater degree in Kenya and Burkina Faso, for example (I.S.C.O. 1989).

Of Dr. Chagula's eight recommendations, no. 1 has been heeded through research and counseling in the field of agroforestry, but it has only had an insignificant impact in Tanzania. No. 2 is a basic principle of decisive importance and is now only beginning to be understood. Professor N. Hudson, a pioneer in the field, noted at I.S.C.O. 6 that the annual increase in a smallholder's harvest should amount to about 50% for him to spontaneously adopt a new and more work-intensive method for his subsistence farming (Hudson 1989).

No. 3 is easy to express but extremely difficult to implement. Generally speaking, water harvesting is the best approach. The large HADO project in Tanzania comprises wide-ranging soil and water conservation in the Dodoma and Kondoa areas. It started in 1973 as a consequence of the DUSER project and Minister Chagula's recommendations nos. 1, 2 and 3. The HADO project is still in progress and has had beneficial effects, thanks to e.g. bans on grazing and switches to farming in the Kondoa area (Östberg 1986, Christiansson 1986). No. 4 has been heeded and led to a general change in water supply policies in some countries but not in others. Nos. 5 and 6 are beginning to be heeded, but there are still numerous reversals. Nos. 7 and 8 concern a concrete case, planned but as yet unimplemented, large-scale expansion of hydroelectric facilities in Tanzania. Recommended studies of environmental impact have been conducted at other power plant projects (Strömquist 1976 and subsequently).

"To the list of measures for improved land use suggested above we now add water harvesting and storage for domestic use and small-scale irrigation. In tropical and subtropical drylands with less than 700 mm of

annual rainfall, we think that water harvesting is a particularly important and appropriate technology together with other measures of conservation. We present and discuss two methods of water harvesting and
storage: runoff-collecting ridges on slopes and sand storage dams in
wadi-beds." (Rapp and Håsteen 1990).

The drylands referred to in the article, from which this quote
was taken, is in a zone with an annual rainfall of 300-700 mm
(e.g. parts of Tanzania, Zimbabwe and Burkina Faso). (See
Figure 4, a simplified map showing the risk of desertification).

A discussion of the comprehensive research involving the
surveying and monitoring of soil destruction and soil conservation being conducted with the aid of remote sensing is beyond
the scope of the present paper. The reader is referred to the work
by U. Helldén (1988) and L. Olsson (1985) for further information on this research.

## Soil conservation for survival, 1989

In November 1989, the sixth international conference on soil
conservation (the 6th I.S.C.O. Conference) was held in Kenya
and Ethiopia. It concentrated on the acute problems of developing countries and their need for soil and water conservation
for survival. The conference attracted more than 300 participants from 42 countries, including many of the leading scholars
and administrators of soil and water conservation agencies in
developing countries. The conference was held by the International Soil Conservation Organization. Both host countries
received comprehensive economic support from Swiss and
Swedish aid organizations. The Conference supplied good
insight into the importance accorded to soil and water conservation internationally and in the affected countries and how this
conservation is being implemented in practice.

The three largest contingents were from Ethiopia, Kenya and
Tanzania. The conference's lectures, discussions and field

excursions can be summarized as follows:

The Scandinavian countries have made highly important contributions to the development of long-term, effective soil conservation measures in East Africa. The greatest progress has been achieved with the soil conservation programs in Kenya's high potential areas near Nairobi. Terracing, fertilization, stable-feeding, fodder-crop cultivation and agroforestry are being conducted there in firmly supported projects. However, the situation is less favorable in Kenya's drylands and in Ethiopia's and Tanzania's drylands and mountainous areas. Despite good will, soil and water conservation is greatly neglected and underdeveloped because of limited resources, smallholder poverty, rapid population growth and political and economic problems. Unfortunately, trends are indicative of even worse poverty and new starvation disasters in the future.

So the need for continued research, teaching and applied projects is very great in these areas.

One field viewed as most promising, and a source of great attention, was water harvesting and storage for cultivation in semi-arid areas with 300-700 mm of annual precipitation, e.g. in the western Sahel zone (Klemm 1989, Reij 1989, Roose 1989 and others).

Two areas overlooked by the I.S.C.O. conference were erosion through mass-movements in mountainous areas and wind erosion in semi-arid areas.

In most contexts, some influence from our DUSER research project in 1968-1972 was still discernible. The integrated work procedures, the concentration on drylands and the emphasis on water harvesting and storage are now generally applied and have achieved good results in certain countries, although not in Tanzania.

Mass-movements, landslides and mudflows in mountainous areas remain under-researched fields that should be assigned greater priority in the future, e.g. in conjunction with efforts to stop forest destruction and its consequences.

## Jan Erik Kihlström

# Environmental pollutants

The increasing public concern about our environment in the sixties created some new terms. Thus, the Swedish equivalent of "environmental pollutant" (miljögift) is a relative newcomer to the Swedish language and is about the same age as the Bank of Sweden Tercentenary Foundation. The term was used in Sweden for the first time in 1963 at the same time as a debate raged in the press about Rachel Carson's book "Silent Spring" (1962). This book made a major contribution to the huge interest in environmental issues that emerged in the 1960's. However, the word was not incorporated in the Swedish Academy's glossary ("Ordlista") until the end of the 1960's.

The guidelines for the Foundation specified that Foundation activities should initially "concentrate on research aimed at expanding knowledge about the impact of technical, economic and social changes on society and on individual citizens". Without any doubt pollution of the environment is caused by such technical, economic and social changes. So it was natural for the Foundation to provide repeated support for studies of environmental changes.

However, the problems of toxic substances in the environment are by no means new and have probably existed about as long as man's material culture, especially associated with the need for tools and implements, has existed. Even the most primitive forms of metallic implements require the processing of mineral and cause deposition of metals in the environment over and above the natural quantities contributed by nature through the erosion of rock. During the pre-industrial era, man's activities only had a limited impact on the environment. Thus, plants and animals were indeed damaged by toxic metallic contamination around the mines of antiquity. Carl Linnaeus made the following expressive comment on the surroundings near Falu Mine after a trip to the area in 1734: "No poet could have depicted Styx, .... nor any theologian Hell, in language grim enough to describe the conditions to be seen here. For poisonous, pungent sulphurous fumes rise up here and pollute the air so that the area cannot be approached without difficulty. It corrodes the earth so no plants can grow nearby". However, such phenomena were very limited, and there was no extensive environmental pollution. Nevertheless, accelerating development led to large-scale industrial operations with accompanying pollution of a completely different magnitude, i.e. both in terms of quantity and distribution areas.

The consequences became even graver when man ultimately learned to make complex chemical substances that never occurred in nature. There are currently a very large number, perhaps 10 million, different chemical substances that cannot be produced by plants and animals. Nor have these substances contributed to biological development in any way. Thus, they are totally alien to nature, so neither plants nor animals have been able to develop any defense against these foreign substances.


## DDT

As long as the synthetic substances were not put to any practical use and remained on laboratory shelves they did not constitute any environmental hazard. This was long the case for many of today's most dangerous environmental pollutants. For example, DDT was synthesized as early as 1874 by the chemist O. Zeidler. However, no one then suspected that it was an efficient insecticide. Nor was DDT put to any practical use for another 60 years. So there was no reason to investigate its possible biological effects.

The Swiss Paul Müller, who worked with plant protection at

the chemical manufacturer Geigy, synthesized DDT once again in 1939, completely unaware of Zeidler's earlier work. However, developments thereafter were governed by Müller's discovery that DDT was an effective insecticide. This capability was used by the Allies in World War II. In a famous radio address from 1944, Prime Minister Churchill declared: "The excellent DDT powder which has been fully experimented with and found to yield astonishing results, will henceforth be used on a great scale by the British forces in Burma and by the American and Australian forces in the Pacific and India in all theatres ..." About the same time, the American Association of Entomology made the following enthusiastic comment on DDT's great benefits: "Never before in the history of entomology has a chemical been discovered that offers such promise to mankind for relief from insect problems as DDT".

Paul Müller was rewarded for his discovery with the Nobel Prize in physiology and medicine in 1948. Today, with the benefit of hindsight, the appropriateness of this reward can be questioned, and perhaps rightly so. But at the time people undoubtedly felt that Müller's discovery had lived up to its great. In the opinion of many people, DDT has meant more in the battle against disease than any other chemical except antibiotics. According to a calculation made in 1953, DDT has saved 5 million lives and prevented 100 million illnesses. In addition insect attacks on harvests and food stockpiles were reduced, thereby contributing to improved conditions in the poorest countries. DDT also had the advantage of being cheap to make. So after its introduction on the civilian market in 1946 it quickly became the most commonly used insecticide.

The way in which chlorinated organic compounds, a category to which DDT belongs, are disseminated in nature was long unknown. Therefore, the discovery of DDT in seals and penguins from Antarctic waters in 1966 was virtually a sensation (Sladen, Menzie and Reichel 1966, George and Frear 1966). Three years later, analyses disclosed that about 2 000 tons of

DDT are trapped in Antarctic ice (Peterle 1969), even though there has never been the slightest need to kill insects in that part of the world. We were subsequently rudely awakened by the discovery that chlorinated organic substances, a category to which PCB and dioxins also belong, could be a serious threat to our environment, not just locally but all over the world.

As might be expected, many insect species soon became resistant to DDT. This development is mainly due to the circumstance that only the most resistant individuals ever get a chance to produce offspring. So the percentage of such individuals increases in every generation – making an insecticide increasingly ineffective.

A number of far-sighted men and women soon began warning about possible disadvantages for DDT. The insect physiologist Wigglesworth (1945) realized that a substance as stable as DDT might accumulate in animals and thus, despite its low degree of toxicity, attain concentration so high that damage was unavoidable. About 1950, scientists such as Bishop (1949) and Hoffman and Merkel (1948) began to suspect that there was a link between damage to aquatic invertebrates and the spraying of dams and lakes with DDT for the purpose of killing insect larvae. After a time, damage ascribed to DDT was found in fish (Crouter and Vernon 1959), birds (Rudd and Genelly 1955) and mammals (Stearns et al. 1947, Wragg 1954).

However, scientists were not the only people who saw the risks and warned about the consequences. Some authors and artists were also far-sighted in predicting more general environmental damage. As early as 1949, the popular Swedish composer Povel Ramel wrote a song."Grisälven" (Mucky river); its subheading was "Miljövisa från 1949" (1949 song of the environment).

In order to determine whether or not there was a link between the observed disturbances in nature and the DDT concentration in damaged animals, chemists had to be able to analyze the very low concentrations of the substance in animal tissue, only amounting to a thousandth of a gram per kilo for DDT (Sladen et al. 1966). Fortunately, sufficiently sensitive and specific analytical methods became available about at the same time as the damage became increasingly apparent. Chemists were then able to confirm a connection between damage and the concentrations of DDT (or its decomposition products) in affected individuals. The evidence for DDT's harmful effects ultimately became so overwhelming, perhaps most spectacularly in the thinning of bird eggshells (Ratcliffe 1967), that the substance was banned in many countries, in Sweden in 1969 (with some exemptions).

But did this ban solve all the problems? Is it really necessary to continue DDT research, especially after the ban was extended and made virtually total in 1975? Well, things are unfortunately not that simple! In the first place, DDT is very stable, and so it persists in the environment, even if concentrations do decline with time. In addition, DDT is not banned in every country, not even in every European country. And we truly live in one world in respect to the spread of environmental pollutants. So DDT can continue to inflict damage whose nature is not completely known as yet. The fact that the danger is not over can be illustrated by a current case. DDT concentrations declined in nature after the introduction of bans and, with minor variations, remained on a low level. But for no apparent reason concentrations began rising again in e.g. guillemot eggs on Stora Karlsö Island off Gotland Island at the beginning of the 1980's (Olsson and Reutergårdh 1986). At that time, however, the environmental chemist Sören Jensen had begun using the wax coating on pine needles for analyses of airborne pollutants, a research project that received financial support from the Foundation (G. Eriksson et al. 1989). The wax coating on pine needles captures a large proportion of the airborne pollutants falling on the tree's locality. This wax is especially good at capturing fat-soluble pollutants, such as DDT. It is possible to distinguish needles formed in each of the last three years. Thus, changes in fallout can be followed from year to year. The same tree can, of course, be revisited for collection of new specimens, so fallout at that particular location can be successively monitored with great accuracy. By sampling needles from different parts of the tree crown, the scientist can obtain information on the direction from which the pollutants came and the direction of the source of pollution. Pines are also so widely spread that the sampling of needles from different locations in Europe makes it possible to compare conditions in different parts of the continent. With the aid of this elegant method, Jensen was able to show that the increasing fallout of DDT at the beginning of the 1980's came from the east and, thus, probably from one or more of the countries in Eastern Europe (G. Eriksson et al. 1989). The temporary employment of DDT for dealing with certain severe insect attacks on forest in the German Democratic Republic was subsequently confirmed. This usage was reflected in changes in DDT concentrations in animals in the Baltic and in the wax coating of pine needles in Central Europe.

In the second place, we now know rather a lot about DDT's properties. We can therefore employ this substance, its spread, decomposition and effects for making more reliable evaluations of the risks presented by chemically similar but otherwise poorly studied substances appearing in nature. This utilization of DDT as a model unexpectedly contributed completely new and important knowledge. In a project supported by the Foundation, an ecotoxicologist in Uppsala, Per Eriksson, discovered that DDT administered to neonatal mice is quickly excreted during their first few days of life (P. Eriksson 1984). But when the animals were about ten days old, DDT excretion slowed considerably, and the substance remained in mouse bodies much longer. If administered a few days later, it was rapidly excreted once again (P. Eriksson and Darnerud 1985). The animals receiving DDT in their 10th day of life subsequently developed behavioral changes and deranged nerve functions as adults (P. Eriksson et al. 1984, P. Eriksson and Nordberg 1986,

P. Eriksson et al. 1990 a, 1990 b). Baby mice are still suckling at 10 days of age and then pick up fat-soluble contaminants, including DDT, in their mother's milk. All living creatures still contain DDT in very small concentrations but large enough to produce this effect in baby mice. However, adults are unlikely to be affected by these low concentrations. The results also showed that even small differences in age may be of decisive importance to the effect exerted by environmental pollutants. The fact that young individuals are usually more sensitive than older ones is well known, but a difference of only a few days was not expected to be so crucial. Nor did the scientists expect the period of enhanced sensitivity to be as brief as just a few days around the 10th day of life. During this period, the growth rate of the brains of baby mice is at a maximum, and this circumstance is presumably decisive. This discovery was also important because other fat-soluble environmental pollutants, such as PCB and chloroparaffins, are transferred from the mother to offspring via the milk (P. Eriksson and Darnerud 1985, P. Eriksson and Nordberg 1986). Therefore, this new knowledge may be important in the assessment of the risk presented by both DDT and even other pollutants to both suckling mice and the breast-fed offspring of other mammalian species.

## PCB

Another of the most frequently discussed environmental pollutants, PCB (*polychlorinated biphenyls*), is actually a whole group of closely related substances in use long before the term "environmental pollutant" had become established. As early as 1929, PCB was being used for industrial applications, primarily due to its exceptional properties as an electrical insulator. At the time, no one believed that PCB could be spread to the external environment or that it might be capable of harming the environment. Knowledge and imagination were too limited to enable people to envisage the impact completely foreign substances might have on the biological environment.

PCB was not found in nature until 1966 as the result of very skilled scientific detective work by Sören Jensen (1966). By that time, the substance group had been in use for more than 30 years before it was found in nature. But, as Jensen pointed out, finding any trace of it in the natural environment was still surprising. In the middle of the 1960's, Jensen was analyzing DDT in biological material. In addition to DDT and other known environmental pollutants, he then found a large number of unidentified substances, similar in some ways to DDT, in his specimens. He assumed that these unknown substances were of biological origin and natural components in the animal material. However, the concentration was low in pike caught in northern Sweden and high in pike caught to the south (Jensen 1972). However, a substance produced naturally in the body of an animal should appear in about the same concentration irrespective of where the animal is caught. An alternative explanation was that the unidentified compounds were decomposition products of DDT and other, chlorinated, organic insecticides. In order to ascertain whether this was actually the case, Jensen analyzed white-tailed eagle feathers from the collection at the Swedish Museum of Natural History. The oldest feathers analyzed were from the 1880's. The unknown substances were found in the white-tailed eagle feathers, but only in feathers collected in 1942 or later, never prior to this year (Jensen 1972). Since modern chlorinated, organic insecticides were not introduced until after the Second World War, these unidentified substances could scarcely belong to this category. However, the concentration increased with increasing levels in the food chain. Thus, concentrations were higher in white-tailed eagles than in pike and higher in pike than in salmon fry. So the evidence suggested that this group of chemical substances was a stable product introduced by man. While this study was in progress, Jensen gained access to increasingly sophisticated assay instruments. In 1966 he was able to show that the unknown compounds could be arranged in a series with increasing molecular weight, each step in the series differing by the mass of one chlorine atom, and that the basic, non-chlorine structure was that of a biphenyl. So the unknown substances were biphenyls containing differing numbers of chlorine atoms, i.e. PCB's.

How then could PCB's elude discovery so long? And why were they not found in specimens taken before 1942 since the substances began to be used in 1929? One explanation is that as long as products containing PCB, such as cables and capacitors, were in use, PCB remained bound to the materials. It was only after the products were scrapped and incinerated that PCB could escape into the environment. It should also be noted here that PCB's, especially the PCB components containing a large amount of chlorine, are extremely resistant to high temperatures and volatile. On the other hand, DDT was discovered in nature after being in use only for a few years. This was undoubtedly because the link in time and space between the use of DDT and its impact on the environment is so clear. It was not hard to suspect a connection when the number of birds and crustaceans suddenly dropped in an area after DDT was employed as an insecticide in forestry and agriculture there. However, PCB has a long period of latency, perhaps 15-20 years from manufacturing until material containing PCB is scrapped. PCB is not released nor able to come into contact with plants and animals before then.

Soon after Jensen's discovery, scientists in different parts of the world began studying PCB's biological effects. The biological damage was then revealed, step by step. We now know that its most serious effects are probably liver damage, reproduction damage studied in Sweden by e.g Mats Olsson, Sören Jensen and J.E. Kihlström et al. (Helle et al. 1976 a, 1976 b, Jensen et al. 1977, Kihlström et al. 1974, 1975) and impairment of the immune response (Nikolaidis et al. 1988). These effects are probably the reason why Baltic seals are endangered.

In Sweden, knowledge about the harmful effects led to a ban on the use of PCB's; it came into force in January 1972. As in the case for DDT, one might then ask whether such an administrative ruling is sufficient for protecting the environment and whether continued research on PCB is a waste of time and money. But for PCB, as for DDT, our experience can teach us more about similar substances, thereby increasing our prospects of making correct risk evaluations in the future. So many scientists in the field called for continued, intensive research on PCB in order to gain knowledge if similar but previously unknown chemical compounds begin appearing as pollutants in nature. Dioxins, the subject of intense discussion in recent years, are so closely related to PCB's that numerous, relatively reliable assumptions can be made about the spread and effects of dioxins on the basis of studies of PCB's. This will make it possible to reduce the need for experimentation with the extremely toxic dioxins.

It was once again found that this continued research yielded new, completely unexpected knowledge about PCB. Two related projects (conducted by J.E. Kihlström and Björn Brunström and Björn Brunström respectively) receiving financial support from the Foundation studied the way in which PCB affects embryonic development in birds. Brunström compared two PCB components, both with four chlorine atoms but at different molecular positions (2,2',4,5'-tetrachlorobiphenyl and 3,3'4,4'-tetrachlorobiphenyl respectively). One of these components, 3,3',4,4'-tetrachlorobiphenyl, proved to be more than 10,000 times more toxic than the other, despite the small differences between them (Brunström et al. 1982, Brunström and Darnerud 1983). The more toxic compound belongs to the category of PCB components usually called "dioxin-like" or coplanar PCB's. In all probability, it is this similarity with dioxin that makes this PCB component so toxic. The most toxic of the coplanar PCB's, 3,3',4,4',5-pentachlorobiphenyl, which has one more chlorine atom, is more than 50,000 times more toxic than 2,2',4,5'-

tetrachlorobiphenyl (Brunström and Andersson 1988, Brunström 1989). These differences in the toxicity of substances that are so chemically similar were truly unexpected. The results also showed that different bird species display very different sensitivities to PCB. Of the species studied, pheasant, herring gull, mallard, goldeneye and black-headed gull are far less sensitive to coplanar PCB components (and therefore to dioxins?) than turkey (Brunström and Lund 1988), whereas at least some domestic chicken breeds are even more sensitive than turkey (Brunström and Reutergårdh 1986). Being aware of these differences is important in the evaluation of risks presented by both PCB's and dioxins.

Dioxins are present in nature in extremely low concentrations and they may not, therefore, despite their toxicity, be the major risk factor as is occasionally claimed in the media. A large volume of data suggests that the dioxin-like PCB components constitute a far greater risk. They are admittedly less toxic than the most toxic dioxins but are present in much higher concentrations. This probably makes them a greater threat. In addition, PCB's will remain in nature for a few more decades, since they unfortunately decompose only very slowly.

It was recently found that effluent from paper mills contains, among other things, a large amount of chlorinated organic compounds that chemically resemble both dioxins and PCB's to varying degrees (National Environment Protection Board 1988). The biggest problem is that more than 90% of these compounds have yet to be identified. So that is why it is extremely important for us to continue the search for and identify as yet unknown environmental pollutants, as well as learn more about the substances already known to us.

Swedish research on environmental pollution and environmental damage, with economic support from the National Environment Protection Board's research committee, research councils, the Swedish Council for Planning and Coordination of Research, the Foundation and others, has expanded consider-

ably since the beginning of the 60's and is on a high international level, sometimes world-leading. Sweden's first chair in ecotoxicology (i.e. the study of toxic substances in the environment) was established at Uppsala University in 1979. The
country now has three additional chairs, viz. one in Lund
(established in 1987), one at the Swedish Museum of Natural
History in Stockholm (established in 1988) and one established
in 1989 by the Swedish Agency for Research Cooperation with
Developing Countries at Stockholm University.

The Swedish public's traditional great interest in nature is
one factor contributing to this rapid expansion. Many nature-
loving amateurs display impressing, wide-ranging knowledge
and great concern about the environment. This concern is even
reflected in legislation. Sweden now has a number of laws and
ordinances regulating the use of chemicals, natural resources
etc. Another expression of this concern is to be found in the
Swedish Penal Code's 19th chapter which states the following:
"Any person posing general danger to plants or animals by
means of some toxic substance ... shall be charged with destruction". Similar provisions were included in the old province
laws. Thus, the Gotland Law, compiled in the 14th century,
noted the following (rendered in modern English): "Any person
who devastates land, which yields 3 marks in rent, without
being in dire straits, shall forfeit his neck and his wife shall
forfeit her place in church ..."

*David H. Ingvar*

# On alcohol research
# – a critical commentary

The goal of alcohol research is obvious: to determine, with biological, behavioral and social scientific methodology, how alcohol affects individuals and groups of individuals and, on the basis of knowledge thus obtained, to draw up guidelines for reducing alcohol abuse. As everyone knows, this abuse is considerable. The cost of alcohol abuse and related effects in Sweden has been estimated at SEK 50-70 000 million (12, 13, 20).

The following analysis has one main message. While previous alcohol research has devoted its attention mainly to the *consequences* – in the human body and in society – of alcohol intake and abuse, a new line of research has become discernible in the past decades. It emphasizes mechanisms in the brain that are ultimately responsible for the fact that the intake of alcohol (and other drugs) evokes pleasant effects, effects mediated by the brain's *reward system*. This constitutes a new approach to understanding alcohol inebriation and the development of abuse. Related to these findings is also increased knowledge about the personality of the alcoholic and about biological and social factors that predispose to abuse. As a result, current alcohol research may inspire new forms for preventing and treating alcohol abuse as well as new, biologically based alcohol policies.

To start with, let me emphasize that contemporary alcohol research is extremely comprehensive, so comprehensive that no single researcher is in a position to overview the entire field. Still, an attempt to evaluate the total picture, despite limitations in the competence of any individual scientist, seems essential, even morally justified in this field as in other research fields. A critical commentary of this type may be particularly warranted in an anthology commemorating the 25th anniversary of the Bank of Sweden Tercentenary Foundation. Over the years, this Foundation has taken numerous initiatives (2) and awarded extensive grants to alcohol research in Sweden.

My views are based on a long-standing interest in alcohol research and in basic biological issues concerning the mechanisms by which alcohol and other intoxicants affect the central nervous system (18, 24, 26). I have participated in both experimental and clinical alcohol research at the Department of Neurophysiology in Lund in collaboration with other university departments (5, 13, 14, 15). Since 1989, the Foundation supports a project on the effect of alcohol on volition.

## Components in alcohol research

Three components are usually discernible in any summary, handbook or review of alcohol research (10, 16, 17, 19, 23, 24, 28):

* Biochemical, cellular and molecular biological studies of the effects of ethyl alcohol on the organism of animals and man.

* Physiological (including neurophysiological), experimental and clinical studies of acute and chronic alcohol intake on individual organs or organ systems, as well as on the entire organism and the entire individual. This sector is dominated by pathophysiology but it also touches upon neuropsychological issues dealing with habituation to the use of alcohol and the development of abuse. The extensive research on treatment in recent years also belongs to this category.

* Sociological studies of the cultural history of alcohol use and its epidemiology and social psychology, including studies of alcohol policies.

### Biochemistry, cell biology and molecular biology

In recent years, the experimental literature on alcohol has grown considerably. It includes abundant data on the molecular effects of alcohol in vitro and in vivo. The effects on individual cell components and the cell membrane predominate. Alcohol appears to have especially deleterious effects on the fetus in utero (24). Cell research has shown that even small doses of alcohol at, or immediately above established limits for exposure to organic solvents, disrupt e.g. lipid metabolism in the liver (10, 13, 17, 28). No significant differences have been found between different kinds of alcoholic beverages (with the exception of absinth). However, beer appears to exert a somewhat slighter effect. But it is the total *amount* of pure alcohol and the *duration* of intake that determine the severity of effects, even down at the cellular level of the organism.

Research on ethyl alcohol metabolism in the organism of animals and man has concentrated on, and continues to concentrate on enzymes that participate in the oxidation of the alcohol molecule (e.g. alcohol dehydrogenase) and on alcohol metabolites (such as acetaldehyde) (8, 11, 24). Several metabolic markers enter the blood (CGT, ASAT, MCV etc.) and can be used successfully as general indicators of alcohol abuse, even in hidden forms (22). This has been utilized in abuse therapy for objectively checking the patient's intake pattern.

Enzyme research indicates genetic differences between different ethnic groups (16, 24). These differences may be related to e.g. the relatively high alcohol tolerance in Europeans and low tolerance in Japanese. This line of research could conceivably shed light on the basic issue of heredity in classic alcoholism, i.e. the question of whether a "talent" for alcohol consumption, and the contrary, poor alcohol tolerance, have genetic basis (16, 24). It should be noted here that adoption studies strongly indicate the presence of hereditary factors in alcohol abuse (16, 24). However, the hereditary aspect in alcoholism has yet to be fully clarified. This is an urgent problem in view of the prophylactic measures such knowledge could make possible.

A recent part of alcohol research that has acquired increasing importance concerns the brain's transmitters (7, 8, 16). Basic discoveries in this area (21) have opened up vast new fields for research on the functional systems of the brain and experimental and clinical research using clinical neurophysiological, neuropsychological and psychiatric methods. To an increasing degree, the results of this research will be directly applicable to matters involving alcohol abuse.

## Physiology and neurophysiology

Observations in animals and man (at different ages) are often similar in many respects (1, 6, 9, 11). A large number of observations have been made of alcohol's cellular and more general effects on different organs and on liver, kidney, stomach, intestine, muscle, heart, blood vessels, blood and the nervous system (10, 17, 22, 28), effects that could be replicated clinically in many respects. Even here, the severity of changes and damage appears to be determined by the magnitude and duration of alcohol intake.

Disturbances in different organ systems interact and potentiate one another. Alcohol may contribute to an increase in blood pressure, and this could, in turn, damage the heart and brain. Gastric and intestinal disturbances may contribute to nutritional derangements which, in some instances, may damage the brain (29), nerves, muscles and heart. In severe cases, this leads to life-threatening conditions, including hepatic coma and alcohol-induced delirium, two well-known causes of death in severe alcoholics (19, 29).

In this sector of alcohol research, the consequences of alcohol abuse predominate. The pathophysiology and sequelae of the abuse have often been studied in detail, in both pathoanatomical and biochemical respects. The alcohol damage can be traced as more or less pronounced molecular abnormalities in the blood, often related to deranged liver metabolism. Protracted alcohol abuse leads to biochemical decomposition in the tissues; their protective mechanisms break down, especially in the brain. This causes functional disruptions in the respective spheres, liver dysfunction, muscle weakness, cardiac arrhythmia, atherosclerosis (possibly), hypertension, intestinal dysfunction (22), defective blood coagulation, damage to brain cells (1, 6, 9, 11, 23, 26) with ensuing disturbances of consciousness and emotion, memory defects and hormone imbalance. Peripheral nerves are also damaged.

Damage of this kind may be greatly aggravated by secondary factors associated with abuse, especially a diet deficient in nutrients and vitamins. This applies especially to brain damage that may be pronounced in the presence of vitamin B deficiency, leading to Wernicke-Korsakoff disease (19, 23, 29). Extensive traumatology also belongs to this sector. Alcohol consumption and alcohol abuse in particular cause a large number of accidents, acts of violence etc. (12, 13).

All told, the first two parts of alcohol research has yielded considerable, often overwhelming knowledge on the ability of alcohol to derange and damage normal, biochemical and physiological activities in the body and give rise to a rich flora of abnormal conditions throughout the entire organism, the central nervous system in particular, not to mention its ability, by virtue of an action on mental function and behavior, to cause physical injury to the abuser and/or other parties.

## Social science research

This sector cannot be fully evaluated by the author of this article, who is a physician/biologist. On the other hand, many years of contact with research foundations (e.g. the Bank of Sweden Tercentenary Foundation, the Swedish Medical Association, Systembolaget's Alcohol Research Foundation etc.) have led to a fairly detailed overview of events in this field. Despite the author's lack of methodological know-how, the following comments may be of some interest.

The cultural history of alcohol consumption is interesting, often entertaining. In recent years, it has been possible to link up this line of research with molecular enzyme research (24). Differences between cultures in respect to alcohol consumption could be due to differing enzyme equipment in ethnic groups.

The question of why e.g. alcohol consumption is so limited in Jews and Arabs, and why this pattern may be disrupted by pressure from the western world, also belongs to the cultural history sphere. Biological and social psychological factors interacting in each individual's central nervous system, i.e. in their brains (17, 28), are discernible behind this observation, as well as behind the widespread alcohol abuse in eskimos, native Americans and minorities exposed to the influence of western cultures.

The epidemiology of alcohol consumption has yet to be investigated adequately, both on a national and international basis (12, 17, 27). Who drinks what, when, and how much? How is alcohol intake related to sociological, cultural, economic and other variables or to values and norms? Many studies have been conducted on these issues, but the pattern behind the data remains unclear. There are e.g. gender differences in the abuse panorama, but their biological, social and psychological background is insufficiently understood. Well-known age differences in alcohol consumption and alcohol effects have been demonstrated, but their physiological and/or psychological determinants have not been fully elucidated. Research on the total consumption of alcohol in society should be mentioned here. Many links have been found between this parameter and the prevalence of acts of violence, liver cirrhosis etc. But it can still be claimed that gaps in knowledge in the behavioral sciences and social research concerning alcohol remain considerable. This contributes to the lack of a deeper understanding of alcohol abuse and methods for preventing, limiting and treating such abuse in Sweden and other countries (12, 23, 27).

## A paradigm shift in alcohol research

In all three sectors into which alcohol research was subdivided above (for the sake of simplicity), the knowledge available is extremely comprehensive, but at the same time fragmented and hard to overview. The detailed knowledge supplied by biochemistry and molecular biology does not help us understand the misery caused by alcohol abuse in suburban communities. The divorce rate for wives of alcoholics cannot be related to the effect of alcohol on the membranes of neurons.

However, it should be emphasized that experimental research on biochemical and cellular effects of alcohol has produced a useful increase in our general knowledge about the pathophysiology of different toxic substances (e.g. solvents) (10, 13, 17, 24). This is valuable in itself. But this research has not explained why some people abuse alcohol and others do not.

One important finding should be mentioned here. Biochemical/molecular research has shown that alcohol damage, including damage to the brain, may be reversible (5, 11, 15). This supports the view that alcohol intake should always be limited and that a large amount of the alcohol damage sustained by the organism may be reversible. Another important finding is the new knowledge on the effect of alcohol on the fetus (24). The view that there is a link between alcohol intake in a mother during pregnancy and alcohol fetopathy has gained wide acceptance. This knowledge is a good example of how systematic research may enhance awareness of the effects of alcohol and thereby contribute to a reduction in abuse and fetal damage with permanent consequences. This fact is clearly discernible in the "Huddinge Project" in Stockholm (2, 23, 24).

Foundations and public agencies have actively encouraged individual scientists to devote time and energy to alcohol research. In view of the limited financing generally available for experimental and clinical research, for basic research in particular, it has been natural for many scientists to respond to invitations from alcohol research foundations. It sometimes seems easier to obtain grants for basic research related to alcohol than for other forms of research. This may have contributed to a some overemphasis in research on the secondary effects of alcohol on the organism.

Commendable attempts have been made by several authorities and organizations (e.g. by the Swedish Society for Alcohol and Drug Research, the Foundation (2), the Swedish Medical Society (8, 24), the Swedish Medical Journal (12)) to summarize and explain to the general public the results obtained by contemporary alcohol research (13). In these overviews, pathological findings and reports on secondary damage to different organ systems and to society have predominated for reasons noted above. The impact of these reviews, often well-presented in the media, is hard to assess. They may have contributed to some degree to diminish the use of alcohol. On the other hand, available figures on alcohol abuse in Sweden and its costs suggest that the dissemination of knowledge about alcohol research has not had any major impact on the amount of abuse. In fact, alcohol consumption in Sweden is now slowly rising once again after a decline at the beginning of the 1980's (3, 12, 20).

About 300 000 Swedes are believed to be over-consumers and about 80 000 are serious abusers according to accepted definitions. Each abuser is surrounded by 3-4 individuals affected by the "waves" generated by the abuse, "waves" in the form of impaired finances, physical and mental abuse, accidents etc. According to pessimistic estimates, this means that something in the order of 250 000 Swedes are "victims" of alcohol abuse in one way or another.

Other sectors in clinical research are similar to alcohol research, sectors involving large diagnostic groups that constitute a major burden on society, sectors that have only made modest progress in the development of causal therapy, despite massive research expenditures of time and money.

Bailar (3) recently subjected cancer research in the U.S. to a far more severe scrutiny than my review of alcohol research in the present paper. Dementia research contributes almost daily to our understanding of the impact of Alzheimer's disease on the brain of the patient, on the patient's personality and on society. But no radical cure is in sight. This also applies to cerebrovascular disorders that lead to tissue death (ischemia) due to blood clots (thromboses) or hemorrhages. We currently know a great deal about the consequences of brain ischemia. But there have been no major gains in treating it.

However, the cited examples, i.e. cancer, organic dementia and cerebrovascular disorders differ radically from the "alcohol disease". The causes of cancer, dementia and vascular occlusion in the brain are not known. But the primary cause of alcohol abuse is well-known. It is alcohol – and the acquired habit of drinking alcohol – that leads to alcoholism in pre-disposed individuals (4, 12, 13, 18, 26, 28).

## The central issue

In my view, alcohol research, like the public agencies and foundations allocating funds for this research, has overemphasized biochemical, molecular, clinical, medical, social and social psychological *consequences* of alcohol use and alcohol abuse. The central issue, i.e. *why people find the effect of alcohol inebriation pleasant*, has recently come into focus. It appears likely that further progress in abuse prophylaxis and early diagnosis of abuse and its somatic consequences will only be made when answers have been found to this difficult question (22). Only then will it be possible to institute broad measures for reducing abuse and to address the alcohol issue as a whole.

A considerable and quite basic misunderstanding should be taken up here, which has prevailed for decades, possibly even centuries, as reflected in ordinary literature, school books and even pharmacological textbooks (10, 19). Here, alcohol is referred to as an "anesthetic" with "narcotic" effects on the central nervous system. Alcohol is considered a "poison" that causes many kinds of damage. The answer to the question of why some people abuse alcohol is to be found in the study of the toxic effects of alcohol. Behind this assertion lies the question-able view (4) that alcohol abuse is *primarily* a "disease". As with other disorders (e.g. infectious diseases, cancer, diabetes etc.), the causes of the disease are therefore to be found by studies of symptoms and pathophysiology.

This view misses the central point that alcohol has an effect (at least initially) that users find enjoyable in the form of relaxation, cheerfulness etc. Claiming that these effects are experienced as positive and that they primarily induce people to use alcohol and, thus, to develop abuse in some cases, is virtually a truism (4, 7, 13).

The idea that the basic issue in alcohol abuse constitutes the inducement, i.e. the positive somatic and psychological effects of alcohol is currently stressed to an increasing degree. Some estimates suggest that 80% or even 90% of all the people who use alcohol are only moderate consumers, i.e. only use it to a limited or moderate degree without any demonstrably adverse effects. Only about 10% of alcohol users consume alcohol to an extent that could be described as "abuse". This small group displays all the consequences described above. It therefore seems obvious that contemporary alcohol research should devote increased attention to the neuropsychology of moderate consumption, i.e. the easily learned experience that alcohol has positive effects (8, 16, 18, 25, 26).

Like the present author, many researchers have found that the current change in alcohol research – from studies of consequences – to neuropsychological and neurobiological research on inebriation – constitutes a paradigm shift of great importance and promise. However, research on the neuropsychology of inebriation, i.e. the positive feelings of pleasure, including expectations thereof, caused by moderate alcohol intake is underrepresented in alcohol research today. It should be noted that such research has only been the subject of experimental clinical studies in the past few decades (7, 13, 25). The functional systems in the central nervous system that are a prerequisite for the feeling of pleasure (and the contrary) in man were discovered already in the early fifties. But extensive experimental and clinical studies entailing systematic exploration of the system referred to as the *reward system* of the brain have only been conducted in the past few decades. As noted above, study of this system constitutes a paradigm shift in alcohol research (8, 16).

The relationship of the reward system to the use and abuse of alcohol and other drugs has inspired several international symposia, including some held in Stockholm – *"Risken att bli alkoholist"* (The risk of becoming an alcoholic) (2) and the Swedish Medical Society's 1987 Berzelius Symposium, "Brain Reward Systems and Abuse" (8) – and also inspired neuropsychological analyses of inebriation (25, 26). Briefly, this research has shown that the reward system produces more transmitters that induce pleasure when the brain is exposed to alcohol (7, 16). This also applies to other central stimulants (amphetamine, heroin, cocaine). Thus, alcohol can be viewed as one of many substances capable of producing a positive, pleasurable "kick". This feeling may be followed by the contrary, i.e. depression. Some theories (7) suggest that certain people respond to the action of alcohol more strongly than others, i.e. their alcohol "talent" is greater. The time course of the stimulating effect of alcohol and the subsequent depressive effect appears to vary. If the development of depression takes a long time, this may create a more sustained desire to continue alcohol intake. Hypotheses such as these are very attractive and are now accessible to quantitative neuropsychological and neurophysiological analyses with modern methods.

Different levels are discernible in research on the reward system. In animal experiments, its anatomic structure, location and function can be mapped with the aid of electrical stimulation and chemical provocation with e.g. drugs (6, 7, 16, 18, 26). Modern brain research offers a powerful arsenal of methods for measuring the effect of alcohol and other drugs on cellular metabolism, down to the level of the individual cell systems in the brain (6, 8, 26). Studies can be made at rest or in complex psychological situations in which the animals, alone or socially interacting, are allowed to chose between alcohol and e.g. sexual stimulation or tasty food. Such methods can also be applied to generations of experimental animals exposed to the effects of alcohol. Animal models have, in fact, already been developed for showing how alcohol abuse can produce a "social legacy" in rats (8, 24).

Such experimental research has its clinical equivalent in neuropsychological analyses of e.g. personality variables (18, 25, 26) and in positron camera imaging of various receptor systems in the brains of normal people and heavy abusers (8, 18, 26). This research is in a phase of intense development in Sweden (Stockholm, Uppsala and Lund) with support from the Foundation.

## Neuropsychology of alcohol abuse

Contemporary brain research has shown that changes in consciousness and awareness due to e.g. alcohol inebriation, can be analyzed in neuropsychological terms in a new way (14). Conscious awareness can be said to consist of three components: memories of the *past*, perception of the *present* and thoughts, plans, visions expectations etc. about the *future*. Various cerebral disturbances, neurological disorders, mental disease and psychological abnormalities, as well as the effect of various poisons including alcohol, alter awareness and its three time components. To some extent, the past, present and future can be located in the brain according to theories published recently (14). The level of activity of the three cited components can be determined by means of direct physiological measurements in the brain itself. Current research has also shown that the emotions can be traced in the brain's functional landscape.

Alcohol intoxication exerts distinct and early effects on the time components of consciousness and on their emotional "color". In principle, alcohol increases perception of the *present* (Sjöstrand). Alcohol shares this effect with many other stimulants, such as amphetamine, cocaine, heroin etc. However, these drugs also have other, very different effects on the brain, effects whose description is beyond the scope of this paper. At the same time, alcohol dampens the perception of past events and the guilt preserved in some memories. In addition, alcohol reduces concepts related to the future and the anxiety people feel about the uncertain future. Alcohol's potentiation of our perception of the *present* is probably a central component in the positive feelings associated with inebriation. Sensory impressions become more pleasant, self-esteem stabilizes, intellectual activities seem more ingenious etc., all well-known effects of a few drinks. When feelings of guilt about past actions and anxiety about the future are subdued, the present emerges in a more attractive light. It may then be tempting for a drinker to seek to re-experience this situation by continuing alcohol intake. An imperative need for a renewal of the pleasurable sensation arises in the nervous system (and minds) of some people, as well as in familiar social situations (13). Guilt about the past and anxiety about the future predominate in the hangover phase following a bout of heavy drinking. This possibly reduces perception of the *present* to a minimum and generates a powerful craving for a "hair of the dog". Thus, a vicious circle is established that leads to continued abuse with well-known and well-explored consequences.

In my view, alcohol research over the next few years should give priority to brain research entailing direct measurements in the brain of the way alcohol alters time components of consciousness and accompanying emotions. Measurement of the distribution of activity in the sober and inebriated brain should lead to a better understanding of the primary, positive effects of alcohol.

The central role played by research on the reward system and on consciousness could be linked to the social sciences (8, 18, 25, 26). Social misery, various forms of deprivation in childhood and an impoverished spiritual climate are known to create neuroses and feelings of guilt. To this must be added, as recent research has shown, other factors promoting abuse, such as poor paternal identification, stereotyped masculinity concepts and sensation seeking behavior (16, 25). Factors such as these, plus the heavy guilt from a person's past and neurotic anxiety about the future, might create individuals who perceive the effects of alcohol inebriation far more positively than people whose childhood lacked psychological and material problems. So better definitions are highly desirable for (i) groups in society in whom severe abuse often develops, and (equally important) (ii) the even larger groups that almost never develop abuse. Which values, which social – and biological – determinants protect people from alcohol abuse and which factors fail to provide protection? Fortunately, many of these issues are becoming the subject of analysis in contemporary alcohol research.

Increased research on the human central nervous system and its reward system (8, 16, 18, 26), as well as on consciousness (14) should relatively rapidly lead to greater understanding of how the experience of alcohol inebriation plays a central role in the development of alcohol abuse. Such knowledge, more than a study of the ultimate consequences of abuse, might be central to efforts to devise preventive measures and improve awareness of the biological and social factors increasing the risk of abuse. Greater knowledge of this kind should not only point to new measures for preventing abuse but even indicate measures for controlling a limited consumption of alcohol, including its positive effects without the development of excessive consumption and abuse.

This approach should also make it possible to devise new information systems aimed at increasing awareness of the nature of alcohol usage and abuse, especially in children and teenagers. If this awareness can be enhanced, future alcohol research might enter a more "profitable" phase than hitherto. To paraphrase the main message in this paper: Alcohol research has had a *past* in which the *consequences* of alcohol abuse have been predominant. In the *present* situation, insight is increasing about the neurobiology and neuropsychology of inebriation, with the emphasis on the reward system of the brain and on individuals who constitute risk groups. If this insight increases, the *future* of alcohol research should develop favorably.

## Summary

Much current alcohol research places the emphasis on biochemical, pathophysiological, psychological and social *consequences* of alcohol abuse. The knowledge available within this sector is extensive. Still, there has been no real decrease in the amount of alcohol abuse in society. In recent years, the central role played by the reward system of the brain for the experience of inebriation and for the development of alcohol abuse has become the subject of attention. At the same time, knowledge has increased on how genetic, psychological and social factors might increase the risk of abuse. The present review stresses that future alcohol research should devote more attention to the central nervous system mechanisms responsible for the positive experience of alcohol intake and less attention to the consequences of abuse.

The author would like to express his thanks to Christer Alling, Mats Berglund, Jörgen Engel, Jesper Persson and Lennart Widén for valuable criticism.

*Bengt Pernow*

# Attempts to prevent cardiovascular disease

Not every disease or health hazard can be eliminated. Many are clearly linked to genetic factors and the latter's attendant characteristics or to the natural ageing process that can be delayed but not prevented. So research in this area must concentrate on attempts to identify factors in the environment and lifestyle that contribute to these diseases and on finding methods for influencing them along lines in which their manifestations are delayed and their consequences mitigated.

Atherosclerosis and the changes it induces in coronary vessels belong to this category of diseases and accounts for more than half of Sweden's total mortality. This percentage has increased throughout the 20th century, both because deaths from other causes, primarily infectious diseases, have declined and because atherosclerotic diseases have increased in absolute terms, largely as a consequence of the increased number of elderly people in our society. Even if most people afflicted by myocardial infarction are more than 70 years of age, this manifestation of atherosclerosis is not merely an affliction of the elderly. It is the main cause of death in men 45 years and older and in women from the age of 65. About one-third of Swedish in-patients facilities are employed for the care of people with cardiovascular disease.

In the light of this situation, it is natural for society to view support for research, whose aim is to shed light on the causes of atherosclerosis and to achieve effective preventive or therapeutic strategies, as an urgent national priority. Here, Swedish research, with the support of the Bank of Sweden Tercentenary

Foundation, and other grant-giving organizations, have produced major results. Basic research on the uptake and metabolism of various lipid fractions in the body have given us greater knowledge about the way in which the atherosclerotic process is initiated and accelerates. Epidemiological research has provided a good, albeit as yet incomplete, picture of the factors that contribute more than others to the fact that atherosclerosis is a major problem for society. New methods have been devised for the diagnosis of prevalence and extent, a prerequisite for future therapeutic advances.

In all these fields, Swedish scientists have made major contributions. Swedish know-how is even used in international collaboration whose aim is to analyze the development of atherosclerotic disorders in a global perspective, identify risk factors and improve the efficacy of preventive measures.

The Foundation's contribution in this field has been made mainly in the form of financial support for two longitudinal projects, the "Göteborg Study" and the "Malmö Study", over many years.

The *Göteborg Study* comprises two major projects, "Men of 1913" and a prospective, primary prevention study. In 1963 Lars Werkö, Lars Wilhelmsen and Gösta Tibblin started the internationally noted "Men of 1913" Study that has given major contributions to our present knowledge about the factors representing an increased risk of becoming ill and dying from myocardial infarction.

The project started with a retrospective review of men born in Göteborg in 1913 and who died before 1963, approx. 25% of whom from myocardial infarction. Of the 50-year old men still alive in 1963, 885 were selected at random and subsequently followed up with repeated checkups and, when necessary, medical treatment.

In 1970, the second Göteborg study was commenced under the motto "Try to prevent heart attacks", a project the Foundation was to support for 14 years. It was based on the experience already gained from the Men of 1913, primarily with respect to the three main risk factors: high blood fat levels, high blood pressure and smoking. A subdivision of the subjects into high-risk and low-risk groups in these respects showed that the former group ran a risk of having a heart attack 30 times greater than the risk for the latter group. Since all of these variables could be influenced, the specific goal of the project was to see if it was possible, by means of interventions addressing these factors, to reduce the number of heart attacks in men living in a major city.

At the time the project started, the situation for heart attack patients was that about one-half died, and survivors were left with serious residual problems. This circumstance had begun to attract international attention. In 1968, two major international congresses were held on the subject, one sponsored by the American Heart Association and one by the W.H.O. Both conferences noted that "at the present time, there is no scientific evidence of the possibility of preventing ischemic heart disease". At the same time, the participating nations were called upon to undertake comprehensive research for the purpose of changing this situation. "It is therefore appropriate to recommend multifactor trials as the quickest means of establishing whether such prevention is possible".

The Göteborg intervention study comprised 30 000 men born 1915-1925. They were subdivided at random into three groups, A, B and C, each containing 10 000 persons. Group A and part of Group B received a questionnaire on hereditary factors, symptoms and living habits. Both were summoned to medical examinations. Treatment of Group A, with respect to hypertension and elevated cholesterol levels, then commenced. Smokers received a program designed to help them break the habit, and physically inactive subjects received exercise counseling. People in the control group, i.e. C, were completely unaware that they were part of the study. During the course of the study, the effects of ongoing treatment were recorded. The result of the project's main purpose, i.e. to assess whether this form of intervention was capable of affecting morbidity and mortality due to myocardial infarction, was checked after 10 years.

Seventy-six percent of the people in Group A who were invited to participate took part in the study. A special review of the people who did not take part disclosed an over-representation for people who were unmarried, divorced or immigrants. A check on them made 27 months after the study's start found a mortality rate three times higher than for the subjects in Groups A-C. Thus, a negative attitude to participation in a health study comprises a number of factors jointly constituting a considerable hazard to health.

The *Malmö project*. In 1967, the Foundation awarded a grant to a project at Malmö General Hospital entailing the collaboration of the Departments of Clinical Physiology, Social Medicine and Pathology under the heading "Epidemiological studies of cardiovascular and pulmonary diseases in Malmö". The Department of Pathology was also part of an international collaborative venture under the auspices of the W.H.O. for the purpose of identifying the incidence of atherosclerosis.

In its initial phase, the Malmö project ascertained the prevalence of atherosclerosis in the region and compared the accuracy of the clinical diagnosis in life and post-mortem findings. The purpose of this comparison was to improve clinical diagnosis. In 1967-83, a comprehensive epidemiological study of cardiovascular and pulmonary disorders in Malmö in men born in 1914 was conducted with Foundation support. This study covered a total of 703 men, i.e. 88 percent of the men invited to participate. Half had medical checkups and treatment to the requisite degree. The other half served as a control group. The effects were measured as the difference between these two groups with respect to mortality, early retirement and the duration of medical treatment during a five-year follow-up period (Lannerstad, Isacsson and Lindell 1979).

Other studies within the framework of the Malmö project addressed the risk of illness due to chronic bronchitis or developing atherosclerosis in neck and leg arteries in relation to social patterns and living habits. In recent years, the importance of various psychosocial factors, primarily the access to a social network and support, to health, morbidity and mortality, has attracted increasing interest (Hansson 1988).

Sven-Olof Isacsson, Lars Janzon, Sven-Erik Lindell and Bertil Steen were in charge of the Malmö project.

## Coronary disease in an international perspective

Morbidity and mortality due to coronary disease displays major geographic variations (Figure 1). Mortality is highest in certain parts of the Soviet Union and other countries in Eastern Europe and lower in Western Europe. The lowest figures have been recorded for Japan and certain countries in Southern Europe,

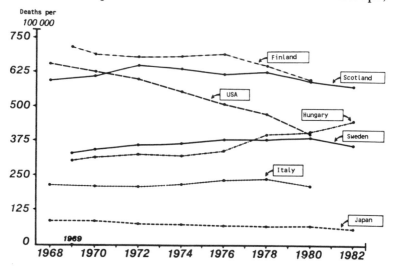

Figure 1. *Deaths due to coronary disease in men, calculated for age-standardized populations in several different countries. From the 1987 "Folkhälsorapport" (Public health report) published by the National Board of Health and Welfare.*

Greece in particular. Sweden is in an intermediate position here. But in our country, as well as in Finland, there are inexplicable geographic differences with greater morbidity in northern counties than in southern counties.

The incidence of morbidity and mortality due to myocardial infarction has not been constant over time. The figure has been falling for the past few decades, especially in the U.S., Canada and certain European countries. The same tendency has even become apparent in Sweden in recent years. These trends are currently being followed-up in a multicenter W.H.O. study in which Swedish epidemiologists are participating.

These changes over time show that coronary disease and other manifestations of the atherosclerotic process are not governed solely by genetic factors and that other factors, apparently susceptible to change, play a major role. This circumstance constitutes a major source of inspiration for research all over the world, research to which Swedes have made major contributions. In view of the subject's highly complex nature, basing conclusions on the results of studies comprising a very large number of subjects monitored for a great many years has been necessary.

## Risk factors in cardiovascular disease

A great deal of research has been devoted to the causal pattern underlying cardiovascular disorders. This research has resulted in the identification of a large number of risk factors, i.e. factors statistically associated with an increased risk of developing a given disease. The results of this research then serve as the basis for preventive or therapeutic measures. Risk factor research works both with retrospective and prospective methods. The term "retrospective" means that diagnoses are extracted from a registry of deaths and cross-tabulated with social or economic factors, living and health habits etc. With the "prospective" method, which yields the most reliable results, a specific population is selected and defined with regard to potential risk factors. This population is then monitored for a number of years, and note is made of their morbidity and mortality. In prospective studies, it is possible to intervene in part of the population selected at random and to analyze whether the adopted intervention has any effect.

Some of the most important risk factors in this context will be briefly described below. This account is largely based on the results obtained from the Göteborg and Malmö projects, both of which having yielded a large number of scientific reports. They jointly supply us with a detailed picture of the risk factor pattern in morbidity and mortality due to cardiovascular disease in Sweden and enable us to compare the situation here with the position in other countries.

*Blood lipids – for better or worse*

Fat in food, an important ingredient in a well-balanced diet, is broken down in the intestine into triglycerides and cholesterol absorbed into the blood. Since these fats are not soluble in water, they are transported attached to special proteins, i.e. lipoproteins. There are different types of lipoproteins. LDL (low density lipoprotein) and HDL (high density lipoprotein) are the most important forms in atherosclerosis. LDL is the form in which cholesterol is transported. HDL has a protective effect on tissues by, among other things, eliminating cholesterol from the walls of blood vessels. So it is sometimes referred to as "benign fat".

Both cholesterol and triglycerides are at the forefront of discussions about the role of fat in the atherosclerosis process. This role will be described in greater detail below, but it should be emphasized that these fats are by no means altogether a bad thing. Triglycerides constitute an important source of energy, and cholesterol plays a major role in a number of processes important to life. Most of the body's cholesterol is found in the membrane constituting the protective envelope surrounding all cells. This membrane is active in the transport of different substances between the blood and cells. Cholesterol is also a constituent in certain hormones and vitamins.

Understanding of cholesterol's central role in the atherosclerosis process has emerged in step with increased knowledge about the way the body forms, transports, utilizes and breaks down this fat fraction. The most important contribution was made by the Nobel laureates Brown and Goldstein (1984) who showed that most cells have special LDL entry points, i.e. receptors, on their surface. The number of LDL receptors is governed by genetic factors. A small number of receptors make it harder for the cells to utilize cholesterol, leading to accumulation in the blood with an increased tendency for atherosclerosis to develop as a result.

Brown and Goldstein were able to clarify this circumstance most convincingly through studies of families with a defect in the gene that regulates the formation of LDL receptors. Some members of these families completely lacked the ability to form these receptors, resulting in severely elevated levels of blood cholesterol and their affliction by atherosclerosis and myocardial infarction in their teens. This extreme form of familial hypercholesterolemia is extremely rare (one person in a million is stricken). More common (one in 500) is the genetic form in which the defect is only inherited by one of the parents. There are 15-20 000 people in Sweden with this form, and all run the risk of early atherosclerosis.

However, a far more common situation is that high levels of cholesterol in the blood result from an interplay between genetic and dietary factors, the latter often being of decisive importance. However, these people seldom achieve the same high cholesterol levels as in the familial form of the disorder, but checking them out is still important because changes in the diet are often the only treatment necessary. Here, it should be emphasized that the development of atherosclerosis is a slow process in the latter group and may continue for decades before the disorder produces any clinical manifestations.

Our present knowledge of the link between cholesterol levels in the blood and the prevalence of atherosclerosis in the heart is based on follow-up studies of individuals with genetic choleste-rol defects and on epidemiological studies comprising large population groups. The first to direct attention to the importance of dietary fat in the development of heart disease was the American epidemiologist Ancel Keys who in 1970 published a study on the situation in seven European countries with clear differences in the prevalence of heart disease. The following year, the now classic Framingham report was published. It shed light on the connection between illness and living conditions in a population outside Boston. These people were subsequently continuously monitored and the results published in a large number of reports.

The Framingham Study inspired a number of similar pro-jects of which the Western Collaborative Study (U.S.) in 1975, the Pooling Project (U.S.) in 1978, the Israeli Prospective Study in 1985 and the Multiple Risk Factor Intervention Trial (MRFIT) (U.S.) in 1986 are noteworthy, in addition to the projects supported by the Foundation. The results of all these projects, based on large population groups, show unequivocally that the cholesterol content of blood plays an essential role in the development of atherosclerosis in both the heart and peripheral blood vessels (Figure 2).

It should be noted that most of these large, epidemiological studies comprised men and that the significance of cholesterol as a risk factor for women is not documented as well. Many studies, not the least Swedish, suggest that triglycerides consti-tute a more important risk factor for women. Thus, a 12-year follow-up study by Lapidus of women in Göteborg failed to find any definite increase in mortality due to heart disease in women

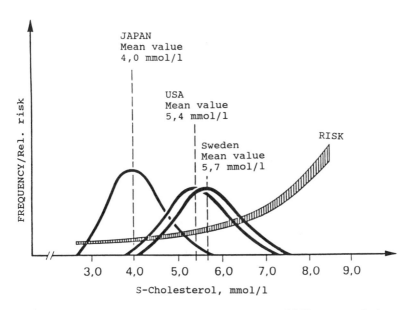

Figure 2. *Cholesterol levels in the blood serum of different populations and the relative risk of morbidity and mortality due to cardiovascular disease. From "Riktlinjer för behandling av hyperkolesterolemi" (Guidelines for treatment of hypercholesterolemia). Hjärt-Lungfonden 1988.*

with high cholesterol values. However, he did find that the risk of myocardial infarction was 3 times greater when blood triglyceride levels were high. Similar results were obtained in the Framingham Study.

## Smoking

There is no longer any doubt that smoking constitutes the greatest single cause of poor health and early death. According to one estimate, one-half million Europeans die every year as a direct result of smoking. The discussion of the adverse effects of smoking has concentrated on the lungs with allergic manifestations and lung cancer as a result. But infarction damage to the heart and brain account for greatest excess mortality in smokers.

The first really convincing report on smoking as a risk factor was published in the 1950's. Increased mortality due to both lung cancer and myocardial infarction was found in 30 000 British physicians, followed for 10 years, who smoked more than 20 cigarettes a day. This study, which attracted considerable interest, was subsequently followed by a number of similar analyses with periods of observation of nearly 20 years in some instances. In 1976, a report, within the framework of the Men of 1913 Study, on a 10-year follow-up of 50-year old men found a definite link between smoking and illness and death from myocardial infarction. The increase in mortality and morbidity was closely correlated with cigarette consumption, heavy smokers displaying an excess mortality of 20%. Since there were relatively few people in this category, the greatest number of deaths ascribable to smoking was found among moderate smokers, an observation that is obviously important to the design of anti-smoking strategies.

Smoking affects morbidity, as well as mortality. The Malmö Study found that both the number of illness days and the consumption of hospital care were greater among smokers than among non-smokers. Some materials have found illness absenteeism to be about 30% higher in male smokers and 45% higher in female smokers than in non-smokers. Even the number of early retirees among the 55-year old men in the Malmö study was much higher among smokers; the correlation with the number of cigarettes smoked a day was good (Figure 3).

The Göteborg and Malmö studies also showed that the increased risk of morbidity and mortality due to cardiovascular disease that accompanies smoking is a reversible process. Studies of ex-smokers unequivocally showed that their mortality after 5 years of abstinence did not differ from the mortality of people who had never smoked. Ex-smokers also displayed lower figures than smokers in respect to the prevalence of early retirement (Figure 3) and illness absenteeism.

The Malmö Study also analyzed the correlation between atherosclerosis of the legs and smoking in 55-year old men. This

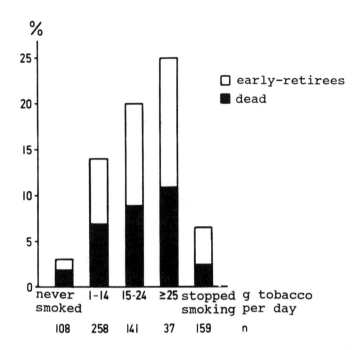

Figure 3. *The percentage of deceased people and early-retirees from 1970-1974 in relation to smoking habits in 1969. The material comprises men born in 1914 and residing in Malmö in 1969. From "Död och sjukdom bland medelålders män" (Mortality and morbidity in middle-aged men). Dissertation by Olof Lannerstad (1978).*

material found that 96% of the people with vascular changes in their legs were smokers, often heavy smokers; the remainder were ex-smokers. In a control group, 15% were smokers. Similar results were obtained by the Framingham Study.

The factors underlying the link between smoking and cardiovascular disease are not fully understood. Some scientists have cited one or more of the components in tobacco smoke as substances capable of contributing to the atherosclerosis process, carbon monoxide, nicotine and tar in particular. However, no definite evidence has as yet been presented to confirm these hypotheses. On the other hand, we know that smoking affects blood circulation via a number of mechanisms that could jointly contribute to the development of cardiovascular disease. The ability of smoking to affect different factors in the blood coagulation process so blood clots more readily form in atherosclerotic vessels has been extensively described. The nicotine in smoke also reduces the blood's oxygen transport capacity.

Some have also claimed that there need not necessarily exist any causal relationship between smoking and cardiovascular disease and that there may be some other pathogenic factor. This factor could be genetic or related to personality. In an effort to clarify the role of genetic factors in this context, Swedish (Birgitta Floderus) and Finnish scientists have monitored identical twins over a long period of time (15-20 years), recorded illness due to heart disease and correlated the incidence to smoking habits. The results showed that the smokers displayed a higher incidence of morbidity and mortality due to myocardial infarction and lung cancer than their twin siblings. This suggests that smoking has a pathogenic effect quite apart from genetic and personality factors.

## Hypertension

Hypertension is an additional risk factor in illness and death from heart disease. After a 10 and 13-year follow-up respectively, both the Framingham and Göteborg Men of 1913 studies found a high correlation in this context. The Malmö Study also found excess mortality among men with high blood pressure. Awareness that hypertension constitutes a risk in the development of cardiovascular disease instigated studies at an early stage of the extent to which hypotensive treatment was able to reduce morbidity and mortality from this disease. A number of early, limited studies were performed in Sweden in this area with positive results. However, there were some ethical doubts about performing comprehensive studies of this kind, since it was felt that a reduction in the blood pressure of people with atherosclerotic vascular occlusion could reduce blood flow, thereby increasing the risk of a heart attack or stroke.

However, two broadly designed, controlled studies of the effect of lowering blood pressure in cases of hypertension were conducted in the U.S. during the 1960's. Subjects in one of these studies had greatly increased blood pressure; half were treated with anti-hypertensive drugs and the others served as untreated controls. The second study comprised people with moderate hypertension and used a similar design. The idea was for the studies to last for five years with continuous reporting of results. However, the first study was called off after only four years, since it found such major differences in mortality from cardiovascular disease to the advantage of the treated group that the withholding of apparently life-saving treatment from the control group was deemed to be unethical. The second study was completed. Even here, the anti-hypertensive treatment proved to have a significant effect on morbidity and mortality due to cardiovascular disease. No adverse effects lending support for the aforementioned fears were found.

After the results of these studies were published in 1967 and 1970 respectively, several other controlled trials were performed, e.g. within the framework of the Göteborg and Malmö studies. All have produced the same results: the treatment of high blood pressure reduces total mortality as well as the development of and death from cardiovascular disease. The significantly reduced mortality found among 55-year old men who received medical checkups and subsequent treatment in the Malmö Study, compared to the control group, was apparently completely due to the anti-hypertensive treatment.

In the light of these well-founded results, it was felt that denying people with hypertension treatment was no longer ethically defensible. Clear guidelines for the way this treatment should be performed were recently published by the Hjärt-lungfonden (Swedish Heart and Lung Fund). Ongoing research in this field is concentrating on comparing different medication, ascertaining the incidence of adverse reactions and determining the long-term and short-term blood pressure level at which the commencement of treatment is deemed reasonable.

## Alcohol

Alcohol as a risk factor in cardiovascular disease has been a subject of contention since the early years of the 20th century and views about its importance have shifted. On the basis of post-mortem findings, alcohol was early claimed to exert a protective effect on the vascular wall. This was based on the observation that people who had died after heavy alcohol consumption often lacked atherosclerotic foci in their blood vessels. However, it was found that this was probably due to the fact that alcoholics often die at an age at which atherosclerosis has not become established.

In the 1970's, reports were published indicating that the risk of becoming ill and dying from cardiovascular disease increased with increasing alcohol consumption. Thus, a 10-year follow-up of the Men of 1913 disclosed far higher mortality in men registered for drinking offenses than in men who were not registered. So, the Malmö Study found higher mortality and a higher incidence of early retirement and illness registration in people who had sought care at an alcohol clinic than in people who did not seek care.

Several materials have found that people consuming moderate amounts of alcohol have a lower incidence of death from cardiovascular disease than both alcoholics and teetotalers. This extraordinary result was found by a number of studies conducted in the 1980's. One of them concerned middle-aged nurses followed for a total of 334 000 person-years. People who drank alcohol had a lower incidence of myocardial and brain infarction than teetotallers. The differences were considerable and persisted after correction for other risk factors.

These results gave rise to the theory that moderate drinking has a protective effect on blood vessels, a view that has gained support in some studies of the effect of alcohol on blood fats. Alcohol does reduce the concentration of the atherosclerogenic LDL factor in blood and increases the protective HDL fraction. However, a critical analysis of these studies identified a number of factors in teetotallers that jointly appear to explain their excess mortality. This group turned out to have a highly heterogenous composition. Thus, it included a number of former heavy consumers of alcohol, people with greater morbidity and a higher incidence of diabetes, liver and pancreas disease etc. They smoked to a greater degree than moderate drinkers, were more overweight and had a higher average blood pressure. These circumstances are characteristic of most teetotaller control materials.

Thus, the link between moderate alcohol consumption and atherosclerosis has not been fully confirmed. So there is every reason to concur with the following statement by the W.H.O.: "The likelihood that moderate alcohol intake results in a reduced risk of developing coronary disease is unfounded and should not be used in encouraging the use of alcohol". This recommendation is even more important in view of the fact that alcohol currently constitutes the biggest medical and social problem in Swedish society.

## Physical inactivity

Early epidemiological studies showed that the incidence of morbidity and mortality due to myocardial infarction was 2-3 times lower in physically active men than in sedentary men. However, these results are hard to interpret and do not constitute reliable proof that exercise protects against myocardial infarction. In the Malmö Study, a high degree of physical activity in leisure time was not related to lower mortality but to a lower incidence of illness registration. However, it is not clear whether or not this is ascribable to the exercise. Generally speaking, physically active people tend to be more health and diet conscious, smoke less, consume less alcohol and weigh less. So identifying physical activity as the main reason for their lower incidence of heart disease is no easy matter.

However, a recently presented, broadly designed, multicenter American study, under the leadership of the Swede L.G. Ekelund, appears to lend added support for the view that poor physical condition is still a risk factor of primary importance to death from heart disease. More than 4 000 men from 30 to 70 years of age were followed for 8.5 years. Poor physical exercise capacity was then found to be linked to a relatively increased risk, even when other risk factors, such as high blood fat levels, smoking, high blood pressure and overweight, were taken into account. The research group also achieved results in a similar study with female subjects that showed better than before that a good level of physical activity reduces the risk of cardiovascular disease.

Even if these studies probably do not constitute the "final verdict" regarding a possible correlation in this respect, there is still sufficient reason to encourage interest in exercise. Regular exercise promotes general well-being, reduces fatigue during exertion and reduces the risk of injuries to the locomotive organs.

## Psychosocial and social factors

Even if the factors cited hitherto do contribute heavily to the high incidence of cardiovascular disease, they are still incapable of explaining more than about half of the cases. For the other half, there is still no reliable explanation. Here, various psychosocial and social factors undoubtedly play a major role, either through direct action on the pathogenic process or indirectly because people in psychosocially demanding environments tend more often to be smokers, have a higher alcohol consumption or develop high blood pressure.

Psychosocial and social factors of relevance to morbidity and mortality due to cardiovascular disease are found in society in general, at the work place and in each person's immediate surroundings.

One widely held view, supported by the findings of some studies from the 1940's, has been that myocardial infarction mainly afflicts men in upper social strata, senior management and businessmen exposed to pressure and stress. However, this does not appear to be the case. A number of studies from England, the U.S. and Scandinavia have apparently found excess mortality in lower social strata and that blue-collar workers are afflicted more often than white-collar workers. This was apparent in one study from northern Karelia (in Finland), noted for its high mortality rate due to cardiovascular disease. A report, published in 1970, on a study in Oslo of 15 000 men from 40 to 49 years found that mortality was highest in taxi and bus drivers and lowest in teachers among the occupational groups studied. The Copenhagen City Heart Study (1978) with 14 000 male and female subjects found excess mortality from heart disease in people with low income and low education. The Whitehall Study (1984) comprising 17 000 civil servants recorded a tripling of the mortality rate for people with low educations compared to people with high educations.

The Göteborg Study found similar results. Its results in respect to the significance of occupation to illness and death due to myocardial infarction were based on more than 7 000 men followed for an average of 12 years. The study found that blue-collar and low-level white-collar workers displayed a far higher incidence of total mortality and morbidity due to myocardial infarction than high-level white-collar workers, even when all other risk factors were taken into account.

This social and occupation-related excess mortality may have different explanations. In most studies, it coincides with an accumulation of different risk factors, smoking in particular, although high blood pressure and elevated blood lipids are equally prevalent in high social and occupational groups. Another factor of probable importance is the difference in living conditions, including dietary habits.

However, the differences disclosed between social and occupational groups are probably related to more general, psychosocial factors. This was shown e.g. in an interview study from Stockholm comprising men who had suffered heart attacks before the age of 45. High demands and stress on the job proved to constitute risk factors only if related to perceived monotony, an inability to have a say and limited opportunities for advancement. Boredom is more dangerous than stress, as Töres Theorell, the person in charge of the Stockholm study, put it.

Another factor in working life of importance to increased morbidity and death from heart disease is shift work. This has been well-documented in two studies conducted by T. Theorell et al. (1982) and A. Knutsson (1989) of the State Institute for Psychosocial Medicine. With the aid of Statistics Sweden (SBC), the former study interviewed 14 500 people, representing different occupations, on their work conditions, perception of their work situation and living habits. Only two work characteristics were found to be significantly associated with morbidity due to myocardial infarction, viz. monotony on the job and shift work. However, smoking was an important variable in this context. This makes it harder to determine the extent to which shift work is an important risk factor in itself. So the study was expanded to encompass nearly one million people in active work ages, selected via the central public health register. A very high correlation was then found between shift work and heart disease. This association persisted even when co-varying factors, such as smoking, income, marital status, place of residence and degree of physical exertion in work were taken into account.

The second study comprised 500 paper mill workers in Sundsvall, Sweden, who were followed from 1968 to 1983 with respect to morbidity caused by myocardial infarction. Even this study produced convincing evidence that people with shift work ran a far greater risk in this respect than others. The effect was statistically significant after 11 to 15 years of exposure to shift work and increased continuously during the 20-year observation period. There was then a dramatic drop in cardiovascular mortality, probably because people who did not enjoy shift work got other jobs. Shift workers also differed in other respects, such as having a higher consumption of cigarettes and higher blood pressure. But the association between myocardial infarction and the number of years of shift work persisted, even when these factors were taken into account.

One factor that has come to the forefront in discussions of total excess mortality, illness and death due to myocardial infarction is the *social network*, a structural concept describing the individual's relationship to her/his social environment. Swedish scientists have made important contributions even here. In 1978, Anne-Marie Bolander at the SCB showed that married men had a lower mortality rate due to cardiovascular disease than unmarried men, divorced men and widowers. The 1986 Göteborg Study yielded similar results: the mortality rate of divorced men was four times greater than for married men. The differences were ascribable in part to smoking, alcohol and social class, but the difference remained significant even after these factors were taken into account.

This problem was the subject of particular attention in a cross-sectional study of the men of 1914 in Malmö where the phenomenon "social network" was defined in both qualitative and quantitative terms. The results showed that men with poorly developed social roots displayed the risk factors related to heart disease, i.e. smoking, hypertension and a low level of physical activity, to a greater extent than people with well-developed social roots. On the other hand, no difference was found regarding blood fats or alcohol habits. Men living alone with limited access to emotional support from friends and relatives displayed a mortality rate 2 to 2.5 times higher than the mortality rate of people who cohabited with someone or who had good social support.

The reason why a defective social network increases morbidity or mortality from heart disease as well as in general is still unknown. Nor do we know which psychophysiological effects accompany a secure social situation. Insecurity does "pave the way" for other risk factors, so defective social support may well have a direct, adverse effect on different immunological and endocrinal mechanisms, thereby making the individual more susceptible to various pathogenic processes.

Extensive attention has been devoted to the importance of *personality type* to morbidity and mortality due to myocardial infarction. Some have claimed that the pattern summarized with the designation "A behavior" predisposes. People belonging to this category are characterized by impatience, ambition, drive and competitiveness. This behavior is largely hereditary but is even learned to some extent. It also appears that the work environment is capable of stimulating the development of this kind of behavior.

Several studies indicate that myocardial infarction is more common in people displaying type A behavior. This was found in the Framingham Study and in Swedish studies. In a 1980 retrospective study of employees at three large Stockholm companies, Kristina Orth-Gomér and T. Theorell found that the risk of myocardial infarction was about twice as great for people with type A than type B behavior, even with the standard risk factors under control. Despite these interesting observations, the relevance of personality type is likely to continue as a subject of contention for many years to come.

## Accumulated risk effect

The factors mentioned above do not merely constitute individual risks. They interact and potentiate one another's effects.

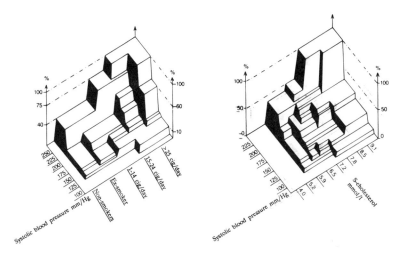

Figure 4. *The risk of falling ill due to myocardial infarction during a 13-year follow-up of men who were 50 years of age at the start of the study. The bar to the left indicates the morbidity risk in relation to blood pressure and smoking habits. The bar to the right indicates the corresponding risk in relation to blood pressure and the blood cholesterol level. From "Rapport från studien 1913 års män". (Report from the Men of 1913 study). Lars Wilhelmsen and Kurt Svärdsudd (1984).*

This synergism was apparent in both the Göteborg and Malmö studies. Figure 4, taken from the Men of 1913 project, illustrates the importance of hypertension, cholesterol and smoking in respect to the risk run by a 50-year old man of being stricken by a heart attack in a 13-year perspective. According to these three-dimensional diagrams, this risk is insignificant if all the factors are kept under control. An increase in two factors leads to a leap in the increased risk of myocardial infarction. As Figure 4 shows, the risk for a non-smoker increased from virtually zero with low blood pressure to about 40% for smokers with high blood pressure. Among heavy smokers, the risk increased much faster, i.e. from about 10% when they had low blood pressure to nearly 100% when they had high blood pressure. The same applies to the correlation between cholesterol and blood pressure (Figure 4).

Accumulated risk is present even with other combinations of

factors. As noted above, various psychosocial factors are often combined with smoking, unsound dietary habits or high alcohol consumption. According to the Göteborg Study, the consumption of both alcohol and tobacco greatly multiplied the risk of death from myocardial infarction compared to the position for non-smoking teetotallers.

## Preventing cardiovascular disease

Knowledge that the development of cardiovascular disease is ascribable to a considerable degree to the action of a number of different risk factors, alone or in concert has stimulated energetic attempts to reduce the incidence of these disorders by means of various preventive or interventive measures. Let me merely mention a few of these studies. They have served as the foundation of our present view of the therapeutic strategies deemed reasonable on the basis of current knowledge.

From 1976 to 1980, a study of more than 15 000 men from 40 to 49 years of age was performed in Oslo. A high-risk group, with respect to cholesterol values, was selected from this group. Eighty percent were smokers. The participants were subdivided at random into two groups, one receiving individual, intensive counseling on diet and the risks of smoking. The other group, a control group, received no counseling. The evaluation performed after 5 years showed that both the blood cholesterol values and the incidence of smoking dropped in both groups, although to a significantly greater degree in the treatment group. The impact on heart attack morbidity and sudden death was striking. There was a 47% drop in the treatment group, a value significantly different from the control group's incidence.

In the American MRFIT Study, nearly 13 000 men from 35 to 57 years were selected from a screening population of more than 360 000 men. They were all high-risk individuals with respect to cholesterol, smoking and high blood pressure. The selected group was divided at random into an intervention group and a control group. The former group was treated intensively with dietary counseling, support for anti-smoking and medicinal treatment of hypertension. Results, found at the end of a 7-year period, were not particularly encouraging. The drop in total risk did indeed amount to 22%, but it did not produce any equivalent reduction in the incidence of mortality due to myocardial infarction, i.e. a drop of only 7%. This value did not differ significantly from the control group's incidence. The MRFIT Study is therefore continuing, but no results have yet been published from the study's latter period.

A multinational intervention study, in which Belgium, England, Italy and Poland participated, was conducted under the auspices of the W.H.O. from 1977 to 1983. This study concentrated on certain industrial sectors and utilized existing medical clinics. The study included more than 60 000 people from 40 to 59 years of age. Intervention consisted of information on existing risk factors and concrete counseling on diet, smoking, physical activity and weight reduction. The results of this collective study were modest. It recorded a 4% decline in myocardial infarction. However, there were some differences between the participating countries. In Belgium, where the most staff was used and individual counseling was most intensive, a statistically significant decline was achieved in both myocardial infarction (25%) and total mortality (18%). This was mainly ascribed to a reduction in blood fats and tobacco consumption. However, these effects were limited to people who had displayed ECG changes during exercise at the start of the study.

The primary prevention Göteborg Study published its final report in 1986 when the three groups, each comprising 10 000 people who had been 47 and 55 years of age at the start, had been followed for 10-12 years. A drop in blood pressure, blood cholesterol level and cigarette consumption was found both in the intervention group and in the two control groups. However, no significant inter-group difference was found in these respects. Nor was there any difference in respect to the number of people who had become ill or died because of heart attacks or in total mortality.

The results of these comprehensive intervention studies are not unequivocal and therefore difficult to interpret. However, it is obvious that the risk factors "smoking" and "blood fats" are variables susceptible to change and that anti-smoking counseling and advice on a sound diet have a good effect. Throughout the entire western world, except in southern Europe, we are witnessing a decline in tobacco consumption. Reducing cholesterol levels in both intervention groups and control groups has also proved to be possible.

But achieving a significant effect on morbidity and mortality due to myocardial infarction, the ultimate objective of all studies, has been more difficult. Only the Oslo Study and parts of the W.H.O. study achieved any significant results in these respects. These depressing findings probably mean that cardiovascular disease is multifactorial to a large degree and that energetic, wide-ranging measures will be needed in order to reduce it. It is also obvious that large groups of people must be followed for a very long period of time before the effect of prevention and intervention measures can be ascertained in terms of reduced illness and death due to cardiovascular disease. The fact that many studies, including the one in Göteborg, have as yet failed to achieve positive results in this respect, despite a clear decline in important risks, must not engender a defeatist attitude regarding the prospects of preventive measures. The Oslo Study and part of the W.H.O. Study show that positive results can indeed be achieved if a major effort is made.

However, the limited results achieved hitherto by the concentration on smoking, diet and blood pressure suggest that psychosocial factors are of predominant importance to morbidity and mortality due to cardiovascular disease. When the situation is viewed as a whole, socially disadvantaged people and people with poor education and poor personal finances are the severely afflicted categories and simultaneously least accessible for prevention and treatment. People interested in their health – or who have relatives with that interest – are afflicted to a lesser degree. So the expenditure of resources should concentrate on the socially disadvantaged. A health-conscious way of life – encompassing moderate eating habits with a well-balanced diet, physical activity, no tobacco and moderate use of alcohol – does contribute to a decline in cardiovascular disease and, when such disease does occur, does mitigate its manifestations.

My thanks to Lars Werkö for valuable comments on this paper.

## David Magnusson

# Individual development in a longitudinal perspective

The overall objective of the research program presented here is to study the way individual characteristics and environmental factors – individually and interacting with one another – govern a person's development from childhood to adulthood and that person's life circumstances as an adult. Here, the study concentrates on the developmental background to somatic and mental health in adulthood, including the development process underlying alcohol problems, crime and mental problems in adulthood. In view of the important role played by education and work in the development process and in the lives of adults, the study devotes special attention to these factors.

Research with the stated general objective has traditionally focused on factors able to improve the ability to predict the individuals likely to have adaptation problems as adults (develop alcohol problems, commit crimes and/or suffer mental difficulties). The present research program does not adopt this approach. Instead, it concentrates on understanding and explaining mechanisms underlying the development process in which individual and environmental factors interact and contribute to the way an individual thinks, feels and acts as an adult.

One common finding of research in this problem field is that people who grew up in certain environments run a greater risk of developing along negative lines, e.g. towards alcohol abuse or criminality, than people from other environments. One important, although frequently overlooked, circumstance is that most of the people from a particular environment do not become criminals or abusers of alcohol. In fact, many of the people who make constructive, highly useful contributions to society are from the very environments believed to predistine to social maladjustment. One central aim of the present research program is to study the individual and environmental factors that – singly and/or in combination with one another – enable most people to overcome adverse external circumstances and develop in a manner benefitting both the individual and society.

## Theoretical perspective

Our theoretical perspective and its impact on the planning and implementation of the research program was described in detail in Magnusson (1988; also see Magnusson and Allen 1983). The central aspects of the program can be summarized as follows:

1. An interactionistic view as the starting point for theory formation and problem analysis. An interactionistic view emphasizes a holistic perspective on individual development as a process characterized by continuous, reciprocal interplay between an individual and her/his environment. This view has far-reaching theoretical, research strategic and methodological consequences.
2. The proximity to important developmental processes and phenomena in real life. At every stage in the study of individual development, our feeling was that addressing central aspects of an individual's development is more important than limiting the investigation to data that fit a particular theory.

These general principles had an impact on planning and implementation in three respects: a) on the choice of research strategy, b) on the content of research in the form of the studied variables and c) the methods used in the processing of data.

a) The first important consequence of this theoretical view is that important aspects of an individual's development cannot be studied except by a follow-up of the individual over a long period of time, i.e. in a longitudinal study. Traditional cross-sectional research has a limited utility and often leads to results that are both pointless and even erroneous, although they may be statistically significant on a very high level. This can be illustrated with models utilizing data from biological variables that have the advantage in this context of being investigatable with objective measures (see Magnusson 1985).

Empirical results from the research program that underline the importance of longitudinal studies of central problems will be described below.

To avoid erroneous conclusions about central aspects in development, the same people must be followed up, sometimes for a very long time. All the data must be for the same individuals because of the highly complex, often non-linear interplay prevailing among individual factors, factors active in the constant interplay process in which people are always involved. This has previously been discussed by e.g. Loevinger (1966), Magnusson (1985) and, recently, by Hinde and Dennis (1986). It should be emphasized that the need for long-term study of the same individuals cannot be side-stepped by the study of the same factors using successive, overlapping cohorts (see Magnusson 1988).

b) The theoretical, interactionistic frame of reference leads to the conclusion that we need to investigate a broad spectrum of variables that simultaneously cover psychological and bio-logical aspects of the way individuals function and important aspects of the social and material environments in which they grow up and live. The importance of not limiting the study to single aspects of development in isolation from the totality is emphasized by results from the present project. Empirical studies clearly show how such analyses can lead to completely erroneous conclusions on the role of individual variables, even when conclusions are supported by strongly significant results (Magnusson and Bergman 1988).

The interactionistic theory also has a definite impact on the selection of the most important individual development aspects that should be studied on each occasion. This selection, like the design of adequate and effective methods for data acquisition, constituted an important part of preparations prior to each phase of intra-project planning. For each age group, data acquisition concentrated on the areas of individual development that, on the basis of experience and psychological knowledge, could be regarded as having particular relevance in a developmental perspective.

c) An important consequence of the theoretical view governing the project's planning and implementation concerned the analyses of data as the basis for conclusions on the developmental process. Traditional developmental psychology research is dominated by the study of variables: individual variables or a set of variables are at the center of research. Variable-oriented research is naturally important and necessary. But it has obvious limitations.

Data processing according to this tradition has mainly concentrated on the use of linear regression models, including factor analysis, for the study of inter-variable relationships and analysis of variance for the study of cause-effect relationships. Two circumstances limit the usefulness of regression analysis models in the present context: the presence of non-linear, complex interactions, often high order, and the presence of inter-individual differences in the rate of maturation. The latter, not the least, could lead to difficult, methodological complications (Magnusson 1985).

One consequence of these circumstances is that the linear regression analysis methods employed in variable-oriented studies must be supplemented with various methods for classifying individuals on the basis of patterns of relevant factors for individual-oriented studies. This approach was empirically applied at an early stage in a study of norms and norm violations (Magnusson, Dunér and Zetterblom 1975). An extensive amount of methodological effort has been made in the project in order to refine usable techniques for this purpose (see Bergman 1987, 1988, Bergman and Magnusson 1984a, b). A number of studies illustrating the merit of a pattern approach and limitations in the traditional variable-oriented approach have previously been reported (Andersson, Bergman and Magnusson 1989, Magnusson 1988, Magnusson and Bergman 1988, in press). Method development and the utilization of methods for pattern analysis have been important features of our study of the development process.

## Data

Complete reports on the planning and implementation of data acquisition have previously been submitted in Magnusson (1981, 1988), Magnusson and Dunér (1981) and Magnusson, Dunér and Zetterblom (1975). The most important source of information was the participants themselves, of course. More than 95% of the information was obtained directly from them. This information was collected in total studies in which all subjects participated and in random studies in which group investigation methods could not be used. Other sources were parents, teachers, friends and public records. Parents supplied important information in a number of questionnaire studies during the school period. Ninety-eight percent of the parents submitted replies to the first questionnaire, distributed when subjects in the main group were about 10 years of age. Teachers collaborated actively during data acquisition and contributed various information on their students during the school period.

On the first data acquisition occasion in 1965, three grades of school children participated. Each school grade comprised about 1 100 children. The oldest of these students were only studied once, in the 8th grade.

The *main* group consisted of the students who were attending the 3rd grade of a school in a town in southern Sweden. Most of these students were therefore about 10 years old at the time of the first study. These students, plus subsequently added students (those who had moved to the town) in the same age cohort, were followed with data collected on them until they reached adulthood. The main group now includes a total of about 1 400 individuals.

Most of the data from the school period were collected with methods that can be used for group administration: tests, inventories, ratings etc. When certain problems were involved, data were obtained with more intensive methods: interviews, observations, individual tests, experiments etc. These data were collected for individuals selected at random as being representative of the main group or who shared some important trait. One such group that was the subject of especially intensive study consisted of children who had early been isolated from or bullied by other children.

Data were collected from the main group during their school years up through the 12th grade. The follow-up of the main group in adulthood comprised a questionnaire study on education, employment, leisure time, family life, social network and alcohol habits, an intensive study of a random sample of 200 subjects who had also been the subject of intensive study at the age of 12-13, and the collection of data from public records on alcohol misdemeanors, crime and psychiatric care. The latter data only cover a very small amount of the total information, i.e. 1-2%. Participants were informed about this data collection. The intensive study comprised an interview with more in-depth examination of the issues illuminated in the questionnaire study, a battery of tests of cognitive functions and field dependency, several personality inventories and a medical examination.

As a result of the selected theoretical perspective, tests of traditional psychological characteristics (intelligence, school performance, interests, educational ambitions, factual behavior etc.) were an important feature in the study of individual factors. These tests were supplemented with data obtained on biological factors, i.e. the hormonal response to stress, physical performance and electrophysiological activity in the brain (measured with EEG). Special interest was also devoted to social relationships and social contact networks.

As far as environment is concerned, social ecological studies mapped the physical environment in school, in leisure time, on the route to and from school etc. for each child. The most important environmental data concerned the family. The traditional measures of socioeconomic conditions (primarily finances and parental education) were supplemented with data shedding light on what could be called the "family climate" (relationships, norms, joint activities etc.).

The group of students who were 13 at the time of the initial data acquisition, designated the *pilot* group, were followed up throughout their school careers up to adulthood. The data collected for this group during the school years concern cognitive and social development, interests and attitudes, norms and norm formation and self-reported crimes and alcohol habits during the teen years. The data for this group also cover certain environmental factors. One essential aspect of the data for this group covers the educational and occupational choice process. This process was also the main subject of a follow-up performed when the subjects were 23 years of age.

## Formal and ethical aspects

A research program of this kind raises a number of questions concerning formal and ethical aspects in respect to the collection and storage of data.

*Information to and consultation with the involved parties.* Throughout the entire project, special effort was made to inform and discuss matters with all involved parties (the participants, school authorities, parents, the Data Inspection Board etc.) well in advance of data acquisition. This collaboration has worked smoothly to date.

To ensure that everyone (students, parents, the school and the public) was well-informed about the study, each collection of data in schools was performed in the following manner. Before the research program commenced, a committee was formed comprising the chairperson of the Parent-Teacher Association, the senior school medical officer, the school psychologist, three teacher representatives, one headmaster-mistress, the school director, the school board's chairperson, a representative of the National Board of Education and the scientific leader in charge of the project. Prior to each study, every feature in the material was discussed and approved by the committee before anything was printed or distributed. The parents were informed at the time they were asked to fill in questionnaires and at a general information meeting. Background information to parents described the purpose of the study and indicated, among other things, the wish to follow the students even after they had completed school. The reference group emphasized the importance of this feature. Data acquisition in the schools was performed by special project representatives. During data acquisition in the classes, students had an opportunity to submit comments. Students who did not wish to answer any questions were not forced to do so. Before the project started, we contacted the editors of the local newspapers and kept them supplied with extensive information throughout the school period. During each data collection, blank copies of the material (tests, questionnaires etc.) distributed to students, parents and the schools were sent to the newspapers.

After participating in the study during their school years, subjects were sent a questionnaire when they were 26-27 years of age. The questionnaire concerned their lives as adults. They were advised that participation was voluntary and that the collected information would be subjected to data processing. A folder, summarizing the results of the previous studies, accompanied the questionnaire. After data acquisition, some of the most important findings were summarized in a booklet sent to all the subjects.

*Data storage and processing.* Right from the start of the project, a great deal of effort was devoted to the storage and checking of data. All information on individuals was immediately coded, making it impossible for anyone without access to the code key to identify a particular subject. All processing comprising information from public records is on unidentifiable files and performed by project staff according to plans reported and reviewed in joint discussions. No results for individual subjects have ever been released, only results for groups of subjects, so no single subject can ever be identified. Data are stored in safes in a room with a burglar alarm.

*Ethical review of the program.* In the spring of 1986, the Committee on Ethics of the Council for Research in the Humanities and Social Sciences was asked to review a number of longitudinal research projects in the social sciences. This scrutiny resulted in a very favorable report on our research project. Information to subjects and the processing of data were described as "exemplary".

## Some results

The most important results of a longitudinal project of the kind described here and comprising development from childhood to adulthood are not available until after a long time. Important issues can be considered and the material's potential utilized only when subject information is available from childhood to adulthood. This means that we have only been able to begin addressing the overriding issues in recent years. In the interim, a considerable number of cross-sectional sub-studies (when adequate) and longitudinal sub-studies with a shorter time span were conducted. The scope of this work is reflected in the number of doctoral theses (5), licentiate theses (13), psychology degrees and the equivalent (57), articles in international journals (34), chapters contributed to printed anthologies (18), published symposium contributions (17) etc.

One important form for reporting the research program's sub-studies has been a series of volumes published by Erlbaum Associates in the U.S. The first of these volumes presents the underlying, theoretical approach, the planning and the implementation of data acquisition plus four examples of studies in which data were used for elucidating central issues (Magnusson 1988). A second volume was recently published (Stattin and Magnusson 1990). A third volume is in press (Gustafson and Magnusson 1991).

*Biological maturation and social development in girls.* One central sub-project concerned the interesting role played by biological maturation in the social development, family formation, education and the occupational lives of girls (Magnusson, Stattin and Allen 1985, 1986). A detailed presentation of this project can be found in the second volume of the project series (Stattin and Magnusson 1990).

Definite differences were found between girls whose biological maturation was early (early-maturing) and late (late-maturing) in respect to various kinds of social behavior in early adolescence. This concerned various types of problem behavior in the home environment (running away, ignoring parental bans etc.), in school (truancy, cheating) and in leisure life (using marijuana and alcohol, shoplifting, hanging around town). Early-maturing girls had cheated, been truants, gotten drunk, tried marijuana etc. far more often than late-maturing girls. At the age of 15, 35% of the early-maturing girls had been drunk on multiple occasions, whereas this was only the case for 6% of the late-maturing girls. In respect to parental relationships and contacts with teachers, conflict-filled contacts with adults were far more common in the early-maturing girls. The early-maturing girls were also less interested in school and less interested in any long, future education.

A detailed analysis of the background to the higher incidence of what could be referred to as a "norm violation" (in relation to a chronological age norm) showed that the differences between girls whose maturity is early and girls whose maturity is late could be explained in terms of the prevailing kind of peer contacts and image of self. Early-maturing girls, more often than other girls, have peers who, like themselves, are more mature than chronological contemporaries. They also mix more frequently with older peers of the opposite sex and with peers who have left school and taken jobs. They also establish heterosexual contacts earlier. In this circle of "advanced" peers, the early-maturing girls were exposed to earlier adaptation to adult behavior than biologically less mature girls of the same age. The contrary applies to late-maturing girls.

The differences in social behavior and social relationships that could be traced between early-maturing and late-maturing girls were concentrated in early adolescence and had evened out considerably by the end of the teen years. In adulthood, there were very few differences in respect to social adaptation and social relationships. So there was no difference between early-maturing and late-maturing girls regarding e.g. self-reported alcohol consumption or registered alcohol abuse in adulthood. This result illustrates the importance of following the same individuals over a long period of time, i.e. to conduct longitudinal research, in order to avoid erroneous conclusions and action. Instead of issuing alarming reports to the parents of early-maturing girls and discussing measures for reducing the risk of adverse future developments, we were able to calm anxious parents and note that problems occurring in this group of girls are no more serious than in other groups when a long view is taken.

Thus, there is a group of early-maturing girls who deviate socially from other girls over a limited period of time. From a biological point of view, these short-term problems are understandable. In biological respects, the early-maturing girls resembled chronologically older groups of teenagers, and their social behavior was not particularly deviant in relation to these groups. Conduct interpreted as problem or deviant behavior, viewed in the light of what is normal for a particular chronological age, can be regarded, when viewed from a biological point of view, nothing more than a change in behavior towards normative patterns in a group of older companions. This change is supported by a self-image of more intensely perceived maturity and a willingness to adopt behavior indicative of a more mature status.

Against this background, it is interesting to note that there were long-term consequences in other areas. The early-maturing girls entered pair-relationships earlier, married earlier, had children earlier and entered the labor market before their late-maturing contemporaries. Major differences in the level of education in adulthood were found. At the age of 26, only 28% of the early-maturing girls had completed three years of upper secondary school, whereas this was the case for 60% of the late-maturing girls. This difference persisted after adjustments for differences in intelligence and domestic background. The circumstance that differences in the level of education could be traced to the influence of maturity during a few teenage years is surprising. But without a longitudinal approach, these tendencies would not have been noticed.

*Educational and occupational careers of girls.* A third volume in the project series, "Female life careers" (Gustafson and Magnusson 1991), now in press, describes a study of the individual and environmental factors in the development of girls that are related to their subsequent development in terms of education and occupation. Central issues are: a) How does the ability of girls, their faith in their own capability and their adaptation to educational requirements change over time? b) What role do the various home environment factors play in education and the development of value systems in this respect? c) What is the long-term relationship between the school performance of girls and their choice of educational option during the school years, on the one hand, and the results of this choice, on the other hand?

The problems were illuminated through the study of development in terms of *patterns* of the variables assumed to be of importance. Whereas certain groups of people display highly stable patterns over time, the patterns of other people change when educational requirements change, then often according to parental expectations. These changes in patterns were studied in the light of theoretical expectations. This way of using theory for predicting results for individuals makes important contributions to research in this field. In addition to the pattern studies, the possible effect of single factors, such as relationships with parents, were studied in order to increase our understanding of the way differences arise between girls with the same intellectual prerequisites in respect to educational aspirations and actual educational careers.

Both these kinds of studies describe the importance of parental value systems in respect to the educational aspirations of daughters and faith in the ability of daughters to move on to further education. One central finding here is that the parental value system concerning education, not the family's socioeconomic standard, is the most potent factor in the home environment. Parental values in respect to the future education of their daughters, are naturally influenced by the girls' actual performance in school. Still, all the girls who had achieved the highest level of education and occupation as adults (26 years of age) came from families in which parents had rated education highest, irrespective of the families' socioeconomic position.

*Social development in boys.* One important aspect of the research program concerned the study of the developmental process leading to later social problems as manifested in criminality, alcohol problems etc. A study of the developmental causes of defective adaptation in adulthood is important for several reasons. Knowledge of this process is needed as input in the design of adequate aid to and treatment of people already engulfed by an adverse developmental process. Of even greater importance is knowledge as a basis for devising home, educational and occupational environments capable of counteracting negative developments.

Earlier research in this field has largely concentrated on the study of single, personal factors manifested at an early stage (such as aggressiveness, hyperactivity, poor performance in relation to intellectual ability) and relationships in the home environment (e.g. alcohol problems, poor parental education, poor finances, divorce, constant moving to new places) and the correlation between these factors and criminality, alcohol problems etc. in adulthood. Frequent reports of findings in this area have often led to premature conclusions about the importance of single factors to future development and have occasionally served as the basis of serious proposals for various countermeasures.

One of the consequences of a theoretical, holistic view of the individual's way of functioning, the starting point in the planning of our research program, is, as previously noted, that the study of single aspects of a person's way of functioning, disconnected from the person's total functioning, has limited explanatory value. What characterizes a person is her/his pattern of factors. Can, in this light, the many pair-wise correlations found between single, person-related factors, or factors in the early environment, and subsequent criminality and alcohol problems be explained by the circumstance that a limited number of young people are characterized by several or all of these factors? A series of studies were performed in order to shed light on this general question. The studies primarily concerned the social development of boys.

Table 1 presents the results of the grouping of 13-year old boys in terms of their pattern of values on a 0-3 scale for six factors for which single, statistically significant correlations with subsequent criminality and alcohol problems have been reported in different contexts.

*Table 1 Grouping of 13-year old boys*

Mean values for individual variables

| Pattern | N | Aggres-siveness | Motor rest-lessness | Poor concen-tration | Poor school interest | Under-achieve-ment | Poor peer relations |
|---|---|---|---|---|---|---|---|
| 1 | 296 | — | — | — | — | — | — |
| 2 | 23 | — | — | — | — | — | 2.4 |
| 3 | 40 | — | — | — | — | 2.6 | — |
| 4 | 61 | 1.3 | 1.4 | — | — | — | — |
| 5 | 41 | — | 1.5 | 2.3 | 1.9 | — | — |
| 6 | 12 | 1.7 | 1.8 | 2.3 | 1.9 | 2.6 | — |
| 7 | 37 | 2.3 | 2.3 | 1.9 | 1.3 | — | — |
| 8 | 22 | 2.2 | 2.7 | 2.6 | 2.4 | — | 1.9 |

Note: – means that the mean value is less than 1.0 on a scale with the values 0, 1, 2 3.

The table shows how each of the 13-year old boys was assigned to one of eight groups, each group characterized by a particular pattern. Several interesting conclusions can be drawn from this table.

It is easy to see that the majority of the boys (296) at 13 years of age fall into a category that does not contain any indicator of behavioral problems. Categories 4-8 are characterized by multidimensional patterns of adaptation problems of varying severity. Only two of the eight groups have a single factor as a characteristic, viz. the groups characterized by poor relationships with peers and underachievement respectively. But it must also be noted that a number of boys with one of these characteristics were not in these groups but in other groups with other factors. This means that we can e.g. identify two groups of boys with poor relationships with friends: one group with this problem alone and one group in which this problem is part of a broader, overriding pattern of behavior. This example clearly illustrates the weakness in treating individual factors as nomothetic variables with the same significance for different individuals, irrespective of the constellation of factors in which they occur.

Table 2 shows the relationship between membership in one of the groups listed in Table 1 for 13 year old boys, on the one hand, and the occurrence in public records on crimes or alcohol problems, on the other hand.

Statistical testing of the results listed in Table 2 shows that only in categories 7 and 8, i.e. boys who as 13-year olds displayed a multidimensional pattern of severe behavioral problems, was the number of boys who as adults were listed in public records for crimes and alcohol problems higher than the figure that could be expected according to a random model. About half of the boys who belonged to category 7 and 8 at the age of 13 are listed in records on crime and somewhat more than one-third of the boys in these categories are listed in records on alcohol problems.

We can also see that the boys who in their school years were in the category characterized by only one indicator of behavioral problems (2 and 3) did not deviate in a significant way from boys who lacked any such indicator (1).

This information shows how statistically significant correlations found between single, early indicators of behavioral problems and subsequent criminality or subsequent alcohol

Table 2. Correlation between development patterns at the age of 13 and registration in crime and alcohol records at 18-23 years of age

| Pattern at 13 | N | Criminality | Alcohol |
|---|---|---|---|
| 1. No problems | 296 | 13.6 | 7.7 |
| 2. Poor peer relations | 23 | 13.0 | 4.3 |
| 3. Underachievement | 40 | 10.0 | 12.5 |
| 4. Moderate aggressiveness and motor restlessness | 61 | 18.0 | 13.1 |
| 5. Poor concentration, poor interest in school | 41 | 30.0 | 27.5 |
| 6. Severe underachievement and poor concentration | 12 | 33.3 | 8.3 |
| 7. Hyperactivity and aggressiveness | 37 | 48.6 | 37.8 |
| 8. Severe, multidimensional problems | 22 | 50.0 | 36.4 |

problems can be explained by the circumstance that these indicators often appear together in one and the same person and that a small number of people account for the single correlations. One behavioral trait for which numerous studies have found a strong correlation with subsequent criminality and alcohol problems is early aggressiveness. This correlation was also found in the present material. When the two groups of boys displaying the heaviest, multidimensional loading (7 and 8) were deleted from the material, the correlation between early aggressiveness and subsequent criminality and alcohol problems dropped to a purely random level.

The research program is currently conducting certain preliminary studies of environmental factors and their role in the individual's development process. The starting point for these studies is that the general principle applying to individual factors also apply here. The role played by a single factor in the early environment (socioeconomic conditions, divorce etc.) depends on the context in which each such factor appears.

*Biological factors and criminality.* One of the important claims in the theory underlying the research program's planning and implementation is that individual development cannot be understood in important respects unless biological factors are included in the models. The merit of this claim has been documented in many of the program's studies. One such example was reported in the study of the rate of biological maturation in girls. Another example will be presented here (Magnusson 1987).

One factor important to an individual's psychological and biological function is the secretion of epinephrine. This takes place in the adrenal medulla, the inner part of the two adrenal glands above the kidneys, and is regulated to a large degree by the individual's perception and interpretation of the situations in which she/he finds her-himself. The interpretation of situations representing demands or threats normally induce an immediate increase in epinephrine output.

We were soon able to identify a significant correlation in 12-13-year old boys between behavioral problems in terms of aggressiveness/motor restlessness/concentration difficulties and low secretion of epinephrine, collected in two different situations in school, i.e. a normal lesson and an examination (Klinteberg and Magnusson 1989). A subsequent comparison of boys who had been registered for crime between the ages of 18 and 26 and other men in respect to epinephrine output at the age of 12-13 produced the results depicted in Figure 1.

Males subsequently registered for crime had a considerably lower epinephrine output at the age of 12-13 than other males. Other analyses disclosed an interesting interplay between epinephrine output, behavior and difficulties in concentration.

The traditional model for the interplay between psychological and biological factors presumes a one-sided cause-effect relationship in which biological factors are assumed to induce psychological effects. Biology comes first, and the individual's perceptions and behavior are the product of biological proces-

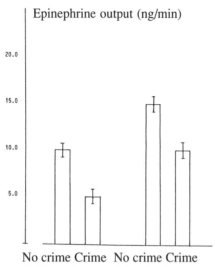

*Figure 1. Epinephrine output (measured in nanograms/min) at 13 years of age in two different situations in school (during an ordinary lesson and during an examination) for people registered for some crime from 18-24 years of age and for people who had not been registered for any crime at the same age.*

ses. One important feature of the interactionistic frame of reference is that the interplay is reciprocal. Psychological and biological factors interact in a continuous, reciprocal process. The traditional interpretation of the results shown in Figure 1 is that they are the product of a biologically inherited factor. An equally reasonable explanation according to interactionistic theory is that the low level of epinephrine in boys who commit crimes is due to derangement and inconsistency in the interplay between the child and the environment in which it learns to function at an early age. If epinephrine output is regulated by perceptions of what leads to reward or punishment, then the environment during infancy, when the individual's functional patterns are established, must operate in a consistent manner, with respect to rules and norms for social behavior, with reward and punishment recurring in a systematic manner, for the individual to function "correctly" in the environment and react adequately as well as physiologically. The importance of this point has also been found in other studies in and outside the research program.

## Research collaboration

Continuous collaboration with scientists in Sweden and abroad is a feature of the program. The planning and implementation of data acquisition could not have been carried out so successfully without the collaboration of a number of scientists from other disciplines. This collaboration is continuing in the analysis of the main issues. Collaboration with other scientists is encompassing foreign scientists to an increasing degree. And visits to the research program by foreign scientists are on the increase. The scientists stay for varying periods of time, participate in the work and/or study the methodology employed. To an increasing extent in recent years, colleagues in the research program are also being invited to present their results and methods at international forums.

## Longitudinal research in perspective

An interactionistic, holistic view of the way individuals develop and function leads to the conclusion that the reciprocal, continuous interaction of intra-individual and extra-individual factors characterizing individual development cannot be successfully studied unless the same individuals are studied in a broad perspective over a long period of time. The validity of this conclusion has been well-confirmed by empirical research. If the starting point for research is an analysis of the phenomena to be studied, this conclusion is hardly far-fetched or advanced. With this starting point it is actually surprising that cross-sectional studies, with the limitations inherent in them and the risks for misleading results and ensuing erroneous interpretations about development processes, have predominated so long.

A review of the research strategy used in other disciplines when the object of study can be characterized as multidetermined, stochastic processes similar to those prevailing in individual development, might prove to be interesting. Any historian who claimed to understand historical developments in Europe at a given time merely by conducting a cross-sectional study with the aid of information from daily newspapers on a given day and with the aid of means and standard deviations for various aspects of historical events would not be taken seriously but become a justified object of derision. A meteorologist who attempted to understand meteorological processes by measuring temperature, wind velocity, relative humidity and other aspects of weather at various locations in Sweden on a given day with the aid of means and standard deviations would probably trigger the same reaction. Cross-sectional studies are obviously important to research on the developmental process in individuals. But comparisons with other research fields illustrate the necessity of supplementing these studies with systematic, longterm, longitudinal studies to a far greater extent than hitherto. For future research to be able to contribute meaningful knowledge on factors governing an individual's development and the way this process operates, the increasing pursuit of such research within the framework of longitudinal research strategy is therefore of central importance.

International awareness of this need has grown rapidly. When the European Science Foundation, after an initiative by Europe's ministers of research, started a series of scientific networks in 1985 as one of its most important tasks, the "European Network on Longitudinal Studies on Individual Development" was the first of a large number of proposals to be accepted and implemented.

In view of the importance of longitudinal research, one

might well ask why more longitudinal studies are not conducted. One important reason is obviously the special demands such projects make on planning and implementation, administrative ability, endurance and cooperativeness. Another reason concerns the reward system.

Generally speaking, rewards in the form of academic merit, such as results attained, are slow to appear and uncertain. The effort involved in longitudinal research is considerable and the risk of failure often very considerable. An error in experimental work is always unpleasant, of course, but can often be "repaired" relatively fast. But an error in a longitudinal project may result in the waste of years of work, errors that are often irreparable.

Moreover, difficulties in finding the requisite, continuous financing probably make many scientists reluctant to conduct longitudinal research. This leads to special problems in longitudinal research of the kind discussed here (problem-oriented research) in comparison to cross-sectional research for two reasons. Firstly, continuous financing is essential. An important prerequisite for the implementation of the longitudinal program presented here has been the continuous financial support by the Foundation. Suspending and resuming a project after a time is only possible in exceptional cases. In any event, the process can seldom be governed by the availability of funding without an adverse impact on results. Secondly, when grant-giving authorities evaluate the costs of different research projects, they tend to accumulate the cost of longitudinal projects in a way that differs from their approach to other types of research in almost every instance. A longitudinal project's need for continuity is so obvious that there is virtually no way to avoid an accumulation of project costs for the period in which the project is conducted. It will then be found that most longitudinal projects, apart from the yield they deliver in longitudinal elucidation of psychological development, generate spinoff effects in the form of cross-sectional studies that would otherwise have cost considerable sums to perform. Another spinoff effect is the possibility of quickly carrying out studies of new problems arising and whose meaningful treatment requires longitudinal data.

Longitudinal research is based on the circumstance that data for the same individuals are collected over time, occasionally over a long period of time. If this vital research is to continue contributing important knowledge on central issues of importance to society, it must have an opportunity to collect, store and utilize relevant data. Technical solutions now make it possible to store and use data in a way in which information is shielded from unauthorized access and from falling into unauthorized hands.

*Torsten Husén*

# Swedish education in an international perspective

## Background

James B. Conant, professor of chemistry at Harvard and its president for many years, has remarked that scientific research is cumulative to a great degree (Conant 1970). Every new study in a particular field attempts to build on previous work. This is not the case to the same extent in the social sciences, he added. In these disciplines, new philosophies and paradigms gain advocacy more readily than in natural science (Husén 1989). And scholars then run the risk of speaking at cross-purposes. In this paper, I shall not discuss the validity of Conant's remarks but merely note that the research process is cumulative even in the social sciences, even though the nature of the cumulation may be different here than in natural sciences. A limited scope research project can grow into an extensive research program. This may, in turn, give rise to the establishment of a new scientific specialty that can be institutionalized and lead to interdisciplinary, international collaboration.

It is in the nature of scientific work that the scholar does not have any idea of what her/his work may lead to. Nor can she or he predict the impact of any new knowledge uncovered by this work. Despite the unpredictability and the seemingly random and erratic nature of this process, I would still like to use a physical metaphor in order to describe it: rings on the water. This phrase strikes me as being more adequate than "cumulative".

I will use the IEA project, a massive attempt to evaluate school systems in different countries on an inter-country basis and supported since 1967 by the Bank of Sweden Tercentenary Foundation, to exemplify the "rings on the water" process. Over the years, this international project, in which research institutions in initially a dozen countries participated, evolved into a wide-ranging program currently comprising more than 40 industrialized and developing countries. The history of the IEA illustrates the way an idea, an individual project, gave rise to new projects that jointly established a new research territory that, in turn, created new institutions (in addition to an international network of collaborating scholars) offering special graduate training and international training programs.

As noted above, the International Association for the Evaluation of Educational Achievement (IEA) received its first grant from the Foundation in 1967. From 1969 to 1989, the IEA had its headquarters in Stockholm at the Department of International Education established through a 1971 Riksdag ruling that expressly cited the Government bill on Swedish involvement in the IEA. The results of this original grant in 1967 will be the subject of my paper. However, some background first! This will not be without interest in clarifying the incentives giving rise to new research.

The initial IEA research should be viewed in the light of the international policy and educational policy situation prevailing around 1960. The Soviet Union's launching of its first Sputnik in 1957 evoked a violent reaction in the U.S. and triggered unbridled criticism of the American school system, of the high school in particular. The fact that the Americans seemed to have fallen behind in space technology was seen as a consequence of the inferior teaching of mathematics and science. Within the space of one year, enormous federal resources were allocated, through the National Defence Education Act, for improvements in teaching these subjects.

In 1960, the industrialized countries' Organization for Economic Co-operation and Development (OECD) began to regard education, technical education and research in particular, as the main factor underlying economic growth, a view propounded very explicitly and clearly in a background document, written for a 1961 OECD policy meeting in Washington, D.C. on the contribution of education to a country's ability to compete on an international basis. One of the document's authors was the Swedish economist Ingvar Svennilson. The same year, the OECD held a conference, in Kungälv hosted by the Swedish Government, on ability and educational opportunity and on making the most of talent.

These events revived interest in a specialty that had long led a languishing and unnoticeable existence: comparative education. The benefits countries could gain by comparing themselves to one another were pointed out. At about the same time, education research relevant to school problems experienced a breakthrough in a number of countries, the U.S. and Sweden in particular. With the support of the Foundation, I recently attempted to document the process in Sweden (Husén 1988). This research was expected to supply the knowledge needed for structural school reforms, e.g. in Sweden by means of the projects supported by the 1957 school commission. Educational research was also ultimately expected to lead to improved and more efficient teaching. As a consequence, not the least of the school commission's favorable evaluation of Swedish educational research, the National Board of Education established a special bureau in 1962 for R & D work on schools. Expectations regarding this research were high, sometimes even euphoric.

Thus, the IEA was established as an international research organization under these auspices. The object was to perform comparative evaluations of national school systems and to supply policy-makers and practitioners with the information required for improving schools. It all started in 1958 when a group of scholars met at the UNESCO Institute for Education in Hamburg in order to discuss evaluation in the school. This was then a new subject for researchers in education. Not even the word "evaluation" had begun to be commonly used in this context. The Hamburg meeting noted that sweeping comparisons were made of the quality of school systems in different countries without access to any empirical data or not even any cross-nationally accepted measurement instruments. So the participants agreed to conduct a feasibility study whose aim was to show whether or not it was possible to devise an international instrument for measuring achievement in countries with different languages and whose results could be computer-processed and analyzed according to a uniform procedure. The feasibility project was conducted from 1959 to 1961 employing a test with one hundred items covering reading comprehension, mathematics, science and geography. The target group was 13-year olds in the respective countries. Among other things, it was found that tests designated by psychologists as "culture-free", displayed much greater inter-country variance than carefully translated verbal tests.

The results of the exploratory study were encouraging. So in 1961, the participating scholars established an international collaborative association encompassing one research institution in each country. Mathematics was selected as the first subject for a full-scale, cross-national comparative study performed on strictly representative random samples of 13- and 18-year olds. The study was conducted from 1963 to 1965. Its findings were published in two volumes in 1967. A number of national reports were also published. It was found that on the average 13-year olds in Sweden and their American counterparts ranked at the bottom among industrial nations. For conservatives this was proof that the most recent Swedish school reform, the introduction of the comprehensive school system, had been a "failure". There were similar scapegoat reactions in the U.S. where doubts were raised about the way federal funds had been used for improving the teaching of mathematics and devising new curricula. But neither the structural reforms in Sweden, covering less than half of 13-year olds at the time, nor the new U.S. curricula that had not yet had time to produce any impact on schools and could therefore not be blamed for the poor results.

In 1967, the IEA started its Six Subject Survey covering science, reading comprehension, literature comprehension, civic knowledge and English and French as foreign languages. The project, supported by the Foundation, comprised 10-, 14- and 18-year olds in 20 countries. Analyses of curricula and the design of international tests were performed by international committees collaborating with national committees for each subject. Representative national random samples of the various school grades were tested in 1970 and 1971. The results were reported in nine volumes (one for each subject plus one method volume, one volume containing case studies of the participating countries and one summarizing volume, see Annotated Bibliography) published 1973-76. A large number of national reports were also published, in Sweden one for each of the investigated subjects in a series entitled "Svensk skola i internationell belysning" (The Swedish school in an international light). Prior to the 1973 and 1975 publications, the Swedish National Board of Education held a meeting for school journalists. This generated immense publicity, especially in 1973, and revitalized the debate on school policies. The study showed that Swedish 14-year olds performed on about the same level as their counterparts in other leading industrial countries. It was also found that the Swedish elite, the top 5% of the 18-19-year olds, held their own in competition with the corresponding elite in other countries. In other words, the opening up of the school system to the masses and offering them 10-12 year basic education did, indeed, lower average achievement compared to an elite system with relatively few students. But the high-performance elite in the mass-education system did not appear to be adversely affected by being taught with other more normal-achieving students. In the 1968 Swedish election campaign, the results of the IEA survey of mathematics were cited by opponents of the mass-education model adopted by the 1962 Riksdag as proof that the model did not work. But better Swedish results in science and reading comprehension led to abandonment of the rather sterile debate on standards that had been triggered by mathematics outcomes a few years earlier.

## Some results

With the limited space available, it would be inappropriate for me to attempt to describe even the main results of 25 years of studies. The main objective of these studies – and this should be underlined – was by no means to hold international knowledge olympics in subjects such as mathematics and science. However, the media sometimes depicted the IEA as the organizer of such contests. The aim of the organization's founding fathers was to seek explanations, on an international, comparative basis, for differences in student achievement between schools and national school systems by looking at differences in resources, curricula, teacher proficiency, teaching methods and, not the least, differences in home background, general cultural background and material standard. After 6-7 years of schooling, students in a typical developing country lag several years behind their counterparts in advanced industrial countries. But even with highly competent teachers the gap would still persist to a large degree because of the strong impact of home background.

With its surveys, the IEA, using multivariate statistical analysis, has sought to explain differences in achievements between students, schools and countries (cf. Härnqvist 1975). Three groups of factors were surveyed: social background, school resources and teaching methods. Social background consistently explained more than the other factors combined. This finding does not mean that schooling does not make any difference. It merely means that there must be a certain amount of balance between resources and methods in relation to the cultural and material standard typical of the society at large.

There were major cross-national differences in respect to the standing of the different subjects and space allotted in curricula and schedules. The IEA's survey of French as a foreign language was able to clarify the importance of the *time factor* on a comparative basis by relating the outcome of teaching, measured with standardized tests, to the number of study years and hours/week. Romania, where French was taught the most number of years and hours/week, displayed the highest average test score, whereas the U.S., only offering two years of French in high school, had the poorest average results. Sweden, with three years of study, was not much better than the U.S. The survey showed that a proficiency subject such as French demands a certain number lesson-hours a week for at least four years to produce acceptable proficiency. The performance of Swedish students in English illustrate this. In a comparison of ten countries in which English was studied as a foreign language, Swedish 14-year olds (whose curriculum includes many years of English) displayed better performance in all respects (reading and understanding, listening and understanding, writing and speaking) than their counterparts in other countries. Dutch students were in second place; like their Swedish counterparts, they also study English for relatively many years.

The IEA repeated the 1964 survey of mathematics in 1980 and its 1970 science survey in 1984. One issue then raised was whether student achievement in these subjects had improved or even declined over time. The results showed that Swedish 13-year olds in 1980 were on the same low level in mathematics as in 1964. But this represented a relative decline, since the level of achievement had risen in most of the other countries. This caused the Minister of Education to appoint a task force to study the problem and submit proposals on countermeasures. The task force found that the competence of teachers had declined considerably as a result of the 1967 teacher training reform when only a 2-year social studies *gymnasium* education was sufficient to qualify for admission to teacher training for the middle grades of the comprehensive school. The only mathematics many teachers on the lower levels of the compulsory comprehensive school knew was what they themselves had learned in comprehensive school. Three years of *gymnasium* are now a requirement for admission to Swedish training programs for comprehensive school teachers.

The traditional, conservative objection to structural educational reforms expanding access to formal education is that the change leads to a decline in standards, i.e. "more means worse"! Obviously, a reform that increases the number of admissions, e.g. from 10-20% to 80-90% of an age cohort in the case of the gymnasium, is bound to lower the *average* level, as the IEA surveys have shown. In the 1970 science survey, the graduating class at a German gymnasium with only 10% of the age cohort enrolled was way above the average for high school seniors in school systems covering about 80% of the same age cohort. But the interesting question is what happens to the *elite*, e.g. the top 5% of an age cohort. The IEA's initial surveys showed that elite graduates of secondary school in mass-education systems, as in the U.S. or Sweden, displayed about the level of achievement as their counterparts in highly selective school systems that only channel a minority into secondary school. In any total evaluation, it should be remembered that the former systems convey the remaining 95% to a higher education level than is the case in the latter system. So the conclusion is: "More does not necessarily mean worse". This statement has a number of educational policy implications.

IEA surveys of *sex differences* in school achievement and attitudes towards different subjects are interesting in the light of the debate on gender roles that has occurred in recent years, especially in the advanced industrialized nations. IEA analyses have mainly involved science subjects and mathematics. One of the IEA's foreign fellowship winners, Alison Kelley, analyzed

(1978) data from the 20 countries participating in the first science survey in 1970. Boys were superior to girls to varying degrees in all the countries and on all three age levels, i.e. 10, 14 and 18 years. But the differences were small or negligible in biology. They were much greater in chemistry and greatest in physics. They increased all the way from the age of 10 up to 18. The pattern was identical in all the countries, industrialized and developing, and within the social strata of the various countries.

However, drawing the conclusion on the basis of these studies that cultural and social factors do not play any role in the development of the differences unquestionably found would be premature. The second science survey, conducted in 1984 and more definitively reported this year (Keeves 1990) showed that sex differences declined from 1970 to 1984 and that attitudes to the subject were related to these differences. The fact that girls like biology better than physics is no coincidence. Another change taking place is that by the 1980's more girls were studying scientific subjects than was the case in 1970.

## Impact on school policy

Any description of the educational policy consequences of the IEA's Six Subject Survey in Sweden and other countries is beyond the scope of this paper. But I might merely mention that the survey did cause some ministries of education to order revisions of national curricula. I described this development in an article in a special issue of the *Comparative Education Review* (Husén 1987). It should be noted that the Swedish research team was asked to present the findings of the survey to the Board of the Foundation and the Royal Swedish Academy of Sciences before the results were published. As chairperson of the IEA and the leader of the Swedish part of the project, I was asked to brief the Minister of Education at the time. This was not the only time the results of the IEA's comparative surveys elicited action by a Government minister. When the results of the second international mathematics survey were published, disclosing terrible results for Swedish 13-year olds, the minister in charge appointed a task force, as mentioned above, to study conditions for mathematics teaching in Sweden.

The IEA surveys have contributed to the policy debate in various international bodies, such as the OECD and UNESCO, not merely in the participating countries. When the OECD decided at the beginning of the 1980's that quality should be given priority in school, it turned to the IEA for data on cross-national criteria for quality evaluations.

When the IEA's reports on the Six Subject Survey were published, the National Academy of Education in the U.S. decided to ask two prominent scholars, Alex Inkeles (1978) and Ellis Page, to review the series of nine volumes reporting on the survey. The *Comparative Education Review*, the leading journal in the field, has twice (1974 and 1987) devoted special issues to IEA surveys.

## Impact on graduate training and scholar exchanges

The activity that initially was a limited research project at the time the Foundation began providing support and whose Swedish section was based at the Stockholm School of Education was soon institutionalized by the establishment of a special chair and a department in international education at Stockholm University. This made it possible for Sweden to commence graduate training with the emphasis on problems in international education. Educational planning in developing countries, in collaboration with the Swedish International Development Agency, soon became an important part of the department's program. Courses were offered in comparative education and on education and development. The department's working language was English right from the start. As a result, a large number of foreign doctoral candidates enrolled in graduate programs. Two scholars who played important administrative and technical roles in the first IEA projects, Neville Postlethwaite and Douglas Pidgeon, both from England, took doctorates on IEA-related subjects even before the department was founded. A few years later, the former, after a number of years with UNESCO, was called to a chair in comparative education at Hamburg University.

In 1971, the Spencer Foundation awarded the IEA fellowships for 5 years for four scholars a year, two post-doctoral and two pre-doctoral. As a result, another half dozen guest scholars produced IEA-related doctoral dissertations. But Swedish doctoral students were also able to use the IEA's databank for interdisciplinary dissertations, such as a thesis on statistical models in multivariate analyses and a comparative study of equality in education. A third doctoral candidate examined a representative random sample of students in the IEA material, studied their choice of higher education and how this choice was related to social background and school achievements. He was able to show how a new elite sector emerged in a system in which an increasing number of people were continuing their education on increasingly higher levels.

In conjunction with the data processing of the Six Subject Survey, the IEA headquarters, where most of the work was performed, was able to extend invitations to a number of leading scholars for brief sojourns in Sweden. They contributed their thinking to the work and scrutinized ongoing analysis efforts. The sociologist James Coleman from Chicago contributed some ideas on multivariate analyses, as Swedish statisticians such as Herman Wold and K.G. Jöreskog also did. The psychologist Lee Cronbach from Stanford contributed ideas on the study of educational achievement. Harald Noah and Harry Passow worked on a series of comparative case studies from different participating countries. Their results were presented in a special volume.

Devising cross-nationally adequate – and valid – achievement tests was a significant research project in itself, covering curriculum analyses, studies of teaching procedures and the methods employed in testing of student competence. Before the field study and data collection from national random samples could be executed, more than two years had to be spent on the preparatory work that contributed an important spill-over effect. As a result of the cross-country experiences gained, in the summer of 1971 the IEA was able to hold a 6-week long international seminar in Gränna on curriculum development and evaluation. It was attended by 150 scholars from about 25 countries, mainly developing countries. The seminar was led by Benjamin Blom, one of the IEA's founding fathers, and coordinated by Neville Postlethwaite, the administrative head of IEA research. Scholars such as Robert Glaser and John Goodlad served as teachers at the seminar. Each country was represented by a team of 4-6 people. As a rule, they were attached to ministries or central public agencies. This meant that the seminar contributed to supplying the respective countries with staff able to take charge of curriculum development and the design of evaluations according to the IEA model.

The IEA also came to play a roll in the promotion of empirical, educational research by holding three summer seminars. The first seminar (held in English) was in Sweden, the second in German in the Federal Republic of Germany and the third in French in France.

At the time of writing, work on the report on the second international science survey is being concluded. This work is being led by a former doctoral candidate in Stockholm, John P. Keeves from Australia, who, after several years as the director of the Australian Council for Educational Research, is now working full-time on the second science project at Stockholm University. The results of this survey served as background material for the international symposium, "Science Education for the 21st Century" held by the Royal Swedish Academy of

Sciences in the beginning of June 1989 as a part of the commemoration of the Academy's 250th anniversary.

Thanks to its international dimension, the IEA has contributed to the development of other networks designed to promote
international collaboration. When the Pergamon Press decided
to publish the "International Encyclopedia of Education: Research and Studies" in 1980, they asked Neville Postlethwaite
and me, previously successive chairpersons of the IEA to serve
as Co-Editors-in-Chief. In recruiting editors and authors we
were able to fall back on the contact network created through the
IEA. After work on the encyclopedia had been completed, an
International Academy of Education was founded for the purpose of further promoting international collaboration in educational research. The IEA supplied the nucleus of this Academy's board of directors.

Educational research has an inherent tendency to be provincial, since its subjects, i.e. schools and teaching, are so intimately related to national cultures and traditions. International
collaboration in educational research does not merely offer a
broader perspective. It also contributes to a questioning of the
general validity of national experiences and research results.

## Some concluding reflections

The previous account tried to show how a project in the
educational field, viz. comparative studies in different countries
of student achievement in subjects such as mathematics and
native language, arose and evolved. Surveys of two subjects,
viz. mathematics and science, were made at intervals of quite a
few years, i.e. 16 years for mathematics and 14 years for
science. This permitted evaluations over time in and between
countries. Both the international and Swedish part of the Six
Subject Survey were generously supported by the Foundation.
In Sweden, this type of research was institutionalized, as pre-

viously noted, through the establishment of a special chair with a department of international education. In most countries, the results of the IEA's comparative surveys have had an impact on the school debate and educational policies.

Cross-country comparisons and analyses of the factors underlying differences in student achievements led to the next major project, also financed by the Foundation, viz. a comparative study of the way educational research and educational policy are related to one another in four countries: the Federal Republic of Germany, Great Britain, Sweden and the U.S. (Husén and Kogan 1984). The next step in the project series, also financed by the Foundation, was a historical study of the relationships between school reforms and educational research in Sweden 1944-62 (Husén 1988).

The two latter projects, especially the first, concentrated on macro level relationships between research and policy-making. Quite recently, I conducted a study of these relationships on the micro level: the way in which the individual scholar perceives her/his role in contacts with policy-makers and administrative decision makers and vice-versa. This study is largely based on interviews with leading representatives of both groups in the same countries as in the first study.

This summing up strikes me as exemplifying a manifestly cumulative feature of social science research, a cumulative process that does not primarily concern theory or method but perspective. This has successively expanded from classroom empiricism via educational policy to educational history. So the metaphor about rings on the water appears to me to be appropriate.

The evolution of my own research over the past 25 years, under the auspices of the Foundation, one project leading to another, has been affected both by a broadening of perspective and by a paradigm shift. Social science in the first two decades after World War II was influenced to a major degree by hard-nosed empiricism. The often undisputed, positivistic aim in psychological and educational research was to collect "hard" data that could be quantified and subjected to advanced statistical analysis. Not surprisingly, the survey method was developed by pollsters and industrial psychologists in the U.S. It was viewed as a "royal route" to valid knowledge about society. So when the IEA began its investigations at the beginning of the 1960's, it started, logically, with a survey project with an international dimension. Standardized achievement tests and questionnaires were already established as data collection instruments. At the time, the databank generated by the Six Subject Survey was the biggest ever arrayed in behavioral science research.

As I pointed out in another context (Husén 1979), the IEA scholars encountered interpretation problems to which the survey method is unable to contribute any valid answers. It does supply large amounts of correlative but no causal information. Why for example are Japanese children better at mathematics and science than Americans, despite far fewer material resources in their schools and much larger classes? What is the importance of the home as "social capital" in the acquisition of knowledge? Answers to such questions call for more qualitative research strategies.

The emergence and development of various research cultures is virtually virgin territory for social science research. An individual scholar – or a group of creative scholars – usually conducts research in an established field. Experience gained in the course of the research often leads to changes in theory and methods. Such results expand horizons and open up new areas. And problems that prove to be more complex than was initially believed may induce scholars to probe more deeply. New scholars enter the field the whole time and are often able to view research work with a fresh outlook and envisage new approaches.

Twenty-five years may seem like a brief period of time for the study of a subject such as the research culture in a country.

But in view of the expansive (or even turbulent) developments some social science disciplines have undergone during this quarter century, the period may have been long enough.

"Rings on the water" in regard to the research described here refers to the successive expansion of a program that was initially an empirical and theoretically and geographically limited task. The theoretical perspective now encompasses a scope far broader than the one studied with "hard data". Numerous countries, especially developing nations, have joined in the work. An activity that was initially a limited, academic specialty is now firmly established as a truly cross-national, institutionalized field of research.

*Kjell Härnqvist*

# Long-term effects
# of education

When we as adults think back to our education, both in school and later in life, one question often comes to mind: just how much do we remember of all the things we learned and once recalled well enough to pass tests and examinations? Many of us who studied German in secondary school can still, almost jokingly, recite the prepositions governing the dative or accusative cases. Whatever Latin we might still remember (if this was also one of our school subjects) enables us to recognize occasional words at degree-presentation ceremonies (held in Latin in Sweden). But ex-humanities students are unlikely to recall much secondary school physics or chemistry. Things are not quite that bad for all subjects, as a few hours of review study often show. But we do not need to delve so deeply into our educational pasts to discover the sketchy nature of our recollection of things once learned.

In contrast, most people have also made the observation that our ability to recall knowledge previously acquired, even casually, without intent and without any need to document learning, is fairly good. Psychology calls this "incidental learning", and this process has considerable power. We may even remember when and where we first encountered this information. A newer concept in psychology, "situated learning" (Brown, Collins and Duguid 1989), reflects the contextual aspects in much learning. Scientific support for this view has been obtained from social anthropology studies of knowledge acquisition in cultures with no formal education system.

## Neglected research field

This mildly paradoxical situation – the contrast between intentional and incidental learning – would appear to be a central issue in educational research, but judging by the literature, the scientific study of the enduring effects of education is still virgin territory. In a review conducted a dozen years ago (Härnqvist 1977), I found very few examples of such research and have recently confirmed that this is still the case (Härnqvist, in press).

The biggest study to date on the enduring effects of education was performed by the American sociologist Herbert Hyman and his colleagues (1975, 1979). The first investigation utilized data from replies to knowledge questions posed in American opinion polls. The results were compared for people with elementary school, high school with graduation and degrees from a college or university. In the highest educational group, an average of about 80% replied correctly. The figure for the lowest group was about 40%. Results for the high school group were about in the middle.

The magnitude of these differences was fairly stable for different birth cohorts, age groups and for men and women. It did not decline much when results were analyzed with subdivision into social categories. However, the study was unable to check the extent to which the different educational groups differed right from the start in respect to general intelligence or learning ability. So no distinction could ultimately be made between the effects of learning and the effects of selection in the educational system. All experience suggests that the latter exerts a very considerable effect.

The second study concerned values and attitudes in people with different educational backgrounds. Even here distinct differences were found which were indicative of broader, more liberal attitudes in moral and social issues in people with a better education. But the lack of control for the effects of selection remained.

The difficulties in achieving this control is probably the most important reason why research on the lasting effects of education is a neglected field. Very few databases are available with which scientists can follow people from their early school years to adulthood and conduct longitudinal studies on an individual basis. The position in Sweden is much better in this respect than in most other countries. This paper, like David Magnusson's elsewhere in this book, provides examples of this.

Another reason for the lack of long-term studies of educational effects is the difficulty in performing objective measurements in representative groups of adults of knowledge, skills and other potential indicators of educational results. However, there is one exception, i.e. the importance of the level of education to occupation and income has been studied with controls for social background and individual prerequisites.

## A model for educational effects

In conjunction with my literature review (Härnqvist 1977), I devised a schematic model which attempted to describe the interplay between learning and selection effects, initially inside and then outside the educational system up to adulthood.

The model started with the position immediately prior to the initial choice situation in school. At this starting point, students can be characterized with a number of variables, such as home background, educational opportunities available in their home towns, intelligence, school performance, interests and motivation – all factors of greater or lesser importance to the choice. This results in the first important channeling of students into different educational pathways and provides them thereafter with differing opportunities for learning. In each alternative, learning occurs which modifies the student's "characteristics". These are important, in turn, to the selection process leading to learning on the next level.

This process continues in a number of such channeling/ learning sequences, usually with more options for students with the best learning prerequisites at the early starting point. Sooner or later, people leave the educational system and are then "sifted" in varying ways, i.e. channeled into jobs offering differing opportunities for applying old knowledge and acquiring new, into social surroundings with differing values and cultural circumstances. Influence, apart from institutionalized pressures, is also constantly exerted simultaneously by family, friends, the media, leisure pursuits etc. The differences we can observe among adults of a given age in respect to knowledge, skills, work habits, interests, attitudes, values and, not the least, occupation and income are the collective result of this complex process lasting for many years.

"Unraveling" this kind of complexity through empirical studies and identifying differences ascribable to the educational system and to factors outside the system's influence is clearly a very difficult matter. But some rough contours are still discernible.

Initial differences in learning ability and differences between different home environments would appear to be beyond the reach of an educational system. But the system's highly hierarchical structure and demands made during the initial school years interact with these factors and affect the circumstances governing the first choice situation.

Learning in school must obviously be taken into account, but no clear distinction can be made between it and successive channeling processes within the system if an empirical study is unable to measure conditions prior to the start of each new stage.

A person's transition from the educational system and channeling into a particular social and occupational environment also represent a kind of educational effect, i.e. education as a "ticket" to various opportunities in adult life. Some theories in the economics of education ascribe greater power to this screening than to knowledge acquisition as such, thus, making it more important to occupational status and income. The entire educational system is then viewed as a test, i.e. a device for screening people for increasingly higher starting positions on the labor market (cf. Winkler 1987).

In contrast, learning in occupational and social contexts should not be included in the impact of formal education, but empirically separating them in the end point's differences between formal levels is obviously difficult.

## Attempt to measure the long-term effects of education

A model with the complexity I just described can lead the researcher in two directions. One could deter from empirical studies, since such studies can never be expected to elucidate all the relevant influences. But the model could also be perceived as an exciting challenge for a researcher, past the point of being concerned about career, provided that basic material is available which meets at least the most important model stipulations and that research-funding bodies are prepared to take a risk. The Bank of Sweden Tercentenary Foundation and the National Board of Universities and Colleges apparently felt that the idea was worth trying, so the LING (Long-term effects of education) Project was launched in 1980.

The longitudinal database available had been compiled at my initiative in the "Individualstatistik" (Individual statistics) project. In collaboration with Statistics Sweden, the project collected its basic data in 1961. The material comprised all the students in Sweden who were born on the 5th, 15th or 25th of some month in 1948. They were normally 6th graders in the Swedish compulsory school system. The project encompassed a total of 11 950 students, i.e. 10% of the 1948 birth cohort. Data from school records supplied information on the education and occupations of parents and on the students' school marks and results from standard, national examination in Swedish, English and mathematics. The students also took three intelligence tests and replied to questions on interests and occupational preferences and how they liked school.

The basic material and special follow-ups have been used in a large number of degree papers, licentiate theses, doctoral theses and journal articles. Some of the more important publications are listed in the References, including two major studies (Härnqvist 1968, Balke-Aurell 1982) which were close to the LING Project's objectives and which investigated the effect of education on changes in intelligence test scores between the ages of 13 and 18 (the latter tests taken in conjunction with mandatory military service and, thus, only by men).

The LING Project's follow-up was performed in 1980 by means of a questionnaire mailed to two-thirds of the basic sample, including all those born on the 15th. In 1982-83 personal interviews were held with about 500 of the participants in special sub-groups.

The postal questionnaire, to which 76% of the addressees responded, concerned the scope and contents of completed education, occupation, work conditions, leisure pursuits, social contact networks and confidence in personal capabilities in different fields. The interviews supplied additional information on some of these issues and also provided data for more objective measurement of verbal skills and ways of thinking. However, posing direct knowledge questions was not possible nor meaningful in any of the contexts. The study was mainly able to shed light on self-reported circumstances.

## Variables in the LING analysis

The model for empirical data analysis was devised so as to be in the closest possible conformity with the schematic model previously described. Path analysis according to LISREL (linear structural relations analysis, Jöreskog and Sörbom 1986) was the statistical method used. Different groups of variables were introduced in chronological order, beginning with the home and ending with self-ratings of capabilities in adulthood, i.e. with the following sequence of clusters summarizing no fewer than about 70 sub-variables or questions. The designations used in tables and diagrams were taken from a more technical report (Härnqvist 1989).

- *The home environment*, measured with two indices:
  (1) Education of mother and father and father's occupation (HOME1)
  (2) The mother's occupation and number of children in the family (HOME2).

- *The initial performance level* based on intelligence tests, achievement tests and marks in the 6th grade, summarized with three variables:
  (1) General level (GL)
  (2) Verbal and linguistic skill (V*)
  (3) Spatial visualization (S*, i.e. the ability to process visual information in three dimensions).

- *Plans prevailing in the 6th grade* (PLAN, i.e. for matriculation, total number of school years).

- *Educational level up to the age of 32* (EDUC), summarized on a scale from 1 (compulsory schooling only without any second foreign language) to 7 (college/university).

- *Working conditions* according to questions on work circumstances and the ability to influence work, summarized with two variables:
  (1) Unsupervised work (SELF-DIRECT)
  (2) Opportunities for advancement (ADVANCE).

- *Adult capabilities* as rated by the participants:
  (1) Various aspects of verbal and linguistic skills in Swedish and English
  (2) Various aspects of civic competence
  (3) Various aspects of practical skills.

In the statistical analysis, different groups of variables were related to one another in the cited sequence in such a way that they were allowed to influence variables at a later point in the model but not the converse (the technical terms for this kind of analysis is "recursive path analysis with latent variables").

In addition to these causal analyses, some questionnaire responses, including those on leisure pursuits, social contacts etc., were processed with more descriptive methods.

## Some results

The results reported here are based on a representative sample comprising persons born on the 15th of any month in 1948. The first task of the analysis was to combine information from the age of 13 so as to optimize the ability of this information to predict differences in the educational level attained in adulthood, in this instance at the age of 32. The results of this stage are illustrated in Figure 1. It refers to male subjects, but the results for women were virtually identical for every point.

The educational and occupational status of parents (HOME1) influenced the children's general level of achievement in the 6th grade (GL), their verbal skills (V*) and plans for non-compulsory education (PLAN). Via these factors, parental status also had an indirect influence on the children's educational level as adults (EDUC). The other home variable, reflecting a tradeoff between a maternal occupation and child-minding (HOME2), influenced performance in the 6th grade but even had a direct impact on the girls' educational level. On the other

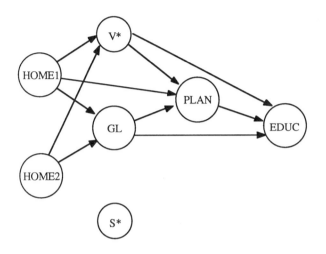

*Figure 1. Path model for background at 13 years and educational level attained at 32 years.*

hand, verbal skills had an indirect influence only on the educational level attained by women. Spatial visualization skill (S*), in contrast to verbal skill, displayed no correlation with other variables in this part of the model.

With factors jointly weighed in this manner, information from the 6th grade was powerfully predictive in respect to the educational level attained in adulthood. It "explained" almost 60% of the variance in the "educational level" variable. Expressed in terms of multiple correlations, it amounted to .77 for men and .76 for women, uncommonly high values for a prediction covering a period of 19 years.

Up to this point, the results showed that we had a powerful control for the prediction of student attainments in passing through the educational system, and this was the main object of this stage, not to arrive at a more subtle picture of the relative importance of different aspects of this information. When extending the analysis to circumstances after concluded formal education, we used the 40% of the educational variance which could *not* be explained by differences in initial levels for the controlled variables as an explanatory variable. This put us in a far better position than e.g. Hyman et al. They did have controls for social background but not for performance at the initial level.

Self-ratings of verbal and linguistic skills could be broken down into a number of mutually independent components which were subsequently related to previous factors in the model. The components were as follows:

- General verbal and linguistic skill
- Proficiency in reading and writing
- Proficiency in English
- Ability to express oneself in spoken and written Swedish.

Table 1 supplies a condensed picture of the relationships between previous factors and linguistic skills. One cross (X) designates significant relationships under .30 (partial regression coefficient); relationships above .30 are designated with 2 crosses.

*Table 1*
*Relationships between explanatory variables and self-ratings of verbal and linguistic skills*

|  | V* | PLAN | EDUC | SELF-DIR | ADVANCE | Explained variance (%) |
|---|---|---|---|---|---|---|
| **Men** | | | | | | |
| GENERAL | X | X | X | X | | 29 |
| READ/WRITE | X | | XX | | | 38 |
| ENGLISH | X | XX | | | X | 25 |
| SPEAK/WRITE SW | | | | | XX | 19 |
| | | | | | | |
| **Women** | | | | | | |
| GENERAL | | X | X | X | | 22 |
| READ/WRITE | XX | | X | | | 18 |
| ENGLISH | X | | X | | | 16 |
| SPEAK/WRITE SW | | | | XX | | 17 |

The first thing noted is that neither the home nor the general level of performance has any direct relationship with self-ratings of linguistic skills, even though they, in certain instances, had an indirect influence on them via subsequent variables in the model. However, the specific verbal factor in 6th grade performance (verbal intelligence test, standard tests and grades in Swedish and English) displayed independent relationships with reading and writing skills and proficiency in English rated 20 years later. Plans for additional theoretical education after the 6th grade had the greatest impact on the men's self-ratings of their proficiency in English.

The strongest relationship in the model proved to be between the level of education in men and their self-ratings of reading and writing skills – a component which was more heavily influenced in women, relatively speaking, by their early verbal and linguistic skills. Work conditions displayed a strong relationship with the ability to express oneself in spoken and written Swedish, although in relation to different factors. Women with unsupervised jobs (often teachers) and men with good promotion prospects (hardly the case for teachers) rated this skill highest.

In my view, these results supply a nuanced picture of the background underlying the ratings of linguistic skills. Education is of independent importance, apart from factors which can be explained by differences in circumstances manifested even at the initial level. But irrespective of the level of education attained, early performance in verbal and linguistic respects still had an impact two decades later. The work conditions of adults, irrespective of employee background and education, had a major effect on self-confidence in the active use of spoken and written Swedish.

It is important to note that indices of verbal and linguistic skills in adulthood were based on ratings performed by the subjects themselves. These ratings reflected the subjects' personal confidence in their proficiency but not necessarily objective circumstances as disclosed in tests. Self-ratings are also affected by e.g. the frame of reference within which ratings are made and by tendencies for replies to be generally positive or negative. Some of these more or less irrelevant influences were captured by the general component, and this is the reason why the comments instead concentrated on the more nuanced indices where the strongest correlations were found.

Rough but by no means unimportant corroborative information can be derived from the computer-transcribed interviews which, from the linguistic point of view, have hitherto only been processed with quantitative methods. But even calculation of the number of words and similar measures produced interesting results.

The total number of words in running text, the number of different words and the number of different "long" words were related to the linguistic ratings. All displayed correlations with the rating of general verbal and linguistic skill, with an ascending degree of correlation in the order cited. Word frequencies were also analyzed in relation to the complete set of explanatory variables. Only "long" words (more than 10 letters when correctly spelled) displayed correlations with the level of education and to a slight degree also with early verbal skill. Figure 2 shows the mean number of "long" words in the interview replies of men and women.

On all levels, both in respect to education and ratings of general linguistic skill, men used far more "long" words in their answers. However, this is more likely to reflect gender-oriented linguistic habits, as feminists assert, than a sign of any superior qualitative ability to use language.

With 1.8 millions words of running text, the spoken language database produced by the LING project must be one of the largest of its kind. The ability to relate language use to background information probably makes it unique. However, I have still been unable to interest any linguist in performing a more qualitative study of this material.

Linguistic skill is obviously an aspect of performance which should generally be influenced by education. Two other proficiency areas were investigated in a similar manner. One dealt

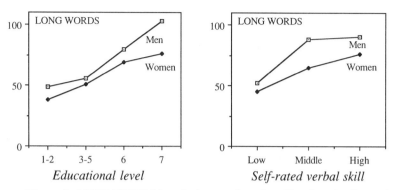

*Figure 2. LONG WORDS in relation to educational level and self-rated skill.*

with what we called "civic competence", i.e. more or less knowing where to turn in contact with public agencies. Some questions concerned contacts for seeking public assistance in various respects. Others concerned procedures for filing complaints when a person was dissatisfied with a particular measure.

The analyses generated both a general component, weighted somewhat in favor of situations in which public assistance is sought, and a more "self-assertive" component based on different complaint situations. The general, more assistance-oriented component displayed higher average values in people from homes with a lower status or who had non-independent jobs, i.e. people with a greater need for public assistance. Familiarity with procedures for exercising one's rights displayed the opposite result. Thus, ratings of civic competence were affected by the respondents' social situation. There was no independent correlation with the level of education.

The second competence area concerned everyday practical skills and had components for domestic skills and practical/mechanical skills. On the average, men differed greatly from women in both respects; there is scarcely any need to indicate in which ways. The most interesting result was that highly educated men rated their domestic skills higher and their practical/

mechanical skills lower than less well educated men. The highly educated men thereby displayed a less gender-related attitude to practical tasks than less well educated men. For the first time in the analysis, spatial visualization skill at the age of 13 displayed relationships here, i.e. a positive correlation with the men's ratings of their mechanical proficiency and a (not equally predictable) negative correlation with the women's ratings of their domestic skills.

Leisure pursuits represent an area which has hitherto been reported in a more descriptive form (Härnqvist 1984). For instance, highly educated people devoted more time to daily newspapers, novels, the theater, concerts, cinema, trade literature and preparations for work. People with a low level of education devoted more time to magazines, TV and sporting events.

To date, the LING Project has not reported any studies of the importance of education to occupation and income, even if data for such studies are available. In Sweden, there have been follow-ups for men in the Malmö Project (Husén 1969, Fägerlind 1975, Tuijnman 1989). The latter analysis covers almost 50 years, probably making it the longest time span ever employed in any study of occupational status attainment. Correlations with social background, intelligence and education changed over time in relation to the men's occupational careers.

## Closing remarks

The persistence of the knowledge, skills, interests, habits and values we acquire in school and in other education depends on the extent to which we have opportunities to use them in occupational and private life. The present study was able to show that people who attained different levels in the educational system differed in various respects in ways which were directly and indirectly related to their education. Moreover – and this is important, these differences can hardly be explained by differences present at the time the people made their original choice of an educational pathway.

However, the study was not much help in making distinctions between the direct and indirect effects of education. What then are the "proceeds" of education? And what is the impact of the subsequent learning occurring as a consequence of skills, habits and values founded in education? Or because that education opened pathways to occupational and social contexts in which this learning could take place?

Specific subject knowledge has not been studied, partly because the knowledge content to which a cross-section of an age cohort is exposed during its education is so heterogenous that no fair comparisons are possible. Comparing even a limited group's knowledge after formal education and its knowledge in adulthood is by no means easy, since knowledge is subject to continuous, qualitative changes and may even be lost, or so it sometimes seems.

However, it would be rash to conclude that knowledge attained in education is of limited importance because people are likely to forget a large part of it anyway. But from a long-range point of view, there is scarcely any support for the often heated arguments advocating moderate curricular changes. In my view, the important thing is that people are presented with opportunities during their education for testing their talents and interests through exposure to a wide-range of educational contents. Some of these contents become enduring knowledge. But even "forgotten" knowledge contributes to a person's development as an individual. These contents provide training in general skills and even first-hand experience as a basis for stepwise decisions on personal preferences and subjects in which greater knowledge and proficiency are desirable. So this is a lasting educational effect as much as anything.

Longitudinal research demands both endurance and continuity. The study described here was made possible through data collected almost 30 years ago. Some members of the original research team are still active in the project which is continuing under new designations and in new spin-off studies. New collections of basic data have laid the foundation for comparisons with age cohorts which grew up and were educated in other circumstances (cf. Emanuelsson and Svensson, in press). This information is important to an understanding of the interaction of the individual and the environment. But it also offers opportunities for studying problems arising in a constantly changing society.

*Gunnar Fant*

# Man's voice and speech

## *Preface*

Nothing is more important than man's speech, the key to the human species' development and culture. Most people take speech for granted. It's just there! We never give it a thought until we meet someone incapable of speech or with some speech impediment. We may even ourselves be afflicted by such problems.

Nothing is as sensitive or as personal as the voice and the way we use it to express ourselves. We enjoy listening to an attractive, expressive voice. And it upsets us when our voice breaks down. The voice changes when we are sad, depressed, tired and tense or have a cold.

Being excluded from normal speech communications is a severe disability, irrespective of whether the problem concerns stammering or voice damage/loss due to some medical problem. For people in the latter category, voice synthesis has acquired major importance (Fant et al. 1980). A voice and speech prosthesis fits into a small computer equipped with a module for text-to-speech conversion. But expectations continue to grow. People are demanding better quality and more personally varied speech synthesis. It may be frustrating for a little girl to need to express herself via a device that is only capable of generating a male voice. Personal emphasis, conveying emotions and stressing important words are other facilities sought.

The development of speech synthesis towards improved quality in general, greater clarity and naturalness and greater flexibility in speech styles and voice types will open up a large range of applications in speech-based information transmission via telephones, public address systems, intercom systems etc. Prevailing techniques mainly use pre-recorded messages. However, general text-to-speech converters offer opportunities for transforming any text into synthetic speech. This technique is currently being utilized by a large number of blind people for "reading" books and newspapers. The demand for individualized synthetic speech is not as great here, but quality improvements would still be welcome.

However, the knowledge base, not computer capacity nor technical design limitations, is the bottleneck in developments. What we hear when we listen to speech is well-hidden in the sound waves. We can indeed perform spectrographic analyses of speech sound waves, but interpreting the results is the problem. The information on speech style, speaker type, voice characteristics, special emphasis and emotional expressiveness are so intimately intermixed with message content that separating these aspects in the analysis of a spectrogram is exceptionally difficult. One difficulty in our research work has been the need to obtain a more profound insight into the mechanisms of speech, the physiological and perceptual prerequisites and the rules linking spoken sounds and stress to observable patterns before we can learn to understand the factors of importance to individualized speech synthesis.

So before we can address the fine detail, we need to develop a more accurate picture of the nature of speech. It would be a naive underestimation of the problem's severity to believe that something requiring a hundred thousand years or more of social evolution could be clarified and described after only a few years of research. There is a vast difference between general, descriptive research on man's ability to express him-/herself and the creation of a working model of real function. The operation of the human brain with its immense capacity and control functions governs the complicated movement patterns of the tongue, lips, palate and vocal cords. The fact that we are capable of detecting shifts in speech and voice quality does not necessarily mean that we know how to describe them in adequate, physical terms for synthetic reproduction by a talking robot.

## Speech as a code

So there is every reason to describe our study of human speech as an effort to break the speech code, i.e. the way, with access to a recording of the acoustic sound pattern of a spoken statement, we are able to interpret what is said and how (Fant 1989). The code encompasses reference patterns for individual linguistic sounds and word stress and rules of how these patterns vary with context, i.e. with all the interacting factors, including preceding and subsequent sounds, syllables and word structures, grammatic and semantic factors etc. Moreover, the speaker's age, sex, physiological prerequisites, speaking style, involvement, intentions and numerous other factors affecting the planning and execution of a message, not the least, in terms of stress and intonation patterns. The communication model provides a schematic view of successive phases of information conversion at the transmitter (speaker) and at the receiver (listener) end, as well as a structural linguistic model of message composition. The code represents the relationship between the smallest components and structures in linguistic descriptions, on the one hand, and the corresponding signal patterns in the speech process, on the other hand, i.e. in articulation, in the sound waves or in the auditory nerve. So inclusion of non-linguistic aspects, such as voice type, speech style, emotional attitude etc., in the concept "code" seems appropriate. These aspects are also based on social conventions.

If the code were fully understood and intellectually comprehensible, we would not have any difficulty in achieving mechanized voice recognition of spoken text. Automatic voice recognition of today mainly concentrates on limited vocabularies comprising individual words uttered with brief inter-word pauses. Good reliability demands calibration with "his master's voice". The technique here is to recognize each word rather than its smaller constituents. The general term "speech code" comprises reference data and rules we can store in a computer and retrieve when needed for addressing a descriptive problem. But even if we currently know a great deal about the speech code, no one is able to read a spectrogram with the same ease as when listening. The difference is actually quite enormous. It may take even an expert on acoustic phonetics hours to decipher the contents of a spectrogram covering a 2.5-second long message with unknown content. We need to utilize all available knowledge about possible linguistic combinations and alternatives as a complement to direct interpretation of details in the sonogram.

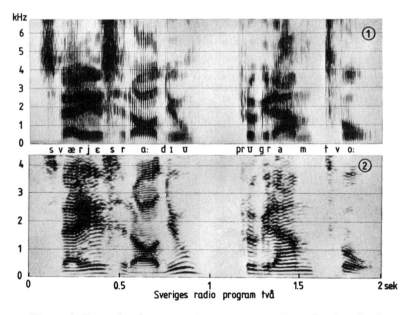

*Figure 1. Example of an acoustic spectrogram. Text:* Sveriges Radio Program två *(The Swedish Broadcasting Company, Radio two). (1) Broad-band analysis – the formant pattern is emphasized. (2) Narrow-band analysis – the pattern of individual harmonics is emphasized.*

Figure 1 shows examples of a spectrogram with the frequency scale on the vertical axis and the time scale on the horizontal axis. In other words, the picture shows how the spectral energy distribution varies within the statement. The values of the relative intensity of spectral components, i.e. the formants, are designated by the degree of blackening. The spectrogram reveals an overall structure of continuous variations with breaks for changing local pattern types. However, the visible structure cannot be directly interpreted as a sequence of spoken sounds. One and the same segment may hide multiple speech sounds. The sounds in *verige* in the word *Sveriges* form a more or less continuous pattern of formant variations without apparent boundaries. When the sound spectrogram became available for experimental research at the beginning of the 1950's and linguists were able to confront their abstract models with physical reality, the effect was almost shocking to some people. Instead of well-differentiated intervals in the speech sounds, the sound spectrogram displayed continuous, hard-to-interpret patterns. With the words of the American linguist Charles Hockett, somewhat condensed: "We may conceive of the sequence of phonemes in speech as a number of differently painted Easter eggs broken one after another, on a conveyer belt. That's the mess we see in the spectrogram".

This is obviously a didactic exaggeration. In fact some language sounds are clearly delineated and relatively easy to recognize, for example the "s" and "sh" sounds. But I recall Hockett's analogy every time I attempt to interpret a spectrogram of an unknown text – a reminder of the limits in our understanding of the speech code. We are unable to handle the code without introducing substantial simplifications. And even if we are rather experienced, we still lack knowledge of the complex of features affecting visible sound patterns and to a different degree our normalizing perception of speech via hearing.

## The mechanism of voice production

Sound production in Man demands a flow of air. Disruption of an otherwise smooth flow of air is the source of the acoustic energy in speech. When air is forced through a narrow passage or encounters an obstacle, such as the teeth, a sibilant sound is formed, such as "s", "sh" and "z". The sound is colored by resonance effects in adjacent air cavities. Voiced speech sounds, such as vowels, derive their energy from the periodic interruption of expiratory air into a series of pulses by the opening and closing action of the vocal cords. The spectral content is determined by resonances of the air cavities between the vocal cords and the lips. The system's natural resonances appear as peaks (formants) in the acoustic spectrum. It should be noted here that speech is even possible during air inspiration, something that can be noted in a shy girl's exclamation of e.g. "Oh".

The location of the formants in the spectrum depends on the shape of the air cavities in the mouth, nose and throat and governs the color and nature of the spoken sound. However, the feature we perceive as the voice fundamental is independent of air cavity resonances and is governed solely by the vibratory frequency of the vocal cords. Changes in the voice fundamental produce melody in singing and intonation in speech.

The harmonics of the voice fundamental also have a physical reality. We can regard a formant range as consisting of one or a few harmonics. The extent to which formants or harmonics appear depends on the type of analysis.

There are two different versions of the spectrogram. The spectrum analysis at the top of Figure 1 was performed with a broad-band filter incapable of distinguishing harmonic components. Instead, the formants, i.e. the spectral peaks, appear. The analysis in the lower spectrogram in Figure 1 was performed with a narrow-band filter discriminating individual harmonics, whereas the formants may be identified secondarily only as an overriding pattern. Conversely, a secondary feature that can be observed in the broad-band spectrogram is the perio-dicity of glottal excitation, i.e. the time domain correspondence of the voice fundamental frequency, F0. A fine structure of ver-tical lines appears. The lines are spaced more closely or further apart, depending on whether the fundamental frequency is high or low. This is because broad-band analysis has a high temporal resolution; it displays the growth and decay of spectral energy within each fundamental period. Each small vertical line repre-sents a fundamental pulse. The distance between two consecu-tive pulses, T0, is, by definition, related to the fundamental frequency, F0, by $F0 = 1/T0$. From the broad-band spectrogram we can estimate F0, at least when this parameter is low, from a local mean value for the inter-pulse distance. In the narrow-band spectrogram, F0 can be directly read as the distance in height between consecutive harmonic component lines.

Thus, the spectrographic pattern is governed both by what has been said, i.e. the utterance, and by the analysis tool employed. We have a choice between a rough spectral analysis with a relatively broad filter supplying detailed temporal resolu-tion and emphasizing formants or a more detailed, narrow-band analysis providing poorer temporal resolution but emphasizing the time-varying pattern of harmonic components, including the voice fundamental. How does the human ear work? Well, like a narrow-band analyzer for low frequencies and like a broad-band analyzer for intermediate and high frequencies. Hearing utilizes a complicated system of simultaneous analysis processes that, on a higher level, extract information-bearing spectral and temporal components, identifying sounds, syl-lables and words. We cannot hear individual formants, but we do perceive sound qualities and, on another perceptual level, hear the voice fundamental frequency F0 and, accordingly, the intonation. Perception thus retrieves the basic dimensions of speech production, i.e. the movements of the speech organs inducing temporal variations in the natural resonances of the vocal tract cavity system, the formants, and the temporal variation in the rate of vocal cord vibrations, in other words F0 and, accordingly, intonation.

In technical terminology, a speech sound is the product of a source and a filtration. Figure 2 indicates that the filter function, i.e. the formant pattern observed in a spectrogram, may be derived from a reconstruction of the shape of the vocal tract cavity system. In pronunciation of the vowel "e" as in eat (the Swedish vowel "i"), illustrated in Figure 2, the tongue is in a forward position and the volume of the oral cavity is less than the volume of the throat. This configuration predestines a low location for the first formant, F1, at about 300 Hz, whereas the second formant, F2, has a relatively high position at about 2 000 Hz. By contrast, F1 in "ah" (the Swedish vowel "a") is close to F2 at intermediate frequencies, approximately 650 and 1 100 Hz. This is because the tongue is in a less forward position, resulting in a narrow throat and an open oral cavity.

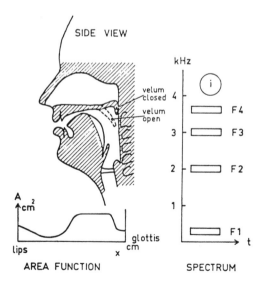

Figure 2. The shape of the air cavities between the vocal cords and the lips determines the frequency of formants as indicated in the highly stylized spectrogram to the right. The vowel is "i", corresponding to a spelled "e".

## Voice qualities

This brief introduction to acoustic phonetics can serve as a background to discussion of our research findings on variability and speaker-specific aspects. Let us return to the functions of the vocal cords. The primary sound source is not the vibrations of the vocal cords but their valvular action, i.e. the periodic opening and closing of the passage between them modulating the expiratory air flow. The primary energy in the voice source is therefore supplied by the pulsating air flow. The amount of air in each individual pulse passing the vocal cord slit, i.e. the glottis, governs the level of the energy in the fundamental, whereas the strength of harmonic components in the formant ranges are mainly governed by the speed and distinctness with which the pulse flow is impeded by vocal cord closure; see Figure 3. The power and brilliance of the voice is accordingly governed by the rapidity and completeness of glottal closure. When closure is incomplete, harmonics and, thus, the formants are weakened. This is typical of a weak, "breathy" voice and contributes to the relative dominance of the fundamental. Noise components are present at the same time.

Normal versus breathy voicing is but one of many dimensions relevant to phoniatrics, comparative linguistics and general speech research. A feature considered pathological in one voice, such as breathiness, may be a normal feature of a particular language or dialect or it may have a distinctive, message-bearing role. The same phenomenon, i.e. aspirative sound formation, is also a necessary phase in all languages at the junction between a vowel and an "h" sound or an unvoiced sound. It is also a normal phase when the voice source shuts down for a pause. The extreme opposite of a "leaky", aspirative voice is the "tense" voice. Here, the vocal cords are prevented from attaining their maximum range of motion, and closure is particularly abrupt and effective. The reduced amount of air in each individual vocal cord pulse makes the fundamental weaker

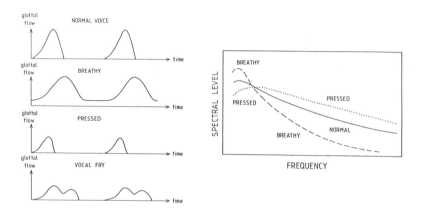

*Figure 3. The shape of vocal cord pulses and the spectrum for normal, breathy, tense and creaky voices.*

than normal, but harmonics are stronger. Tense voice production may be damaging to the vocal cords, but it does have a linguistic function in certain types of stress realizations. Combined with an extremely low F0, the result is a creaky voice, often with double glottal pulses (see Fig. 3) that also serves a linguistic purpose e.g. in designating a juncture between voiced segments, i.e. two vowels.

An important part of our research work has concerned the development of technical models of the voice source permitting realistic resynthesis. Developing the necessary know-how from speech analysis is a difficult, time-consuming task. Our department plays an internationally leading role in this field. We have also penetrated more deeply into theory and measurements than is apparent from the simplified presentation above (Fant 1982, 1986, 1988). A comprehensive, theoretical study has been undertaken to determine to what extent voice source and sound shaping are mutually dependent. Independence is only an initial approximation. Each individual air pulse passing the vocal cords excites air cavity resonances but is also affected by the resonances. One result is the development of minor perturbations, i.e. changes in the amplitude, shape and timing of successive air pulses. These micro-variations contribute to some extent to the character of the voice.

Source-filter interaction is of major importance to e.g. a soprano's singing voice. To avoid losing output volume, a soprano singing a high-frequency note must adapt her articulation so that the fundamental is reinforced by the first formant. Additional gain is obtained through the aerodynamic course of events at the vocal cords. When F0 coincides with F1, source-filter interaction results in smaller air consumption. Under these conditions, the soprano is capable of holding the note longer.

## The female voice and the male voice

One task within the framework of our Foundation-supported project was to develop the know-how necessary for synthesizing female voices for text reading systems. This is no simple task. As we know, auditory perception is not related to physical reality in any simple way. In our experience, there are situations in which it may be difficult to determine whether a person we hear on the radio, telephone or a recording is a man or a woman, a boy or a girl. There are clearly borderline cases. If we cannot see Zarah Leander (a Swedish, female singer with a deep, dark voice) but merely hear her voice (without knowing the singer's identity), it is hard to identify the sound as the voice of a woman. On the telephone, it is not always easy to hear whether a speaker is a boy or a girl.

What do these gender differences consist of? The most prominent difference is that the frequency of the voice fundamental, F0, of an adult woman is somewhat less than an octave on the average, about 80% higher than for an adult man. Another major difference is in the formant pattern. The somewhat shorter vocal tract in woman, i.e. the length of the air column from the vocal cords to the lips, also accounts for somewhat higher (an average of 20%) formant frequencies. In

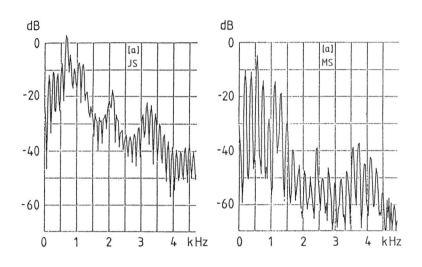

*Figure 4. The spectrum of the vowel sound "ah". A male voice to the left and female voice to the right.*

addition, the formant patterns of women and men are not proportional.

The gender differences in a formant, e.g. in F1, are vowel-dependent to a great degree. It is maximal in vowels, such as the "a" in "had" (the Swedish "ä") and minimal or even negative for the vowel sound "u" in "do" (the Swedish "o"). The same deviations from proportionality found in tenors compared to basses, suggesting analogous physiological relationships. When a boy's voice begins to break, his vocal cords grow, and the pitch of the fundamental drops. In my own case, I changed from a soprano to a bass. During puberty, the position of the larynx drops in males, thereby lengthening the throat cavity. This is one of the factors contributing to non-proportional scaling of the formant frequencies. Speech production also appears to be controlled by perceptual demands for equivalent phonetic quality with an effect on articulation as a result – a compensatory mechanism.

There are also differences in the shape of voice pulses and, thus, in the source spectrum. In a feminine voice, the harmonics of the voice source are weak in relation to the fundamental, and the previously discussed properties in a "leaky", "breathy" voice production are found; cf. Figure 4 and Figure 3. Physiological studies performed at e.g. the Phoniatrics Unit at Huddinge Hospital have confirmed the leakage tendency. The vocal cords in women seldom achieve complete closure in their maximum closure phase. This tendency has been confirmed by our aerodynamic recordings. The incomplete closure also has an effect on formant frequencies and may cause resonances from the sub-glottal system, i.e. from the tracheal airways, to appear. In addition, formant peaks are less sharply delineated; they are flattened somewhat. The less complete vocal cord closure also leads to a relatively higher proportion of unvoiced intervals in the female voice compared to voiced intervals.

All these conditions may be found to greater or lesser degrees, but inter-individual differences are considerable. As we know, there are masculine female voices and effeminate male voices. The pitch, i.e. the average F0 for a speaker, need not necessarily co-vary with the formant pattern's average scaling factor. Men with a small head and, thus, relatively high-scaled formants may have a relatively low F0, and a large woman with a large head may have a voice with a high pitch, i.e. a high F0. Such abnormal combinations can generally be corrected by voice training.

There are also purely behavioral differences with no clear physiological or perceptual explanation, for example a feminine way of speaking. Such voice patterns have not been the subject of much study. One example is that Italian women tend to centralize the back vowels "u" and "oo" as evident from a relatively high location for F2. One study in which we participated showed that gender differences are far less striking in Finnish children than in Swedish or American children. This was seen in experiments in which subject groups of different nationalities listened to identical recordings of spontaneous remarks in conversations with boys and girls. We still only have vague ideas about what a feminine way of speaking entails. The prosodic framework, i.e. the intonation and emphasis structure rather than individual sounds, may play an important role. We also know that imitation of prosodic patterns are of decisive importance to the technique used by professional impersonators.

## Reading and stress

One of our tasks comprised an attempt to obtain objective standards and programmable rules for good reading and, in this context, to study individual variations in speaking styles. The prosody, i.e. the stress structure, intonation, pauses and phrasing, more than the clarity of individual sounds, is the factor that catches the attention of someone listening to a good reader. These considerations were the reasons why we started our project "God svenska" (Good Swedish). A brief excerpt from a novel by Kerstin Ekman was read by a total of 16 people, several of whom with professional experience. One of the latter, our reference speaker (ÅJ), combined great clarity and a pleasant manner with a natural speaking style. An actor and a teacher contributed with examples of a more dramatic and personally varied speaking style.

The fluctuations between stressed and unstressed words and syllables is an apparent property of speech and reading. A stressed word generally contains a single stressed syllable. The emphasis normally falls on content words, i.e. nouns, adjectives and main verbs, whereas function words, such as articles, prepositions, conjunctions, adverbs and auxiliary verbs, lose their stress in running speech. The fluctuations between stressed and unstressed syllables form characteristic, quasi-rhythmic patterns.

The degree of stress placed on an individual syllable is reflected in its duration, F0 pattern and several other para-

SYLLABIC STRESS. OBJECTIVE AND SUBJECTIVE.

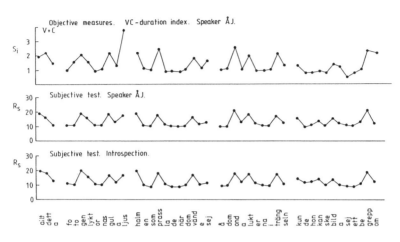

*Figure 5. Syllabic stress in a long sentence. Normalized duration values at the top. Subjectively estimated stress values in the middle. Introspectively estimated values in silent text reading at the bottom.*

meters. Here, we will concentrate on duration related to the subjectively estimated degree of stress. An appropriate object for duration measurement is the syllable's vowel (V) plus the following consonant (C) that carry a larger part of the prolongation effect produced by increased stress and providing good correlation with subjective estimates. See Figure 5. This figure comprises a long sentence with five sub-phrases. We normalized the duration of the V-C interval so that the mean value of unstressed syllables was 1 and the mean value of stressed syllables was 2. Intermediate values were interpolated linearly through comparison of the current duration and reference values. These values depend on speaking tempo, but their magnitude is 110 ms for an unstressed syllable and 220 ms for a stressed syllable.

Subjective estimation of our reference reader's reading was performed by a total of 14 people who utilized the same scale, expanded ten times, as in the objective test. Figure 5 shows, not unexpectedly, that correlation between objective and subjective estimates was very good. The profiles are largely identical. One interesting observation is that the typical prolongation of the terminal syllable in a phrase was not reflected in the subjective test. It is taken for granted.

The profile at the bottom in Figure 5 shows the results of the 14 subjects' introspective estimates during silent reading before listening to the reader. The similarity to the curve obtained from the reading is striking. One might suspect that estimates of the reading were based more on expectations than on active listening. However, supplementary tests when the group listened to readings of the same phrase by different speakers disclosed that the stress variations observed in the duration patterns were also reflected in the perceptual estimates.

Adequate contrast is a prerequisite for distinct speech. When stress emphasis increases, the duration difference between stressed and unstressed syllables increases. The stressed syllable simultaneously acquires greater intensity, and the fundamental frequency pattern, i.e. the F0 curve, shifts towards a higher pitch and greater movement within the stressed word. Contrast between syllables is not the only thing to consider. The qualitative contrast between consonants and a subsequent and/ or preceding vowel, as seen in the spectrogram, is also by stress. Relative intensity values are also affected. A consonant normally requires a closure in the mouth, throat or lips, but closure may not be complete due to de-emphasis. The more open articulation of a voiced, unstressed consonant induces increased physical intensity, thus i.e. the contrast between consonants and adjacent vowels declines. The Swedish phrase "ge igen", normally pronounced "jeIjen (in IPA symbols), is reduced to "jeien" and, with further de-emphasis, to "jeen". Entire speech sounds, syllables and even entire words are often dropped in spontaneous speech in situations when they are not needed for comprehension without speakers always being aware that this happens. Pronunciation simplifications as extensive as this is hardly recommended in careful reading of a text aloud, but even skilled, experienced speakers reduce unimportant words, especially when they read at fast rates and encounter semantically irrelevant phrases. These natural fluctuations are hard to simulate in synthetic speech.

Here, we can identify two speaker-specific characteristics, viz. the average contrast between stressed and unstressed syllables and the ability to vary stress in a natural way according to the demands of text contents. But stress strategies also vary, e.g. in the proportion between the available means of expression, i.e. contrasts in segment lengths, intensity, voice fundamental frequency and acoustic patterns. The easiest variable to quantify is duration. This also appears to be the most important variable in Swedish. In this language, the consonant following a stressed vowel is often prolonged more than the vowel. But interindividual differences may be considerable here.

We have found language-specific variation. In English, prolongation of the consonant preceding the stressed vowel is almost as great as prolongation of the consonant immediately after this vowel. The situation is more complicated in French. In a stressed syllable at the end of a phrase before a pause, the consonant following the stressed vowel is lengthened, whereas in other positions mainly the consonant preceding the vowel is lengthened. In French, however, the basic determinant of stress is the intonation pattern, i.e. the temporal course of F0 variations.

## Phrasing and pauses

The relative emphasis of individual syllables is only one detail in a large frame of temporal patterns of fluctuations between stressed and unstressed words and between emphasized and suppressed parts of a phrase or entire phrases. The temporal pattern also includes tempo variations and marking of junctions between successive phrases, sentences and paragraphs. Pauses of varying length and more global intonation patterns constitute the most important expressive device for dividing the read text into segments of appropriate lengths. In an intonational phrase, the pitch of F0 starts moderately high or on a high level and then gradually sinks towards a low level at the end of the phrase. Within a phrase, local F0 pattern variations add to the realization of stress. In Swedish, the specific word accents, i.e. grave as in the word "bana" (Eng. = track, i.e. bàh-na), or acute, as in the Swedish word "banan" (Eng. = banana, i.e. bah-nán) Word accent differentiates a number of Swedish homographs, such as "anden" which means "spirit" when the accent is grave and a "duck" when the accent is acute. See Figure 6.

A word or a group of words may be emphasized within an intonation phrase, as marked by a rise in F0 and an increase in duration. The role of pauses as boundary markers is obvious. But there are other junction cues, such as a prolongation of the terminal sounds immediately prior to a pause. A single such prolongation of a terminal sound, without any pause, is a sufficient indicator of a phrase junction. In such instances, one also finds a local and sudden drop in F0 within the junction

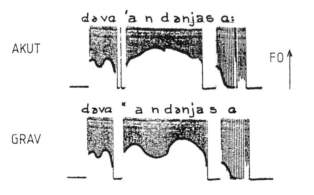

"Det var anden jag sa"

*Figure 6. Example of the voice fundamental F0's profile when word accent is acute or grave. Text: "Det var anden jag sa" (It was* anden *I said).*

interval; an instance of laryngealization perceived as a voice creak.

A previously little noticed phenomenon is the circumstance that pauses are part of a basic rhythmic pattern in reading aloud. The fluctuations between stressed and unstressed syllables gives speech a quasi-rhythmic structure. The distances between stressed syllables do indeed vary considerably, depending on the number of speech sounds or syllables in such a stressed interval, from 0.2 second to 1 second, but the mean value within a sentence is rather constant and amounts to about 0.5 second. This average distance between stressed syllables has an obvious rhythmic function in poetry. In the analysis of prose, inter-stress periodicity is less apparent but gains support when pauses are considered as an integral part of the temporal pattern.

In our investigation of prose read aloud, we found a tendency for pauses between phrases and clauses within a sentence to amount to 0.5 second or a little less. With a rhythmically sensitive reader, good agreement is obtained between the basic rhythmic interval and the sum of pause duration and sound prolongation immediately prior to a pause. Any pause inserted should fit the rhythmic continuum. If sound prolongation before the pause increases, pause duration tends to be reduced to the same degree. The analogy with music is obvious (Nord, Kruckenberg and Fant 1989). A prolongation of the note immediately preceding a pause is compensated by a shorter pause.

Tempo can vary in music, thereby affecting pause durations. But what about speech? Is the rhythmic reference a constant that happens to coincide with the average duration of the stressed intervals or does it vary with local tempo? We have some evidence suggesting that the latter hypothesis may be valid.

Another interesting observation we made is that long pauses, usually between complete sentences, do not vary arbitrarily but in distinct quanta so that the duration of pause plus the pre-pause prolongation tends to vary by a factor of two, three, four or five times the basic rhythmic interval. We have also found some evidence for this tendency in English and French (Fant, Kruck-enberg and Nord 1989). The tendency is most pronounced in rhythmically sensitive readers. However, a number of questions remain unanswered regarding the rhythmic reference and its dependency on speech tempo. In any event, the music analogy remains with pauses comprising multiples of a half or a whole beat. Music, song, speech and poetry have a natural, common foundation in rhythmic structures that are now beginning to emerge with increasing clarity.

## Knowledge and applications

Our project began as a study of the human voice and speech with the aim of attaining more natural speech quality in speech synthesis with individualization of voice types and stress elements in text-to-speech conversion system. This would be especially desirable in a personal aid for mutes. A great deal of work has been devoted to improvements in models of the voice source in speech. Our work has served as guidance for research groups in England, France, Japan and the U.S. But a good model of the anatomical structures in human voice formation is not enough. We need a great deal more knowledge about how these tools are used in connected speech as a part of the overall code and what constitutes a good voice.

For this purpose, we have worked especially hard on the development of methodology, including coordinated studies of speech as a physical phenomenon and the perception of phonetic and speaker-specific categories.

This long-term approach is not only beneficial to synthesis technology with various applications. Studying speech as a code with general laws and social conventions is also a matter of general scientific relevance. One of many applications is in computerized voice recognition and interpretation of speech. Our studies of speech prosody have also contributed to basic

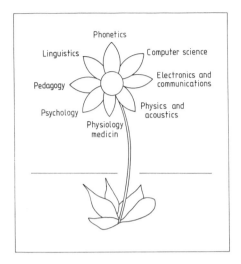

*Figure 7. An interdisciplinary flower*

knowledge in linguistics and phonetics with applications in e.g. language instruction. We have recently initiated studies of stress patterns and syllabic structure in English and French translations of a Swedish text that display similarities and differences in the way stress is produced in the three languages. These contrastive pronunciation studies will probably be incorporated into an EC project.

The humanistic aspect should not be underestimated. Our studies of the stress structures in prose read aloud provides a good basis for work on poetry reading. We have already started such a project (Kruckenberg, Fant and Nord 1989).

Few research fields are as interdisciplinary as the study of the human voice and speech. The technical and scientific part of this study has an important coordinating role in theory formation and development of measurement methods providing support for linguistics and phonetics and even for medical voice research, rehabilitation and pedagogics, as symbolically illustrated in Figure 7. The music acoustics group at our department have made major contributions to voice research, not only to research on the singing voice but even to fundamental studies of the function of the vocal cords. The "Vocal Fold Physiology Conference" held in Stockholm at the end of July 1989 is an example of a medically oriented activity supported by the Foundation. It was held under the auspices of the Royal Institute of Technology in Stockholm (KTH) in collaboration with the Phoniatrics Clinic at Huddinge Hospital. The conference was a major success. Our internationally leading role in the field was acknowledged. A workshop on a similar theme was held in Katthammarsvik on the island of Gotland in 1985.

Better rules for individually adapted text-to-speech synthesis, especially with respect to rules for the synthesis of different types of male, female and children's voices, are examples of technical applications of our project. Our grant from the Foundation has also contributed to the financing of a doctoral dissertation on articulatory and physiologically based speech synthesis (Qiguang Lin). Other scholars who have contributed to our Foundation project are Jan Gauffin and Johan Liljencrants in respect to the function of the vocal cords, Inger Karlsson and Christer Gobl in respect to voice source analysis and the female voice and Anita Kruckenberg in the study of stress structures in prose read aloud.

Two cultures meet in our interdisciplinary work, i.e. technology and the humanities, in a joint search for knowledge about the human voice and speech, the very foundation of our society and a prerequisite for communications. The knowledge acquired is needed for the development of communication aids for several groups of disabled people and is a support for rehabilitation. Speech research is an important and exciting field whose exploration will probably never be completed. A small child masters what scholars have been unable to fully understand or adequately describe. We have a great deal to learn, but the evolution of technology and increasing collaboration across established disciplinary boundaries should have a stimulating effect.

*Inger Rosengren*

# Language and pragmatics

## Background and structure of the research program

The international research program "Sprache und Pragmatik" has been conducted since 1987 with support from the Bank of Sweden Tercentenary Foundation. The program is being coordinated by the Department of German in Lund. It is based on the results of five international symposia of the same name that were held in Lund from 1978 to 1986. The program is also based on the Lund project "Fackspråklig kommunikation (FAK)" (Technical language communications) financed by the Foundation from 1978 to 1983.

The aim of the research program is to supply a systematic description of the relationship between grammatical and pragmatic or communicative competence. In other words, we intend to describe the grammatical properties to which particular communicative functions are attributed. The program encompasses four sub-projects comprising 23 scholars from the Federal Republic of Germany (BRD), the German Democratic Republic (DDR), Norway and Sweden. Each of the first three projects concerns a specific area within the program framework and is subdivided into sub-projects. The fourth project has a somewhat different structure. The results of the program are published in the S & P report series (Sprache und Pragmatik).

The projects are as follows:

1. Sentence and illocution. Project Director: Inger Rosengren, Lund.
2. Word order and information structure. Project Director: Marga Reis, Tübingen.

3. Language structure and text structure. Project Director: Wolfgang Motsch, Berlin (DDR).
4. Language structure, text structure and knowledge systems in an integrated model for automatic language processing. Project Director: Wolfgang Koch, Lund.

Project 1 will attempt to supply a theoretically well-founded description of the linguistic units we employ in language communication, i.e. clauses and sentences in particular. The project also intends to describe the smallest units in pragmatics.

Project 2 addresses the actual information structuring in the grammatical unit described in Project 1, i.e. what is emphasized and what is pure background. The hypothesis is that this structuring has a grammatical basis. However, its function is pragmatic.

The task of Project 3 is to examine the structure a text may display. Does each text have a hierarchic structure? If so: which units form the hierarchy, and what does this hierarchy look like? How do we know how to construct a text?

Project 4 (separately financed by the Foundation) intends to construct an abstract food preparation robot capable of reading a recipe in German or Swedish, preparing the dish in question and translating the recipe into the other language.

## *What is a language?*

Languages are there to be used. With their aid, we express our emotions, thoughts and needs and attempt to influence our surrounding. Language is obviously not the only instrument we can use for this purpose. However, it is our most important communicative instrument and a prerequisite for the formation of societies and groups. According to the founder of generative theory, Noam Chomsky (see e.g. 1986), our language is based on a universal, genetically determined language faculty. Underlying principles are identical for all languages. These principles contain parameters that, depending on where we are born and raised, i.e. the individual language to which we are exposed, are fixed through confrontation with concrete linguistic phenomena. The result is a grammatical system consisting of several components: the phonological, the syntactic, the semantic component and the lexicon. With the aid of these components we combine units to form expressions, phrases and sentences we subsequently employ in communications in order to achieve our communicative objectives.

In addition to knowledge about the grammatical system (grammatical competence), all language users also possess implicit knowledge about pragmatic or communicative rules (the pragmatic system) governing the use of specific languages (pragmatic competence). Thus, grammatical and pragmatic competence jointly constitute our linguistic competence. When communications take place, this competence interacts with several non-linguistic systems. Investigation and description of this interaction requires detailed knowledge of the various systems in the interaction. The goal of the research program "Sprache und Pragmatik" is to contribute to this description.

## Which sub-field will the research program address?

In the large research field discussed above, the research program has focused on text structuring or text formation, viewed as a complex "speech act" encompassing both the structuring of illocutions (speech acts) and the structuring of the information embedded in the illocutions (see Searle 1975, Katz 1977, Bierwisch 1980, Grice 1979, Levinson 1983). In this way, we will systematically examine both the boundaries of, and relationship between, grammar and pragmatics in a central field (see Motsch, Reis and Rosengren 1989). The aim is theoretical. We wish to develop a model that adequately describes text structure composed of smaller units.

The questions we have to ask are:

(a) Are the two systems autonomous (two modules) or can one be deduced in some way from the other?

(b) If the systems are independent of one another, what do these modules look like, what are the relevant units in the respective modules, and what rules apply when the systems are related to one another?

(c) Which other modules interact with these modules when communication takes place?

Project work is based on the hypothesis that two modular structures, systematically related to one another, are involved. As far as the internal structure of grammar is concerned, however, we know far more about this subject than about pragmatics. Our view of the relationship between the two modules and the non-linguistic modules can be illustrated with this simple model (Figure 1).

The model is read from left to right. It describes both

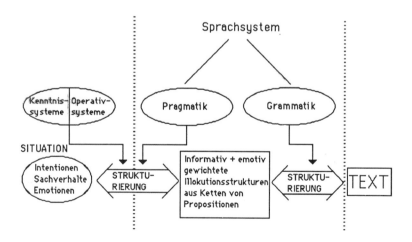

*Figure 1. Model of text structuring.*

language production and language reception. Every utterance can be analyzed with respect to its grammatical and pragmatic structure. The operative systems, as well as the knowledge systems we use, which influence us in the production and reception of text, are outside language. Text is then the product of interaction between all the modules in the communications process: intention, (propositional) content and affective attitudes. The text itself, i.e. the result of this interaction with the speaker's individual information, then becomes an individual unit from which the effect of individual modules can only be deduced by means of abstraction.

Our hypotheses restrict our investigative area and determine our objectives. To summarize, we intend to investigate in detail the internal structure of the modules, their mutual interaction and interaction with other modules and, thus, their effect on the final communicative product: the text.

## What are the concrete issues to be discussed?

To answer this question in non-technical terms is not easy, since non-technical paraphrasing always entails simplification.

Quite obviously, the planned sub-projects within each project could as a rule not start before there was a theoretical basis for each project. So every project commenced with general and basic, theoretical questions.

*Project 1* concentrated on the detailed description of the grammatical unit used, according to the basic model, in communication, both with a view to its grammatical structure and pragmatic function.

We form sentences with the aid of grammar. So the sentence obviously plays a major role in communications. But what a sentence actually is and the boundary between its grammatically determined structure, on the one hand, and its pragmatic function, on the other, (if there is any such boundary) is by no means obvious (cf. Altmann 1987, Motsch and Pasch 1987). Thus, we had to decide what constitutes a sentence type (see Reis and Rosengren 1988, Reis 1990, Brandt et al. 1989, Falkenberg 1989a; 1989b, Liedtke 1989). In addition, we had to develop a model for the semantics of sentence type, since sentence type is related to its pragmatic function via semantics (see Rehbock 1989, Brandt, Rosengren and Zimmermann 1989). The problem can be illustrated with the aid of sentences such as (1) to (9). Please note that these are only examples or exemplifications.

(1)  He has just experienced the biggest setback in his life.
(2)  Has he just experienced a new setback?
(3)  Who hasn't experienced setbacks like that?
(4)  You'll have to take your setbacks like everyone else.
(5)  Try to take your setbacks like a man!
(6)  What a lot of setbacks he has had lately!
(7)  Poor fellow, he has had to put up with an awful lot!
(8)  Go through the same things he has, and you'll see for yourself!
(9)  Would you like to feel how it feels?

All the sentences are related to or could be related to setbacks: (1) claims something. (2) asks, in principle, about the same thing. Example (3) is a rhetorical question, i.e. a question to be perceived as a statement. (4) and (5) are requests though, but with a different type of sentence. Example (6) should primarily be interpreted as an exclamation, even though it begins with an interrogative word. (7) makes basically the same statement, although in a different way. Example (8) should be perceived as a conditional statement. But it could also be a rejection of something the addressee said. (9), possibly a threat, makes no mention of any setback.

It is easy to see that partially different sentence types are involved. But how many sentence types are there, and what is the role of sentence type in an utterance's communicative function?

The same problem can also be illustrated from the pragmatic point of view. The following examples only represent a fraction of the many ways a request to leave the car at home this morning could be expressed.

(10) Make sure you leave the car at home tomorrow! I need it.
(11) The car has to be at home tomorrow! I need it.
(12) Don't take the car tomorrow! I need it.
(13) Can't you leave the car at home tomorrow? I need it.
(14) Would you please not take the car tomorrow?
(15) The car stays at home tomorrow. I need it.
(16) You have to use your bike tomorrow. I need the car.
(17) It's going to rain tomorrow, and I have to go to town.

There are several different types of sentences here too, and the propositional content varies. (17) does not even mention the car. This sentence can only be interpreted adequately if you are aware of the context in which it is uttered.

What factors enable us to interpret sentences such as (1) to (17) the way we do? Sentence type (declarative, interrogative, imperative) cannot be the only factor. Since the function of these sentences can generally be interpreted without context, function, on the other hand, cannot be merely the product of contextual factors. It seems reasonable to assume that there is a pragmatic sub-module that interacts with the grammatical module. In which case, how much or what part of the pragmatic function is governed by sentence type and sentence meaning and how much is contributed by the pragmatic module? In order to obtain answers to such questions, we have to know what sentence type is and the significance of sentence type. We also have to know what a speech act is and which speech act types there are.

So questions we have to ask are: How do we define sentence type? What is the meaning conveyed by sentence type? Which speech act types are there? How are they defined? What contribution does sentence type make to the communicative function?

What other elements in a sentence contribute to this function? How does sentence type and speech act types relate to one another? To what extent do non-linguistic modules contribute to the function of utterances?

Only after we acquire a satisfactory definition of the grammatical units enabling people to perform speech acts, only after we successfully define what a speech act is and which speech act types exist, will we be in a position to lay the foundation for more detailed studies in the field. This definitional work will also create prerequisites for approaching Project 3, i.e. the issue of how linguistic units can be combined to form texts.

This brief problem inventory provides an overview of the ground to be covered by Project 1. In the past two years, project members have worked on the general issues. The syntactic structure of the basic sentence types was defined within the framework of the government-binding (GB) theory, and the semantic structure within the framework of categorial grammar (a logical semantic calculus).

Outlining these theories here would be beyond the scope of this paper. Suffice it to say that they allow us to describe the relevant differences between sentence types.

Our aim in the year to come is, by addressing the individual issues in detail, to obtain a better definition of a speech act. In our view, a definition of sentence types must be available before the types of uses can be defined. An important step in this direction is a major paper by one of the project members who describes how a sentence's semantic structure can form the starting point for its linkage to a speech act type.

*Project 2*, like Project 1, started with an analysis of general problems. The project is studying, among other things, information structuring with the main starting point in sentences (Höhle 1982, Reis 1987, Rosengren 1989). Here, a number of typical examples can also serve as a greatly simplified illustration of a highly complex problem. Words in italics are stressed.

(19) Peter has never been to the *Vatican*.
(20) *Peter* has never been to the Vatican.
(21) Peter has *never* been to the Vatican.
(22) Peter has never *previously* been to the Vatican.
(23) Only *Peter* has been to the Vatican.
(24) I've never given that problem a thought before.
(25) Never did I give a thought to problems like that one.
(26) I was the one who'd never given a thought to problems like that one before.

We can see that the stress is on different words in sentences (19) to (23). This circumstance appears to be the reason why we interpret them somewhat differently. The difference between e.g. (19) and (20) lies in the fact that (20) emphasizes that Peter is the one who has never been to the Vatican, the implication being that others have. But there is no special emphasis of this type in (19) (although the word *Vatican* is stressed). Are the communicative differences between (19) and (20) related to semantic differences? This hardly seems to be the case. What about (22)? Even though the sentence looks as though it were negated, the reader could interpret it to mean that Peter has probably been to the Vatican *now*. The point made is that he has not previously paid it a visit. Stress on the word *never* in (21) emphasizes, correspondingly, that Peter has never visited the Vatican at any time. (23) indicates that many other potential visitors have never visited the Vatican.

The effect of changes in word order can be studied in (24) to (26). In (25), emphasis is on the first word. A similar effect is achieved in (26) compared with (24) by the use of a cleft sentence.

The task of Project 2 is to achieve more detailed rules on information structuring of this type. Therefore, the project first produced detailed descriptions of the grammatical and pragmatic parts of information structuring. In other words, we need to identify the grammatical properties that give the sentences different pragmatic functions and where these properties play a role in a grammatical model. We also need to identify the pragmatic functions which stress placement and word order may have.

To some extent, pragmatic function is related to the context in which a sentence occurs. The function may be to emphasize something in the sentence as being new information as opposed to old information. How much is perceived as new information depends partly on context. However, stress and word order may have other informative functions. Project 2 obviously works in fields touching on Project 1. But it also has links to Projects 3 and 4.

*Project 3* has the task of examining how sentences or, more accurately, speech acts, can be combined to form texts (see e.g. Gülich and Kotschi 1987, Drescher and Kotschi 1988, Motsch 1989). The project can build on results from the previous project, "Fackspråklig kommunikation (FAK)" (Technical language communications) (see Brandt et al.1983). The members of this project developed, in collaboration with scholars from the Akademie der Wissenschaften in Berlin who now are members of the program, a model describing text as a hierarchy of speech acts.

Despite its brevity, the following text has a relatively complex structure.

(27) Cheese thrives best when stored in a refrigerator. However, it should be taken out in good time before it is eaten. Keep the paper/foil on until the cheese is served. Serve the cheese on a decorative glass plate and garnish it with radishes and olives. This combination of colors makes the dish a joy to the eye.

This is an instructive text consisting of at least two parts: one part describing how to treat the cheese and another describing how it should be served. The project's task is to determine which modules are responsible for text structure and which general principles govern text formation out of smaller units.

Since the text does not consist of sentences but of pragmatic units, such as speech acts (illocutions) and combinations of illocutions, the relationship between sentence and text is not direct. On the other hand, illocutions are carried by sentences. They are also combined by grammatical devices, such as conjunctions and adverbs, forming larger units. If the sentence is the largest unit in grammar and illocution the smallest unit in pragmatics, the contact point between grammar and pragmatics is the sentence and illocution. Since text consists of illocution structures, it is itself a (global) speech act. Illocutions in turn are obviously linearized according to certain principles.

As suggested above, text also has a global information structure that is the product of interaction between different sentences with, in turn, varying information structures. Moreover, text contents also have an argumentative structure.

Thus, a text can be viewed on an abstract and static plane as the result of interaction between illocution structure, information structure and argumentation structure in which the illocutions, arranged according to certain principles and realized by sentences, form the information-bearing units.

However, texts are dynamic units whose structure is as a rule built up successively. They are formed and understood at the moment communication occurs. So they also reflect the communication process. An important part of the project's work, therefore, is to describe the principles governing changes of direction in communication, due to text production or reception itself, reflected in e.g. turn-taking signals, summaries, paraphrasing and correction).

The aim of *Project 4* is to describe, in concrete terms, the linguistic and non-linguistic contributions made by the different modules to text structure. Since the goal of the project is to analyze and produce texts, the project will have to tackle the difficult problem of where to set the boundaries between linguistic competence and our conceptual image of reality.

The project is based on a number of German and Swedish recipes. For the computer to be able to interpret a food recipe and then execute the instructions in the recipe, the computer must be able to understand the connection between the linguistic message and the kitchen environment that is a prerequisite for food preparation. It must know e.g. which tools can be used for performing a task such as *chopping onions*. It must also understand that the tasks described in the following simple steps in a simple recipe are actually highly complex and that e.g. *slowly* only refers to part of this complex task, i.e. the act of adding flour to a sauce. In other words, the idea is not for the sauce to be stirred slowly but for the flour to be slowly added to the sauce.

(30) Stir the flour slowly into the sauce.

As regards the type of text, German recipes differ from Swedish recipes in a number of interesting respects. A computer can therefore not translate word by word. It must be familiar with the rules of usage applying to linguistic expressions in the recipes in both languages. In German, you do not *chop* an onion, you *slice* it. German often uses infinitive phrases where Swedish has imperative sentences.

(31) Die kleingeschnittenen Zwiebeln in die Soße geben.

The computer must also understand that the adjective *kleingeschnittenen* (finely chopped) comprises an implicit instruction that is explicit in the Swedish recipe.

By devising a concrete model, in a limited area, of the way in which a computer comprehends a recipe in German or Swedish and executes recipe instructions, we obtain insight into what a person needs to know in order to understand a recipe and execute recipe instructions. We also obtain a picture of how much of this knowledge is linguistic and how much is non-linguistic. So Project 4 supplies factual information on the way the different modules interact and what each module contains. It can, therefore, test the validity of theoretical assumptions about the borderline between linguistic and non-linguistic knowledge (also see Schank 1977, Blume and Jakob 1983, Tremblay and Sorensen 1985, Cercone and MacCalla 1987, Bierwisch 1988, Koch 1988a, 1988b, Andric, Hansson and Koch 1989).

## *Why the selected design for our research program and how does the program work?*

The description of the different projects shows that the current problem field, despite all the restrictions imposed on text and text structure, is very large. It was obvious to me at an early stage that no single scholar or small group of scholars would be able to overview the entire field simultaneously. As a result of the heavy theorization and rapid developments in linguistics, it is becoming increasingly difficult for anyone to master any major field.

So it was obvious that many researchers with varying specialties would be needed in order cover the research field in a satisfactory manner: specialists in modern grammatical theory, pragmatic theory and computational linguistics. As a result, the idea of starting a major research program comprising multiple, suitably staffed projects gradually evolved. A program of this size could not be expected to finance all the research with research grants. Since program members would be specialists, my assumption was that they would be able to perform the research within the framework of their ordinary positions. This proved to be a correct assumption. The project directors had no difficulty in attracting interested scholars to the respective projects.

Each project director was to be responsible for her/his

project and objectives, naturally with due regard paid to the general program framework. My own task in the research program was, on the basis of the basic hypotheses and in collaboration with the project leaders, to ensure that the individual projects and sub-projects supplied new insight on the global relationship between grammar and pragmatics. Right from the start, the project leader for Project 2 has also participated actively in the organization of the program. As a result, the program became cohesive much faster than otherwise would have been the case.

The program is being financed by the Foundation and Deutsche Forschungsgemeinschaft (DFG). The project leader for Project 2 reports to the DFG. Foundation funds are used only to cover the cost of the organization and some of the program's meetings, in addition to costs for two part-time (50%) assistants.

The program has now been in operation for a little more than two years. We have had three annual sessions for all the project members. In addition, each project has had a meeting at least once a year, sometimes more often. During the first year, we sought common, firm, unambiguous frames of reference, while simultaneously getting to know one another. Each project also had to deal with its own theoretical basic issues, in relation to the program's basic hypotheses and the sub-hypotheses in the other projects. Today we have a far more solid theoretical foundation. Certain general results for the whole field are now becoming apparent.

Productivity has been high. To date, 15 issues of the S&P containing a total of 28 individual articles have been published. Many of the articles in reports have subsequently been published in international journals and books. However, equally important is perhaps the fact that a program of this size has scientific and social consequences. Contacts with international research have increased considerably, especially for Lund. We have become an interesting scientific partner in a very different way than was previously the case and are now hosts to more scholars from Germany than before. In this way, our doctoral candidates have better direct access to the research frontier than previously. This is a very desirable side-effect of the program.

One question is how a program this large works in reality. Let me merely mention one example illustrating this.

In the autumn of 1988, all the program leaders gathered in Berlin for four days for program symposium no. 2. This symposium addressed general issues in plenary session and more specialized topics at internal project meetings. At a plenary session, each project described its work during the year in such a way that issues and solutions important to the entire program were taken up. At this program meeting, it was not too hard to see how future work should be conducted.

Project 1 submitted a joint project report in which we addressed a small but central, empirical issue. With this work, we laid the foundation for a number of papers – still with the aim of creating a common, theoretical foundation – written by individual project members. This work was then discussed at a 1989 project meeting in the DDR where Project 1 met with the members of a project from the Akademie der Wissenschaften in Berlin in order to discuss common issues. The leaders of Projects 2 and 3 also participated in this meeting. Here the leader of Project 2 took up an issue whose nature encompasses both Projects 1 and 2. After this meeting, the individual project members completed their papers.

At the same time, a member of Project 1 began a major, theoretical paper based on the results of the work discussed at the project meeting.

During the summer, the leader of Project 1 met with her group in order to discuss the plenary presentation at the third annual meeting in October 1989 and with the leader and members of Project 2 in order to discuss papers written after the DDR meeting, especially a paper whose subject belonged to both Projects 1 and 2. All of these papers, plus papers written in

Project 2, served as the basis for plenary discussions at the third program meeting which took place in October 1989.

The results achieved pointed towards Project 3, i.e. the project whose task it is to produce a detailed description of text structuring. This project, in the same way as the other projects, had studied different theoretical models. The October 1989 program meeting resulted in more detailed guidelines for this project, a project highly dependent on the results of Projects 1 and 2.

To summarize, the linking of four separate projects into a coordinated program has led to intensive research across project boundaries. Since this cooperation across project boundaries has become increasingly intense, the projects play a less prominent role than before. The program "Sprache und Pragmatik" will become an organic whole. This shift from project to program is continuing and will pave the way for joint program results.

*Sture Allén*

# From grapheme to lexeme

When the Bank of Sweden Tercentenary Foundation celebrates its 25th birthday, the Department of Computational Linguistics at Göteborg University (Språkdata) will have been in existence for 24 years. Its precursor, the Research Group for Modern Swedish, was founded in 1966 with the aid of a grant from the then recently established Foundation. The project was called "Datamaskinell undersökning av tidningsprosa" (Computational investigation of newspaper prose).

In the years around 1960, several specialists in Nordic languages at different establishments in Sweden began addressing contemporary language usage and theoretical and methodological matters from a more international point of view. We had been trained according to a powerful philological tradition, and this had worked to good effect. At the time, I was studying interesting text philological problems for my dissertation on Johan Ekeblad's letters from the middle of the 17th century. However, the new signals were enticing, too. A completely new tool had also emerged, the computer. It had proved to be a major asset in my dissertation preparations and merited use for other applications.

There were many fields to investigate. Of these, phonology and morphology had attracted considerable international attention. Syntax had only been treated sparingly. Graphonomic studies were only conducted sporadically. Semantics and lexicology (not lexicography) were virtually dormant.

While still working on my dissertation, I outlined a project combining my (philological) interest in words, graphonomic studies, interest in contemporary language and curiosity about the computer's capabilities as an aid in linguistic research. This was what ultimately became the "Datamaskinell undersökning av tidningsprosa" project.

The following questions were asked: Which lexical units, in the broad sense of the term, occur in Swedish, represented by a large body of text? How common are they and how are they distributed in different kinds of texts? The main aim was to publish the results in a book on frequency.

The material was taken from five morning newspapers whose language could be described as "standard". I used the designation *bruksprosa,* "utility prose", to describe this type of Swedish. The newspapers represented three regions, viz. Stockholm, Göteborg and Malmö, Sweden's three main cities. The texts covered all of 1965 according to a specially prepared scheme and comprised a total of one million words of running text.

I had previously received a grant from the Swedish Council for Research in the Humanities to finance the requisite data acquisition. The texts were supplied in the form of punched paper tape from the newspapers' composing rooms. So we were able to avoid costly and time-consuming data entry of subject text. The acquisition procedure is even more convenient nowadays. In the project's initial phase, we were able to use some software from the previous years.

## "Nusvensk frekvensordbok" 1-2: Words and more words

Qualitative issues, especially the design of criteria for the linguistic units to be studied, consumed a considerable amount of time and energy. The strategy devised for the project is shown, somewhat simplified, in Figure 1.

The starting point for the descriptive model was the character sequence forming the text. This sequence was segmented into strings between two consecutive blank positions. The criterion

| Main phases | Descriptive levels, main criteria, lexical parts | | |
|---|---|---|---|
| | 1 Words | 2 Collocations | 3 Word elements |
| I Segmentation | *Graphic words* Syntagmatic contrast /NFO 1/ | *Combinations* Recurrence /NFO 3/ | *Graphic morphs* Commutation /NFO 4/ |
| II Separation | *Homograph components* Grammar /NFO 1/ | *Constructions* Grammar /NFO 3/ | *Homomorph components* Grammar /NFO 4/ |
| III Classification | *Lemmas* Grammar /NFO 2/ | — | *Formal morphemes* Grammar /NFO 4/ |
| IV Differentiation | — | *Idioms* Semantics /NFO 3/ | *Polysemy components* Semantics /NFO 4/ |

*Figure 1. Project strategy.*

can be called "syntagmatic contrast". We deleted punctuation marks etc. from the text words obtained this way (*lever!* and *lever*) became *LEVER*), the distinction between upper and lower case was neutralized (*lever* and *Lever* became *LEVER*) and hyphenated words were recombined (*le- ver* and *lev- er* became *LEVER*). We called the units graphic words. They constituted the first descriptive level.

The second word level was attained through the analysis of grammatical ambiguity, homography. Here, for example, the singular noun *koppar* (copper) could be distinguished from the homograph *koppar*, the plural form of the noun *kopp* (i.e. cup). In the corresponding manner, the singular noun *basar* (with stress on the second syllable, i.e. bazaar) was separated from *basar* (basses), the plural form of a singular noun, and *basar* (supervise), the present form of a verb; the adverb *åt* (tight) was separated from the preposition *åt* (to) and the verb form *åt* (ate) etc. The noun *lever* (liver) was distinguished from the verb form *lever* (live). The units on this level were referred to as "homograph components". The analysis was performed as a review, occurrence by occurrence, of a computerized concordance for the entire material. However, a sample was examined in respect to the occurrences of each of the 24 most common homographs, leading in turn to estimates of frequency and a calculation of confidence intervals.

The two cited descriptive levels were presented, along with quantitative information, in the first part of the *Nusvensk frekvensordbok baserad på tidningstext* (Frequency Dictionary of Present-Day Swedish based on newspaper material) (NFO 1, 1970). In addition. grapheme frequencies were listed in one of the appendices. We found that the elements in inflectional morphology – e a n t r s – predominated by a wide margin. They jointly accounted for 51% of all grapheme occurrences in the text.

Generally speaking, homography is one of the most characteristic properties of language. It is so widespread that two words out of three (according to our analysis) in a running Swedish text are homographic. All kinds of examples are encountered, from obvious cases such as *lever* to a more sophisticated phenomenon such as *leverans*. This example is related both to the verb *leverera* (deliver) and to the combination of *lever* (liver) and *ans* (care) to form the noun *leverans* with a theoretical but probably never used meaning (care of the liver).

There were two main types of quantitative information: "frequency" and "distribution". The observed frequency (F), i.e. the number of times a word occurred in the studied material, was a basic parameter. Since one and the same frequency value may reflect completely different distributions in sub-texts, indication of a measure of the units' distribution was also important.

We selected two types of measures of distribution, "dispersion" and "contribution". The dispersion value (D), based on the number of sub-texts, the mean value and the standard deviation, can range from 1 for a perfect distribution among sub-texts and 0 for occurrence in a single sub-text. "Sub-texts" were the five newspapers contributing to the corpus and the six topic areas into which the material was subdivided. "Contribution" was our term for a rough measure of distribution indicating which and, thus, how many sub-texts had contributed to a particular unit's frequency.

"Frequency" and "distribution" were merged in such a way that the observed frequency was multiplied by the dispersion among newspapers. The resulting value was called a "modified frequency" (Fmod). Units with an Fmod value of at least 4.125 were referred to as "basic vocabulary" and presented in particular detail. The stated minimum value was the value obtained when a unit had one occurrence in each newspaper.

Homographic separation increased the number of observed units. However, bringing inflectional forms and variant forms together in the same basic forms, lemmas, was clearly a matter of great interest. Both *lever*'s were assigned to separate lemmas: the noun *lever* and the verb *leva*. *Lev, leva, levande, levat, levde, leve, lever, levt* etc. were listed under the latter. The verb form *ge* (give) had the most forms found (24): *gav, gavs, ger, ges* (infinitive and present), *gett* (past participle), *giv, giva, givande, give, given, gives, givet, givit, givna* (perfect participle, neuter, non-neuter and plural), *gåve* etc. This procedure was performed automatically for the most part on the basis of a review of Swedish morphology. The program assigned 97% of the word forms to the correct lemma. This was naturally a great help, but the results still had to be scrutinized as a whole, since errors had to be identified (as when the system interpreted the "or" syllable in *flygmajor* (air force major) as a plural ending and assigned

| Onr | Enhet | Fmod | F | DT | DÄ | Tidn | Ämn | Sub |
|---|---|---|---|---|---|---|---|---|
| 4289 | kärnvapen *nn -et* | 12.48 | 18 | .693 | .174 | 1–5 | 123 | 3 |
| 8178 | kärra *nn -n* | 4.338 | 6 | .723 | .171 | 1345 | 56 | 2 |
| 4335 | kärv *av -t* | 12.31 | 17 | .724 | .627 | 1235 | 1–6 | 6 |
| 3076 | kö *nn -n* | 20.79 | 25 | .832 | .487 | 1–5 | 1345 | 5 |
| 7372 | köa *vb -ad* | 5.149 | 10 | .515 | .281 | 235 | 35 | 6 |
| 2071 | kök *nn -et* | 36.26 | 79 | .459 | .306 | 1–5 | 2356 | 6 |
| 6648 | kölvatten *nn -et* | 6.098 | 9 | .678 | .534 | 1235 | 235 | 2 |
| 3749 | kön *nn -et* | 15.51 | 25 | .620 | .803 | 1–5 | 1–6 | 5 |
| 7840 | könsroll *nn -en* | 4.661 | 10 | .466 | .539 | 1234 | 1236 | 4 |
| 2868 | köp *nn -et* | 23.00 | 27 | .852 | .732 | 1–5 | 1–6 | 2 |
| 357 | köpa *vb -te* | 234.6 | 259 | .906 | .666 | 1–5 | 1–6 | 12 |
| 3083 | köpare *nn -n* | 20.73 | 28 | .740 | .298 | 1–5 | 12345 | 5 |
| 1479 | Köpenhamn *pm -s* | 56.40 | 72 | .783 | .780 | 1–5 | 1–6 | 2 |
| 7412 | köping *nn -en* | 5.079 | 9 | .564 | .609 | 1235 | 2345 | 5 |
| 4636 | köpman *nn -en* | 11.05 | 18 | .614 | .394 | 1–5 | 2456 | 5 |
| 3824 | kör *nn -en* | 14.91 | 24 | .621 | .441 | 1–5 | 2356 | 5 |
| 816 | köra *vb -de* | 105.0 | 140 | .750 | .611 | 1–5 | 1–6 | 12 |

*Figure 2. From the Basic vocabulary in alphabetical order (NFO 2).*

*flygmajor* to a newly created (and non-existent) lemma (*flygma-ja*). The one million words of running text gave us 103 000 graphic words subdivided into 112 000 different homograph components listed under 71 000 different lemmas. The results on the lemma level were presented in NFO 2 (1971).

Figure 2 provides an extract from the list of "Basic vocabulary in alphabetical order". The following abbreviations were used: Onr (serial number, i.e. ranking based on Fmod), DT (newspaper dispersion), DÄ (topic-area dispersion), Tidn (contribution from newspapers), Ämn (contribution from topic areas) and Sub (number of occurrences of sublemma forms, i.e. inflection and variant forms).

A selection of the material in NFO 1-2 was published in the book *Tiotusen i topp* (Top ten thousand) (1972). The book also contains some specially processed material.

## "Nusvensk frekvensordbok" 3: Collocations

Words seldom function on an individual basis in communications. Many words are strongly linked to one another. A typical example in Swedish is the word *del*: *en del av förklaringen till* (part of the explanation for), *få del av* (receive information on), *ta del av* (study), *en betydande del av* (an important part of), *en hel del* (a considerable amount), *för en del år sedan* (some years ago), *för min del* (for my part), *i denna del av världen* (in this part of the world) etc. So the next phase of the project concentrated on linked words (collocations).

The basic methodological idea was to identify recurrent collocations in the corpus, probably producing a large number of lexically interesting units. The presence in the material of at least two identical examples was referred to as "recurrence". Sequences complying with this criterion were called "combinations". The recurrence criterion proved to be overwhelmingly fruitful. We obtained 660 000 examples of recurrent combinations, from phraseologically relevant examples, as exemplified above, to phraseologically irrelevant combinations like *det inte att* (it not that).

Our job became to separate the wheat from the chaff. The phraseologically relevant collocations are at the same time lexically selected and grammatically well-formed. Our grammatical criteria can be grouped in four categories: noun phrases, verb phrases, connectives and sentences. Seventeen types emerged: *den stora frågan* (the main issue), *i linje med* (in accordance with), *ta form* (take shape), *sköta om* (care for), *kommer att fortsätta* (will continue), *för att undersöka* (in order to investigate), *är på väg* (is in the process of), *mycket ung* (very young), *även om* (even if), *om också* (even though), *för att* (in order to), *men låt oss inte gå händelserna i förväg* (but let's not get ahead of ourselves), *det är givet att* (obviously), *kort sagt* (briefly), *som människa* (as a person), *jo då* (yes indeed).

Subsequent processing of the constructions entailed rather complex phases due in part to unit overlapping. The recurrent phrase *umgås med sina vänner* (meet with her/his friends) comprises the recurrent collocations *umgås med* and *med sina vänner*. This problem had to be resolved and assigned some transparent form of presentation. Discontinuously linked words,

| Enhet | F | Fx | För | Enhet | F | Fx | För |
|---|---|---|---|---|---|---|---|
| LIGGER 258/563 | | | | ligger inte i | 2 | 2 | 2 |
| ligger bakom* ab | 5 | 3 | 5 | ligger kanske | 2 | 2 | 2 |
| ligger bakom* pp | 14 | 14 | 13 | ligger kring | 2 | 2 | 2 |
| ligger bra till | 3 | 3 | 3 | ligger mellan* pp | 7 | 7 | 7 |
| ligger dock | 5 | 5 | 5 | ligger nu | 2 | 2 | 2 |
| ligger där | 3 | 3 | 3 | ligger nära | 8 | 2 | 8 |
| ligger däremot | 3 | 3 | 2 | ligger nära till hands | 6 | 2 | 6 |
| ligger emellertid | 3 | 1 | 3 | ligger närmare | 4 | 4 | 4 |
| ligger emellertid inte | 2 | 2 | 2 | ligger närmast | 3 | 3 | 3 |
| ligger för* pp | 3 | 3 | 3 | ligger också | 11 | 11 | 11 |
| ligger för närvarande | 3 | 1 | 3 | ligger oftast | 2 | 2 | 2 |
| ligger för närvarande hos | 2 | 2 | 2 | ligger omgivet av | 2 | 2 | 2 |
| ligger före* pp | 2 | 2 | 2 | ligger på* ab | 1 | 1 | 1 |
| ligger givetvis | 2 | 2 | 2 | ligger på* pp | 39 | 35 | 38 |
| ligger hela tiden | 2 | 2 | 2 | ligger på ett annat plan | 2 | 2 | 2 |
| ligger helt enkelt | 2 | 2 | 1 | ligger på gränsen till | 2 | 2 | 2 |
| ligger helt i linje med | 3 | 3 | 3 | ligger som | 3 | 3 | 2 |
| ligger hos | 4 | 4 | 4 | ligger till grund för | 4 | 4 | 4 |
| ligger i* pp | 69 | 56 | 65 | ligger under* pp | 7 | 7 | 7 |
| ligger i att | 7 | 7 | 7 | ligger utanför* pp | 3 | 3 | 3 |
| ligger i dag | 2 | 2 | 2 | ligger vid* pp | 7 | 7 | 7 |
| ligger i linje med | 2 | 2 | 2 | ligger väl framme | 2 | 2 | 2 |
| ligger i sakens natur | 4 | 4 | 4 | ligger väl till for | 2 | 2 | 2 |
| ligger inom | 5 | 5 | 4 | ligger öster om | 2 | 2 | 2 |
| ligger inte | 9 | 5 | 9 | ligger över* pp | 3 | 3 | 3 |
| ligger inte heller | 2 | 2 | 2 | det ligger nära till hands att | 4 | 4 | 4 |
| | | | | som ligger bakom* ab | 2 | 2 | 2 |

*Figure 3. From the Dictionary by words forming the units (NFO 3).*

in phrases such as *ta (x) ställning* (take a stand) and *på (x) sätt* (in a way) in e.g. *på ett eller annat sätt* (in one way or another), were another factor requiring special attention. So we decided to list recurrent examples of these linked words in their complete form.

The analysis on this descriptive level yielded 50 000 different constructions with 180 000 instances as "maximum-length units" examples. We extracted idioms from this comprehensive material, i.e. constructions whose meaning cannot be inferred from the meaning of component words. One example is *i elfte timmen* (at the last moment, literally: in the eleventh hour). We applied the criterion restrictively and obtained 300 units with 1 700 examples. Collocations in the form of combinations, constructions and idioms were presented in NFO 3 (1975).

Figure 3 shows an example from the list *"Lexikon per i enheterna ingående ord"* (Dictionary by words forming the units). Here, F stands for the total observed frequency, Fx for the observed frequency unit as a maximum-length unit and För for the number of authors using the respective construction (a kind of contribution information). The total number of authors amounted to 569. The entry "258/563" means that 258 of the 563 examples of *ligger* (lie) in the text are linked to the listed constructions. We called the quotient (46% here) the "constructional tendency".

As the Figure shows, the constructions were not lemmatized. This is because the units were no longer individual words but collocations. It would have been impractical to reduce e.g. *tillfälligheternas spel* (the result of coincidence) to *tillfällighet spel* and misleading to group *i tiden* (up to date) with *i tid* (in time).

One impression given by the study of the collocations was that the very large number of recurrent constructions represent a fundamental aspect of human speech. It is then necessary to envisage an enormous amount of standard collocations in each person's mental dictionary that are retrieved in communications. In another context, I referred to this phenomenon as language's *ostinato* as opposed to its *capriccio*, i.e. its creative aspects. Any psychologically credible model for linguistic production and perception must take this into account as a major factor. It has also proved to be an increasingly interesting factor in the development of e.g. systems for computerized translation.

## "Nusvensk frekvensordbok" 4: Word elements

The final phase of the NFO project directed its attention to the inner structure of words. The behavior of non-compounds as independent units and their interplay with other units in collocations had to be supplemented with an examination of their role as word elements. This would supply a far more complete picture of the actual use of the units in language.

The lemmas' entry forms in the NFO 2, with certain units deleted, such as foreign units, proper names, abbreviations and numbers, served as the material for the analysis. As a result,

55 000 lemmas were analyzed. Their text frequency amounted to 930 000, i.e. they covered 93% of the corpus.

The lemmas' entry forms consist of a small number of different kinds of word elements: prefixes, base morphs, derivational suffixes, links and, in certain instances, inflection suffixes (viz. in words such as "flerveck*ors*skägg"). In order to establish the boundaries between elements, we utilized, with certain limitations, commutation, i.e. series such as chefs*doma*-re (chief magistrate), lär*dom*saptit (appetite for learning), ung-*dom*lig (youthful), folksjuk*dom* (epidemic illness), *dom*stol (court) and *dom* (judgement). Segmentation was performed on an interactive basis by an adaptive program, i.e. a program that noted and utilized decisions made in the course of the analysis. It was based on a model for permissible character combinations (graphotactics) and was able to approximate word elements. The analysis produced 7 800 graphic morphs with a textual incidence of 1 652 000.

The separation into homomorph components, performed in conjunction with the segmentation, applied to the various types of word elements: base morphs, suffixes etc. We derived a base morph from *dom* and a noun-formative suffix, as in *sjukdom* (illness). Both *lever* and *lev* became base morphs, of course. A total of 7 900 base morphs and 560 different affixes were found. 460 of the latter were derivational suffixes and 240 of these noun-formative. The switches between prefixes, base morphs, links and suffixes can be illustrated with the following example (a single word): *o lyck s fall s för säkr ing s av del ning* (accident insurance department).

The material for the classification into formal morphemes consisted of the base morphemes. Different kinds of variation served as criteria. Examples of these types are *elv(a)* (eleven) / *elf(te)* (eleven[th]), *fabel* (fable) / *fabul(ös)* (fabul[ous]), *ess* (ace [in cards]) / *äss* (ace), *simm(a)* (to swim) / *sim(ning)* (swimm[ing]), *(upp)bär(a)* (e.g. bear [up]) / *(bil)bur(en)* (carri[ed] [by car]). Processing yielded 5 300 different units with 6 100 variants. This work was described in NFO 4 (1980).

The final descriptive level, the most interesting of all in respect to word elements, was achieved when we performed a semantic differentiation of the formal morphemes found to be polysemic. For any differentiation to be possible, paraphrasing the identified main meaning (kernel sense), and keeping it separate from other main meanings based on the same formal morpheme, had to be possible. In this way, we obtained three polysemy components for one typical example, *tipp*: *tipp* 1 as in *svanstipp* (tip of the tail), *tipp* 2 as in *topptippad* (guessed to be a likely winner etc.) and *tipp* 3 as in *slamtippning* (sludge dumping). The main listing in the NFO 4 recorded all 8 300 identified units with all their occurrences in the lemmas' entry forms. The listing was actually an advanced, semantic concordance for word elements. It is interesting to note that an ordinary Chinese dictionary contains about 10 000 (word) characters. The similarity of the numbers is not merely a coincidence.

Several lines from the list are shown in Figure 4. Ftext means the observed frequency in the text, and Flex designates the number of different lemmas in which the unit occurs.

In the highly sketchy review of the various phases, criteria and descriptive levels provided above, the thousands of individual components in the bustling life of language, the constant surprises, the recurrent model adjustments and the constantly growing volume of application conventions, could barely be touched on. But they were the things we worked with daily.

On a total of 4 400 pages the four volumes of the NFO describes 150 different processing operations on different descriptive levels with varying kinds of quantitative information, depending on the circumstances. No corresponding work appears to have been reported for any other language.

Our research results were published in the *Data Linguistica* series (Almqvist & Wiksell International) established with the publication of NFO 1 in 1970. The series is also a general forum for the subject and comprises reports on linguistic studies of text

| Enhet och kontext | Ftext | Flex | Enhet och kontext | Ftext | Flex |
|---|---|---|---|---|---|
| **lev** | **1386** | **141** | *lev* nad s reg el *nn -er* | 1 | |
| lev 'äga organisk existens' | 651 | 55 | *lev* nad s standard *nn -en* | 16 | |
| *lev* a *vb -de* | 454 | | *lev* nad s sätt *nn -et* | 2 | |
| *lev* a nde *ab* | 1 | | *lev* nad s teckn ing *nn -en* | 4 | |
| *lev* a nde *nn -t* | 1 | | *lev* nad s trött *av -t* | 1 | |
| *lev* a nde gör a *vb -de* | 6 | | *lev* nad s van a *nn -n* | 6 | |
| *lev* e bröd *nn -et* | 10 | | *lev* nad s vill kor *nn -et* | 3 | |
| *lev* e rop *nn -et* | 1 | | *lev* nad s vis dom *nn -en* | 2 | |
| *lev* erne *nn -t* | 5 | | *lev* nad s ålder *nn -n* | 1 | |
| *lev* nad *nn -en* | 3 | | *lev* nad s öd e *nn -t* | 2 | |
| *lev* nad s ban a *nn -n* | 3 | | efter *lev* a *vb -de* | 3 | |
| *lev* nad s be skriv ning *nn* | | | efter *lev* nad *nn -en* | 5 | |
| *-t* | 1 | | fort *lev* a *vb -de* | 4 | |
| *lev* nad s bild *nn -en* | 1 | | fram *lev* a *vb -de* | 2 | |
| *lev* nad s för håll a nde *nn* | | | in *lev* else *nn -n* | 22 | |
| *-t* | 5 | | in *lev* else för måg a *nn -n* | 1 | |
| *lev* nad s glad *av -t* | 2 | | kvar *lev* a *nn -n* | 9 | |
| *lev* nad s konst *nn -en* | 5 | | kvar *lev* a *vb -de* | 1 | |
| *lev* nad s konst när *nn -en* | 4 | | ren *lev* nad s man *nn -en* | 1 | |
| *lev* nad s kost nad *nn -en* | 1 | | sam *lev* nad *nn -en* | 7 | |
| *lev* nad s kost nad s in | | | sam *lev* nad s norm *nn -en* | 1 | |
| dex *nn -et* | 1 | | träd *lev* a nde *av -ø* | 2 | |
| *lev* nad s lopp *nn -et* | 1 | | väl *lev* nad s man *nn -en* | 1 | |
| *lev* nad s lyck a *nn -n* | 1 | | öken *lev* a nde *av -ø* | 1 | |
| *lev* nad s minn e *nn -t* | 1 | | över *lev* a *vb -de* | 35 | |
| *lev* nad s mönster *nn -et* | 1 | | gen om *lev* a *vb -de* | 2 | |
| *lev* nad s niv å *nn -n* | 1 | | halv ut *lev* d *av -t* | 1 | |
| *lev* nad s norm *nn -en* | 1 | | liv s *lev* a nde *av -ø* | 1 | |
| *lev* nad s om kost nad *nn* | | | samm an *lev* nad *nn -en* | 1 | |
| *-en* | 1 | | drif t s ut *lev* else *nn -n* | 1 | |
| *lev* nad s om ständ ig | | | | | |
| het *nn -en* | 1 | | | | |

*Figure 4. From the Dictionary with contexts (NFO 4).*

bodies (Swedish and foreign) and on theoretical and methodological work. Eighteen volumes have been published to date.

## Institution

Activities acquired a more solid foundation as early as 1970 when the Research Council established a research position in linguistic data processing technology. Two years later, a chair in computational linguistics was appointed at the Council. The Unit for Computational Linguistics at Göteborg University's Department of Nordic Languages was established and the research group began working within its framework. The group was formally dissolved in 1976 after termination of the Foundation grant that had been a strong source of support for a decade. However, the team continued working. Parallel projects were launched, especially the Algorithmic Text Analysis project that concentrated on automatic morphological analysis; the Syntactic Tagging (SynTag) project supported by the Foundation and dealing with syntactic analysis and tagging of part of the NFO corpus; Swedish Names that supplied material for the *Förnamnsboken* and other processed material; O.S.A. dealing with the data acquisition, storage and structuring of the Swedish Academy's *Ordbok*; *Lexikon för invandrare* (Lexin); *Lexikalisk databas/Svensk ordbok; A lexicon-oriented parser for Swedish*; and *Translator's Aid*; the latter two in collaboration with Anna Sågvall Hein.

The demand for linguistic data grew continuously. Notes to public authorities expressing the need for a service unit led to the establishment in 1975 of the Logotek language bank with two permanent employees. Over the years, this unit has supplied many people in research, language cultivation and the business sector (the graphical industry not the least) with information. It has extensive material to draw on: text covering more than 30 million running words from newspapers, novels, Riksdag minutes, legislation etc. with comprehensive lexical processing of this material. The results of completed projects are also stored. For example, the unit's manager, Martin Gellerstam, is the editor of the *Svenska Akademiens Ordlista* (Swedish Academy's glossary), and the language bank regularly provides assistance in support of the ongoing publication of the complete works of August Strindberg.

A curriculum for research education in the subject as an alternative in general linguistics was adopted in 1973. Consolidation in the field continued thereafter on a national and international basis. In 1977, the unit was transformed into an independent university department. A new curriculum was then adopted for researcher training in the subject as an independent discipline. Two years after the department was established, the professorship was transferred to Göteborg University. The popular designation "Språkdata" had been used for many years and was deemed suitable even for the new department. Today, about twenty persons work at the department. When I was appointed the Permanent Secretary of the Swedish Academy in 1986, I took a 75% leave-of-absence from my professorship. My substitute until the end of 1989 was Anna Sågvall Hein. Martin Gellerstam took over as my substitute in the spring of 1990.

The designation *"språkvetenskaplig databehandling"* arose before the term *"datalingvistik"* had become established in Swedish. Both are equivalent to the English term "computational linguistics". *"Datalingvistik"* comprises computerized upgrading of linguistic know-how, lexical know-how not the least, and the empirical know-how required for successful development of systems for analysis, synthesis, dialogue and translation, including the simulation of linguistic processes. The various activities overlap. The use of the term *"språkvetenskaplig databehandling"* indicates that the discipline is linguistics, making it a subject in the humanities.

Of the people who obtained their scientific training through work in our projects, many have submitted dissertations on subjects outside the institute framework. I have never had any objection to this interdisciplinary approach, since I feel that the results still benefitted the humanities.

Basic training in the subject was long in the form of orientation reviews and subsequently as single courses. In 1984, however, a computational linguistics line, i.e. a four-year program qualifying participants for admission to research education, was introduced. The program collaborates with the Linguistics, Philosophy and Information Processing Departments.

## Swedish dictionary

After the NFO in which meaning played an important role, especially in the fourth part, the differences between the various meanings of word elements in particular, it was natural for us to ask a question that had always been "in the air": What do words really mean if examined closely? The time seemed ripe for a semantic attack on the words we had processed in so many qualitative and quantitative ways. The result was the *Lexikalisk databas/Svensk ordbok* (Lexical database/Swedish dictionary) project.

From one point of view, this new project filled a gap in our strategy, viz. differentiation on the word level. However, the project was not any corpus study. Instead, it collected material from many quarters. So no quantitative information was involved. Nor were word meanings the only subject addressed. The project was to supply information on constructions, idioms and morphemes.

I drew up the project plan in 1976. The interim report was completed the following year. Esselte Studium decided to finance most of the project, and work was able to start in 1978. It was conducted until 1986 when *Svensk Ordbok* (SOB) (Swedish dictionary) was published. However, work continued thereafter the whole time, albeit on a reduced scale. A dictionary is never finished.

The SOB emphasis is on the definitions of the meaning of words. The lemmas were selected as entry words according to our previous definition. But a lemma is based on the formal properties of words and therefore had to be supplemented with a semantic unit. "Lexeme" was selected as the term for a kernel sense of a lemma. A lemma can thus encompass one or more lexemes.

Different definition formats were developed for different types of words. One important guideline designated that defined words would be interchangeable with their definition in sentence contexts. We also strived to limit and control the circularity (unavoidable in principle) in definitions.

One or more shades of meaning could be stated in the lexemes. These items were regarded as being derived from kernel senses by means of e.g. expansion or transfer. They were presented in the same way as the kernel senses through a cyclical structure for the lexical articles.

A characteristic feature of the general language is that word meanings are rather vaguely delineated. Putting it another way, word usage is highly flexible in language. This also applies to jargon that has entered the general language. Language users cannot be expected to employ terms like *predikat* (predicate), *export* or *elektromekanisk* (electromechanical) in ways exactly corresponding to the usage in the respective fields. A dictionary should reflect general language usage, but special comments can be included when the usage of certain words in general language differs from usage in jargon, comments such as "not in scient. contexts" for e.g. *stjärna* (star), "more stringently def. in math." for e.g. *derivata* (derivative) etc.

The SOB preface describes the book as a report from a research field. The nature of language is such that new contexts are constantly being discovered and refinements can be made without end. Language is also constantly "mobile". However, we did find that our overall theoretical and methodological concepts were valid. In eight years, we had performed a selection of entry words, written 66 000 definitions of kernel senses, specified 25 000 shades of meaning (expansions etc.), processed 4 000 idioms, specified 25 000 indirectly defined morphological examples (word-formation examples), selected 100 000 sentence examples and supplied information on style and usage, as well as, in a number of cases, on the technical field and language from which entries were borrowed. The result was a 1 500 page volume. This extremely laborious processing of Swedish vocabulary in such a relatively brief period of time would not have been possible without the experience gained from the NFO project.

Figure 5 shows the verb *leva* (to live) plus several particle verbs. The small square (□) designates the shade of meaning, an asterisk (*) an idiom and a tilde (~) a repetition of the entire entry form.

**lev/a** verb *-de, -t* el. *-at* **1** vara vid liv ⟨jfr **liv 1**⟩: *överleva; -er dina föräldrar ännu?; hon -de ytterligare två år; man -er bara en gång* ▫ ofta med tonvikt på livsinnehållet: *de -er ett stillsamt liv; man ska ~ som man lär; de -er under ytterst knappa villkor; ~ på existensminimum; ~ livets glada dagar* ▫ spec. njuta av livet: *hon hade arbetat hela sitt liv och aldrig haft tid att ~; det kändes som om han skulle börja ~ igen* ▫ spec. äv. ha sin tillvaro förlagd (till) viss plats: *de -er numera på landet; att ~ i storstaden* ✭ *få veta att man -er bli hårt ansatt; hur -er världen med dig?* hur har du det? ⟨vard.⟩; ~ *för ngn/ngt* helt ägna sitt liv åt ngn/ngt; ~ *livet* utnyttja livets glädjeämnen, roa sig; ~ *rullan/loppan* festa, svira ⟨vard.⟩ **2** (göra intryck av att) vara fylld av liv och kraft om platser m. m.: *stadens centrum -er igen; badorten -er upp på sommaren* ▫ spec. om konstnärligt verk e. d. ha förmåga att fängsla: *han är död, men hans böcker -er; sångerna skall alltid ~ inom oss; tyvärr -er inte hans romanfigurer* ▫ äv. (i tävlingssammanhang) om boll e. d. ˙vara i spel ▫ äv. om tävling e. d. (alltjämt) vara spännande: *när NN reducerade till 2−1 -de matchen plötsligt igen* **3** med prep. livnära sig på visst sätt: *det är svårt för två att ~ på en lön; ~ på grönsaker; ~ på räntor; de hade inget att ~ av* ▫ äv. överfört, spec. stimuleras (av): ~ *på gamla minnen* ▫ spec. äv. ha såsom förutsättning: *romanen -er helt på personskildringarna* ✭ ~ *på luft* livnära sig på (nästan) ingenting **4** med

prep. el. partikel ha såsom (nära) umgängespartner: *flera familjer måste ~ tillsammans i det lilla huset* ▫ särsk. ha såsom sexuell partner: *hon -er ihop med en äldre man; de -de tillsammans i många år innan de gifte sig; makarna hade -t samman i 30 år* ▫ äv. med avs. på abstrakta företeelser ständigt sysselsätta sig (med): *jämlikhetsfrågorna har hon -t med i många år* ▫ spec. med avs. på negativa företeelser uthärda: *mänskligheten måste ~ med kärnvapenhotet* **5** vara livlig (och föra oväsen) ⟨syn. stoja⟩ ⟨vard.⟩: *det var värst vad barnen -er i kväll* ▫ äv. överfört om naturföreteelse: *vinden -er i trädkronorna* ▫ spec. om segel fladdra (utan att fyllas av vinden)

**lev/a me'd** verb *-de, -t* el. *-at* • ofta med prep. med stor inlevelse höra eller se: *barnen -de helt med i pjäsen*

**lev/a om'** verb *-de, -t* el. *-at* särsk. föra ett utsvävande liv ⟨syn. svira⟩: *när han fick arvet åkte han till Paris och -de om ordentligt*

**lev/a sig in'** verb *-de, -t* el. *-at* • med prep. med stor inlevelse föreställa sig: *han kunde inte ~ i hennes situation; en skådespelare som helt -er sig in i sina roller*

**lev/a upp'** verb *-de, -t* el. *-at* **1** få nya krafter el. nytt liv: *efter framgången -de hon upp en smula; den gamla sången -er upp på nytt* **2** göra slut på tillgångar e. d. ⟨syn. förslösa⟩: *han -de upp hela arvet* **3** med prep. **till** motsvara: *han kunde inte ~ till förväntningarna*

**lev/a u't** verb *-de, -t* el. *-at* • ge fritt utlopp för känslor, aggressioner e. d.: ~ *sina drifter*

*Figure 5. From Svensk ordbok.*

There was obviously a need for a dictionary like the SOB. Nearly 70 000 copies have been sold to date. Many readers have accepted our invitation at the beginning of the book to send us their comments and suggestions. New editions benefit from their observations. The dialogue continues.

## Contacts

At the initiative of our department, Nordic summer schools in linguistic data processing were held for a number of years in the 1970's and 1980's. The first course was held in Marstrand in 1972. In the summer of 1977, the course was held in Palo Alto, California, where we have important contacts. As a result of these and other activities, Nordic collaboration was built up and has been of considerable importance to the field's development.

Among other things, this Nordic collaboration led to the start of the Nordic Computational Linguistics conferences. The first such conference was held in Göteborg in 1977 and the most recent one in Reykjavik in 1989.

Having an opportunity to arrange a Nobel Symposium with participation by scholars on the highest international level was a great experience. The theme I selected was "Text Processing". The symposium was held at IBM's Nordic Education Center on Lidingö Island in 1980. Six years later, another Nobel Symposium was held there. This time, the theme was "Possible Worlds in Arts and Sciences".

The Association for Literary and Linguistic Computing (ALLC) is an international organization in the research field. Among other things, the ALLC publishes a journal and holds conferences. The XIVth International ALLC Conference was held in Göteborg in 1987. The conference series referred to as COLING (International Conference on Computational Linguistics) also offers numerous opportunities for establishing international contacts.

The Lexicographica series (Max Niemeyer Verlag, Tübingen) is another contact forum. I have been its co-editor since its inception in 1984. Twenty-nine volumes have appeared to date.

In recent years, the Council of Europe has become involved in the field nowadays called "language industries". One important reason for this development is the need to protect Europe's linguistic diversity in an information industry in which English predominates. We are part of a committee conducting a computational linguistics project under the Council's aegis.

One of the biggest international research and development programs in our field concerns the EC's computerized translation project, Eurotra. 150 scholars in twelve countries are working on the project on a long-term basis. We have been asked to evaluate the project's (computational) linguistic results in two phases.

## The future

The original used in printing the SOB was generated by software using the lexical database. This database is in itself an interesting subject for research opening up opportunities for detailed investigations of the vocabulary's semantic structure. The strict formats for definitions of the different kinds of words make it possible to examine, after analysis of the definitions in various respects (disambiguation, lemmatization, syntactic tagging), e.g. functional classes and hierarchical classes in the vocabulary. Examples of an instrumental, functional class are *spetta* "bryta med spett" (break up with a crowbar), *skyffla* "flytta med skyffel" (move with a shovel) and *kratta* "jämna med kratta" (smooth with a rake). Examples of the numerous hierarchical classes are *kasack* (a long garment) – *plagg* (garment) – *föremål* (object) – *företeelse* (fact) – *ngt* (someth.) in an ascending degree of abstraction, i.e. *ngt* (an abbreviation for *något* – something) is at the top in this context. A thesaurus, based on a language's semantics (and not on a tentative description of the world), is a dream. It would represent the completion of a line of research pursued for many years. Many potential applications in different kinds of knowledge-based systems, semantic parsing (sentence analysis), text generation and computerized translation, as well as in other contexts, spring immediately to mind and are likely to acquire increasing importance in the Department's future research work.

This is the state of the research frontier at the present time. Similar projects are being launched in different parts of the world, although usually based on dictionaries already in print and not on any dynamic, modifiable, lexical database. One decisive factor is that the lexicon and lexical semantics are being recognized as central parts of the increasingly comprehensive computational linguistic systems being devised.

In closing, let me note that I have had the pleasure of sharing the research adventure with a rather large number of like-minded scholars over the years. In my work on this paper, they were never far from my thoughts.

*Bengt Sigurd*

# Social reforms and Newspeak

When George Orwell coined the term "Newspeak" (the title of an appendix in his book "1984", published in 1941), he created a word which was to become famous all over the world as the designation of linguistic manipulation whose purpose is to impose a particular ideology on people and prevent them from thinking in any other way. But Orwell also pointed to an interesting research field for socially oriented linguistics, semantics, pragmatics and sociolinguistics and re-raised the old discussion about the power of language over thought. A number of Newspeak studies have examined the language in dictatorships, Stalin's Soviet Union in particular, in which linguistic directives were intended as devices for controlling the people's thinking and contributed to the obliteration of history (see e.g. Oppenheimer 1961-62). Another field attracting great interest is the language differences between East and West Germany where words such as *Kommunismus* (Communism), *Friede* (Peace) and *Demokratie* (Democracy) had very different meanings in the respective countries (for an overview, see Stedje 1989). Even Hitler's language purification campaign, in which e.g. the word *Auto* (of Greek origin) was to be replaced by the Germanic term *Kraftwagen*, is a frequently cited example of Newspeak.

Bolinger's widely used textbook, "Aspects of Language" (1975), contains a chapter, *Mind in the grip of language*, that, in turn, contains a section called *Control by language*. Here, Bolinger discusses the possible effect of different designation strategies, as when a South American calls a screwdriver an *atornillador* (screwing in device) and a Spaniard uses the term *destornillador* (screw remover), or the bias of the word *man* in words like *horsemanship* (women still display "horsemanship" when they go riding). A well-known Swedish example is *justeringsman* (minutes checker), now somewhat facetiously changed to *justeringsperson* with varying degrees of success. Another example is the perverse use of the term *sköterska* (nurse, i.e. a noun with a feminine ending; there is no equivalent masculine noun with the same meaning) even for male nurses ("Sister Kent"). Since higher education terms will be discussed below, it is interesting to note that some American universities have replaced the term *credit* because they feel it evokes excessively economic associations.

For a number of years, the Bank of Sweden Tercentenary Foundation supported a project concentrating on a kind of Newspeak. It was called "Verbala reformer" (Verbal reforms) and studied the linguistic side of social reforms. The most interesting feature of this project is the fact that it had some influence on higher education in Sweden, viz. by contributing to the reintroduction of the undergraduate degree *filosofie kandidat* (usually abbreviated "fil. kand.", roughly equivalent to a Bachelor of Arts or Science). The project was led by the author. Anna Orrling Welander served as a project assistant. The project was based on the observation that reforms in society often have an objective side and a linguistic side. Ideological keywords and words for important phenomena and changes are linked to the objective changes politicians strive to achieve. These keywords bear up the reforms and signal their ideology.

The Swedish public is undoubtedly aware that new words are often introduced in conjunction with reforms, such as the nominal term *obligatorium* (obligatory measure) in conjunction with the obligatory health insurance program. The public probably feels that these words sometimes reflect only cosmetic changes intended to obscure what is really involved. Letters to the Editor in newspapers often cite such words. Typical words in this context are *lokalvårdare* (literally: one who cares for localities, i.e. a euphemism for an "office cleaner" or "charwoman"), *revitalization area* (an area where all the trees have been cut down), *disponibel bruksarea* (available utilization area, i.e. floor space in a residence), *lågpresterande* (poor performance, i.e. bad), *servicehus* (a kind of old-age home that has replaced the *poorhouse* of yesteryear to some extent), *engångsskatt* (non-recurrent tax, i.e. an extra tax that could indeed recur), *miljöavgift* (environment conservation fee, i.e. a tax that could certainly be used for non-conservation purpose) and *tillfälligt sparande* (temporary saving, i.e. a form of saving some people refer to as "compulsory saving"). But the public may still not be aware of the extent to which it is manipulated with the aid of verbal tricks. And politicians are probably not fully aware that their reform proposals have a material side and a verbal side and that the success of their proposals depends as much on verbal aspects as on material aspects.

The Foundation project "Verbala Reformer" yielded material and comments on word selection terminology and word formation. The project also yielded fragments of a general linguistic denotation theory as can be glimpsed in Orrling Welander's paper on slang words (1983). The "Verbala Reformer" project found an excellent object for study in the Higher Education reform of 1977 and subsequently. The present paper will concentrate on this reform. But the "Verbala Reformer" project also studied slang words, since they have been found to shed interesting light on official reform language. Slang words ridicule the event or person they denote, whereas the aim of reform words is just the opposite: to induce positive attitudes.

The results of the "Verbala Reformer" project were employed in discussions in the "UHÄ:s Planeringsberedning för kultur- och informationsyrken" (National Board of Universities and Colleges [UHÄ] Planning Committee for Cultural and Information Occupations), of which the author was a member for a time, and in articles and debates in the media (see the

References). The most important of these publications was probably the article "Högskolan som verbal reform" (Higher education as a verbal reform) in the journal "Forskning och Framsteg" (FoF) 8/1981.

The present article is based to a large degree on the article in "Forskning och Framsteg", but it also supplies some glimpses of the decision-making process in the UHÄ.

## Keywords in higher education reforms of the 1970's

If a writer wishes to denote persons in a discourse, he can often designate them with a pronoun, e.g.: "*De* skall anmäla sig till ämnesinstitutionerna" (*They* are to register at the respective departments). But in other instances, the persons must be designated by the mention of some characteristic property or some typical activity. A longer sentence with a relative pronoun could then be used, e.g.: "*De som studerar/vill studera* skall anmäla sig till ämnesinstitutionerna" (*Those who are studying/wish to study* are to register at the respective departments). A noun can also be used as the subject of the sentence, such as *student* (student) or *studerande* (the present participle of the verb "to study", used here as a noun: "a person or persons studying"), e.g. "*Studenter/Studerande* skall anmäla sig till ämnesinstitutionerna". Some subtleties of meaning are often lost when a statement is compressed in a nominal label this way, but everyday communication would not work if people did not have a large vocabulary of short words and stock expressions to call upon or were unable to construct new expressions as needed. See Brown "How shall a thing be called?" (1958).

However, one of the characteristic features of simple, short words is the circumstance that they can readily acquire positive or negative connotations. It is for this purpose reformers attempt to suppress certain words and invent new ones designed to reflect the spirit of their reforms. For reform opponents, however, the new words are tainted by the spirit of the reforms, and opponents try not to let themselves be fooled by the new labels. Reformers frequently employ these keywords in order to show that they are insiders, and opponents find it easy to identify adherents through their choice of words.

Many examples of linguistic manipulation can be found in the higher education reforms of the 1970's, i.e. new words used frequently or incorporated into regulations or other words that were suppressed. In the 1970's, reformers felt that the connotations of the word *student* were far too bourgeois (the designation was previously used for graduates from the former, elite upper secondary school only attended by a minority of Swedish teenagers). So the word *student* is found only exceptionally in new regulations just after 1977, and many university bureaucrats devoted considerable time and energy to deleting the word *student* whenever it was used, by force of habit, in curricula etc. The reformers tried to introduce the term *studerande* as an alternative. But reformers were unsuccessful in eradicating the word *student*, and the words are used interchangeably today. The difference between the Swedish words *student* and a *studerande* is that a *student* has completed high school education and matriculated, whereas a *studerande* is still studying somewhere at some level in the educational system (making the term "studerande" a more accurate equivalent of the English term "student"). It is hard not to suspect that the reformers were also anxious to blur the distinction between people who had concluded their education and those who continued to study as they tried to blur the distinction between different educational levels by using the word *högskolan* (literally, "high school" but meaning "higher education" here) for all higher, theoretical education and post-high school practical vocation training.

The 1977 Higher Education reform is a verbal reform to a great degree, i.e. a reform that advocates attempted to implement through the introduction of new terms, the deletion of old terms, or assignment of new meanings to old terms. The reformers wanted to replace the word *universitet* (university) with the word *högskola* whenever possible. The entire higher education system would be referred to as *högskolan*, even if the supervising authority retained the name *Universitets- och Högskoleämbetet* (National Board of Universities and Colleges), abbreviated UHÄ. Its director was also allowed to retain the title *Universitetskansler* (Chancellor of the Swedish Universities), even though logic dictates that he should have been called *Högskolekansler* or *Universitets- och Högskolekansler.*

In Swedish higher education, the term *universitet* has been the designation for institutions in Lund and Uppsala for many centuries. The Swedish names of a number of Swedish schools of higher education contain the noun *högskola*, such as "Kungl. Tekniska Högskolan" in Stockholm (Royal Institute of Technology), "Chalmers Tekniska Högskola" in Göteborg (Chalmers Institute of Technology) and the "Lärarhögskolan i Stockholm" (Stockholm School of Education). These institutes have a typical professional or vocational orientation. There were also institutes of higher education that called themselves "akademier" (academies), such as the "Musikaliska Akademien" (Royal Academy of Music) and "Konstakademien" (Royal Academy of Art). But the educational reformers in 1977 felt that *högskola* was a term with the right sound, even though there was already a confusing word, *folkhögskola* (literally folk high school) denoting lower level institutions of a different type. The higher education reformers also ignored the fact that the word *högskola* could be confused with the English term *high school*, leading to problems in international communications. So that was what could happen in 1977 when reformers disregarded the importance to Sweden of having institutions, educational programs and degrees in conformity with the international system.

## The new "higher education degree" and old "fil.kand."

In 1978, the UHÄ adopted a decision in which undergraduate degrees were introduced for certain professions, such as the *läkarexamen* and *logopedexamen* (higher education degree in medicine and degree in logopedics respectively), but most degree designations had to follow the pattern "Högskoleexamen på X-linjen" ("higher education degree in X"), so the "fil.kand." (bachelor of arts or science), "med.kand." (bachelor of medicine), and "teol.kand." (bachelor of theology) degrees were abolished. This was an ideological decision. The old degree designations were felt to be "too bourgeois or academic".

Criticism of the abolition of the "fil.kand." degree was prompt. The new proposal was felt to be clumsy. The need for an internationally acceptable degree to present to public agencies and employers was considerable. Humanities graduates were at a disadvantage because their typical degree, the "fil.kand.", had been abolished. The stack of certificates from completed *enstaka kurser* ("separate courses", see below), which was the only thing students who did not follow a certain line could get, did not impress Swedish or foreign authorities or employers who were accustomed to diplomas on fancy paper and a seal. Many university teachers also failed to notice that the "fil.kand." degree had been abolished and the general public found it hard to believe that the educational authorities had abolished an old, well-established degree like "fil.kand".

In 1982, the author suggested to the UHÄ Planning Committee for Cultural and Information Occupations that the "fil.kand." degree be reintroduced. My arguments showed how the Higher Education reform's vocabulary had caused problems for students, university teachers and employers in Sweden and abroad. This ultimately led to a commission on a new educational line in the humanities, even though this was not my original inten-

*Figure 1. Old and new words for university students (drawing from Forskning och Framsteg).*

tion. The ensuing proposal on a humanities program was circulated for comments but received little support. However, almost every official comment felt that the proposed degree designation "fil.kand." was excellent. The proposal to reintroduce the "fil.kand." degree was discussed in many quarters in the media (see the References). UHÄ took note of the response and cited the "fil.kand." degree in a positive light in its budget request for 1986. The 1986 budget bill responded by directing the UHÄ to undertake a review of degree designations. This was quickly accomplished, and the "fil.kand." degree was reintroduced (with new demands on credits), and soon became a popular degree with many students.

Studying the way more or less official designations for "students/studerande" over the years is interesting. The drawing above indicates differences in language usage.

## Lines/programs and "separate courses"

Another important consequence of the 1977 reform was the sharp distinction drawn between narrow, professional ("useful") education and free (unrestricted) studies. Every aspect of the new system reflects this subdivision, for example, in the difference between *utbildningslinjer* (vocational education lines) and *enstaka kurser* (separate courses). In the old system, students studied subjects in the various disciplines, such as mathematics, physics, astronomy, political science, sociology, psychology, Nordic languages, semitic languages etc., and combined them into e.g. a "fil.kand." (B.A. degree). The new system, as clearly reflected in the terminology used, was contrary to the old system's subject-orientation.

Defining professional training programs for physicians, architects, engineers, jurists and teachers was not difficult. The new system worked well for these professions, since they received more funds and top priority. New professional programs for actors, musicians and media producers also received good funding, since they represented a definite adaptation to certain occupations. However, the subdivision was disastrous for students of social science and the humanities; their labor market is far more varied. With the aid of the term *enstaka kurser*, the funding system transformed the humanities into a second-rate field. The situation was not improved by political rhetoric on the importance of the humanities.

Only one line of training was offered in the humanities, viz. the "kulturkommunikationslinje" (training program for cultural communications), whose name was subsequently changed to "kulturvetarlinje" (program for cultural workers). But this still seems like a desperate attempt to incorporate free studies in a constricted educational system and most students with these talents prefer "free" studies. In Lund, about 75 students are admitted to the "kulturvetarlinje" each term, whereas there are more than 2 000 students taking separate courses, despite every attempt to counteract this trend. It is interesting to note that even the students admitted to the "kulturvetarlinje" prefer the "fil.kand." title option now that it is available.

Separate courses only receive half the funding allotted to professional programs, and study counsellors never hesitate in describing *enstaka* courses as second-rate (or even "wooly") courses. The word *enstaka* ("unique", "separate") indicates that a course is only given on some separate occasion and held by temporary teachers. However, this is not the case in humanities departments. Large departments were forced to "squeeze" their traditional core courses (now referred to as 20-credit courses, 40-credit courses etc.) into the confines of "separate course". University teachers who experienced the proposals submitted at the end of the 1970's never envisaged the enormous impact the artificial subdivision into programs and separate courses was to have. The social sciences and humanities are still struggling to achieve funding of equal magnitude for all university courses.

## Slang designations and designations for professions

The "Verbala Reformer" project shed light on language usage in the old and new higher education systems and attempted to identify guiding principles and values in word formation. The project also examined language usage in the 1982 Social Services Act, as well as titles and designations for professions.

The creativity required by reformers when they coin new terminology has a parallel in the inventiveness displayed by slang, the difference being that slang has the opposite connotation. Whereas bureaucrats strive to find abstract words that alter a program's or profession's status, slang words utilize concrete, human foibles as their starting point in ridiculing an event or profession. The 1982 Social Services Act referred to *övervakare* (literally: a person who watches over [someone], i.e. a parole officer) as a *kontaktperson* (contact person). But slang used less flattering terms for these occupations. A government commission suggested using the terms *vaktkonstapel* (prison guard) or *vårdare* (keeper) for a *fångvaktare* (jailer), but inmates prefer calling this officer the Swedish equivalent of "screw". As a consequence of these observations the "Verbala Reformer" project also examined the inverted world of slang; the results were reported in Anna Orrling Welander's article "Prälle, svartrock, himlalots – om slang för yrken" (1983).

People need designations of varying dignity for different situations and purposes. Official designations are not always useful in every context. Fortunately, language users invent appropriate words, including slang words, a process serving as a kind of safety valve.

The "Verbala Reformer" project also studied occupational designation at different times as background for an analysis of occupational titles in academia and the occupational designations laid down in the 1982 Social Services Act. Anna Orrling (unpublished manuscript) studied the help wanted ads in certain newspapers in 1930, 1940, 1950, 1960, 1970 and 1980 and made several interesting observations. In the 1930's and 1940's, there were still occupational designations containing the word *jungfru* (maid, single woman), *arbeterska* (female worker), *expeditrice* (female salesperson in a shop or store), *mamsell* (miss) and *dräng* (farm hand, male laborer). Numerous occupational designations contained the word *biträde* (assistant), such as *affärsbiträde, manufakturbiträde, konditoribiträde, grammofonbiträde, skobiträde, kassabiträde, kontorsbiträde* and *husfrubiträde*. The term *biträde* is still useful in new compound words, as in the Social Services Act's *vårdbiträde* (orderly). But *biträde* is often replaced nowadays with *assistent* (assistant) as illustrated by words such as *personalassistent, hemvårdsassistent, fritidsassistent, forskningsassistent, laboratorieassistent* and *barnomsorgsassistent*.

The use of occupational designations containing the word *konsulent* (consultant), such as *personalkonsulent, säljkonsulent, hemslöjdskonsulent* and *läkemedelskonsulent* is increasing

– as is the word *konsult*. This is also the case for occupational designations containing the word *chef* (manager), as in *försälj-
ningschef, platschef, fritidschef, servicechef, driftschef, avdel-
ningschef, sektionschef* and *datachef*. Certain initial words in
compounds, such as *service,fritids* (leisure time), *daghems* (day
nursery) and, of course, *data* (data processing), are typical of
our time.

In the 1930's, there were numerous occupational designations showing that the occupations were for women (e.g.
*arbeterska, bagerska, försäljerska, frisörska, flicka [kontors-
flicka, skrivmaskinsflicka], mamsell, expeditrice, fru* and *frö-
ken*). Gender-specific occupational designations have largely
disappeared in modern Swedish (apart from *sköterska* and
*barnmorska* [midwife]). The contemporary, equal opportunity
Swedish society appears to prefer non-gender designations for
professions.

## Words in the Social Services Act

The "Verbala Reformer" project also examined the vocabulary
in the 1982 Social Services Act (certain observations about its
vocabulary were also published in Gellerstam 1984). The fact
that vocabulary in the social services field has always been the
subject of spontaneous or guided development is well-known.
Attempts to make some "touchy" subjects more acceptable by
giving them new names, to introduce new values or obscure
what things are really about can be suspected. For example, the
new Social Services Act replaces the term *fosterhem* (foster-
home) with *familjehem* (family home), probably to convey a
more intimate (familiar) impression and to divert thinking from
"fostering", a concept virtually abolished in school regulations
from this period. Neither the term *fosterbarn* (foster-child) nor
*fosterföräldrar* (foster-parents) occur in the 1982 Social Services Act. Does this mean that these children are to be called

Social reforms and Newspeak · 409

*barn i familjehem* (children in family homes) and parents to be called *familjehemsföräldrar* (family home parents)?

The term *socialvård* (social care) was replaced with *social-tjänst* (social service) in the 1982 Social Services Act. *Hemsa-marit* (home helper) was replaced with *vårdbiträde* (orderly), a change that is hard to understand and that has hardly caught on. Are trade unions opposed to the connotations associated with the word *samarit* (metaphorical use of the Biblical word "Samaritan")? The term *ålderdomshem* (old-age home) was replaced by *servicehus* (service building) that in fact designates something entirely different. *Pensionärer* (old age pensioners) are not mentioned in the Social Services Act at all. Things previously called *barnhem* (orphanage) and *ungdomshem* (juvenile home) are now referred to as *hem för vård eller boende* (homes for care or residency), a long and clumsy term that has not proved to be popular with welfare workers or the public. Some people refer to these homes as "paragraph 12 homes" because they are mentioned in paragraph 12 of the Social Services Act. This shows how impossible it is to have a long noun phrase as the designation for something to which people frequently refer. However, this phrase did contribute to the spread in the use of the word *boende* (residency) in Swedish.

The term *omsorg* (care) is being used to an increasing degree e.g. in words such as *barnomsorg* and *äldreomsorg*. But the bureaucratic designation *Omsorgsstyrelsen* (a social welfare board for the retarded) was offensive to many people, at least initially. The intimate sense originally conveyed by *omsorg* has faded somewhat in the course of time.

## Conclusions

The "Verbala Reformer" project yielded two important conclusions. One is that the study of the new vocabulary accompanying social reforms with linguistic (semantic, pragmatic and sociolinguistic) methods is fruitful. The impact of this vocabulary on the language and thinking of people may be considerable in a relatively monolingual, media-fixated, tightly controlled country like Sweden. People interested in instituting some reform would find it worthwhile to give careful thought to the vocabulary they wish to use in convincing the citizenry of the reform's merit and inducing them to think and act in the desired way. Forecasts can be made about the survival and impact of words. People who choose to resist a reform and even re-introduce an earlier system would do well to study the reform's vocabulary so as to reveal the philosophy underlying terms. The studies of the Higher Education reform's vocabulary published by the "Verbala Reformer" project did indeed direct attention to the terminology's underlying ideology and disadvantages. It was easier to show why the humanities were misfavored and what students were missing out on. The reintroduction of the "fil.kand." degree then became easier.

The second conclusion – and the one that may be most interesting to the Foundation – is that scientific projects can actually bring about social change. This is naturally nothing new where technical projects are concerned. Just think of the effects produced by inventions such as the telephone, automobile, transistor, TV, computers and satellite communications. But finding that a purely descriptive, linguistic project had an impact on society is something new. So the conclusion must be that even projects such as these are capable of conveying benefits.

*Svante Lindqvist*

# History of technology as an academic discipline

## *Introduction*

The importance of research support is not necessarily in proportion to the size of the financial grant. Even a relatively modest sum can, if disbursed at the right time, be of major importance to the instigation of research in new, important fields. Analogously, a foundation's decision to support unconventional projects may have a long-term impact on the initiation of interdisciplinary research. If a new project results in the increased recruitment of scholars to a new field, the result of such a measure could ultimately be counted in man-years, conceivably in entire research careers. Effects would then extend beyond the face value of grants, if the latter could have been translated into a number of man-months. The point in time and the nature of a project could therefore be more important factors than grant magnitude in the establishment of new fields of research.

One example of support given at the right time to an unconventional project was the 1984 decision by the Bank of Sweden Tercentenary Foundation to support a guest chair in the history of technology at the Royal Institute of Technology (KTH). The professorship was established for an American scholar, Professor Thomas P. Hughes of the University of Pennsylvania. The idea was for him to spend three weeks a year at the KTH, giving lectures and holding seminars. The purpose of the guest professorship was to stimulate interest in the history of technology and research in history of technology in Sweden.

The Foundation declared itself willing to support the project over a five-year period. In its presentation of the project in the spring of 1984, the Foundation wrote: "Opportunities for continuous contacts with scholars, graduate students and students are important, in our view". The presentation also noted that the guest professorship would promote international contacts in the field of humanistic studies of technology. The grant, SEK 40 000 a year for 5 years, is far below the average for projects receiving support from the Foundation in the 1980's. (The average size of annual grant in 1989 amounted to about SEK 300 000.) As the following will show, this was still a grant that made a major contribution to establishment of history of technology as an academic discipline in Sweden.

## Growth of history of technology as an academic discipline

As early as 1937, Torsten Althin, the first director of the National Museum of Science and Technology, suggested that "research and teaching in the history of engineering be made the subject of the same or similar public attention and assume the same position in the social machinery" as traditional history subjects, i.e. general history, the history of law, economic history, history of art etc. The National Museum of Science and Technology had been founded in 1924 at the initiative of industry as one phase in the attempts by Swedish engineers at the beginning of the century to gain recognition as a professional group. Pointing to the profession's long traditions and its historical importance to the nation's social and economic development was one of several ways to enhance the status of engineers.

Torsten Althin had obtained his museological training under Sigurd Erixon at the Nordic Museum. In 1934, Erixon became a professor of Nordic and comparative ethnography, a subject that had emerged as an academic parallel to the Nordic Museum and Skansen. In 1941, the Institute for Nordic Ethnology was founded in close association with the museum. Althin hoped that the National Museum of Science and Technology would acquire an academic equivalent in a subject dealing with the history of engineering. This never happened. One reason was the inherent contradiction in the very idea: on the one hand, industry's interest in elucidating the background of modern technological development in "its own" museum and, on the other hand, a museum's traditional needs and attitudes towards collecting, documenting and teaching through exhibitions.

The National Museum of Science and Technology was built up along the same lines as the Deutsches Museum in Munich. In many respects, the former was a smaller scale copy of its famous model, although architecturally inspired by the functionalism of the 1930's. However, the Museum's contents were influenced by its founders and financing. The subdivision into various basic exhibitions largely followed Swedish industry's subdivision into sectors, and the relative size of the basic exhibitions reflected the position of the respective industrial sectors. The Museum became something of a mirror of industrial Sweden of the 1930's rather than a showcase for the historical importance of the different areas of technology. The historical aspect became of subordinate importance. As a result, Museum activities never acquired strong support in the academic world. Thus, the National Museum of Science and Technology differed greatly from other Swedish museums, such as the National Museum of Fine Arts, the National Historical Museums and the Swedish Museum of Natural History, all with academic equivalents at universities.

Sigvard Strandh, Althin's successor at the National Museum of Science and Technology's, was keenly aware of this problem. At the end of the 1960's, Strandh vainly attempted to interest various university departments in the Museum's activities. Among other things, lecturers and doctoral candidates at Stockholm University's department of history were invited to discussions at the Museum of important research tasks. Referring to the Museum's needs, Hans Lindblad (Lib.), submitted a bill (no. 967) in the upper house in 1970 in which he suggested that "the Riksdag propose that the King-in-Council establish a research and education department in history of technology at some appropriate institution". However, this initiative, like many others at this time, was fruitless.

This situation changed in the 1970's. The reason was, quite simply, increased awareness of the importance of technology to the environment and society. The 1950's simplified view of technology, reflected in terms like the "Atomic Age" and "Plastic Age", followed by the environmental debate of the 1960's, was superseded by a wish for deeper understanding of technological change. At the universities, scholars in different disciplines developed an interest in technology. One example of this new interest was e.g. the "Attitudes to Technology" symposium held by the Foundation (Sörbom 1978). The increasing interest in technology in the 1970's as a social and cultural phenomenon also fostered the need for a historical dimension: historical case studies that deepened our understanding of technology and its evolution, as well as inquiries into the roots of the modern technological society.

One result of this new historical interest at the universities was the project "Engineers and Scientists in the Industrial Revolution", financed by the Foundation. Within the project, three important books were published, books that can be described as the beginning of modern research in history of technology in Sweden (Torstendahl 1975, Runeby 1976, Eriksson 1978). The Foundation was also important to the inception and contents of the new interdisciplinary research established at Linköping University at the end of the 1970's. In the 1980's, the Technology and Social Change department (Tema T) there developed into the country's liveliest department for the study of technology. As the following remarks show, it also became of major importance to the research in history of technology.

At the engineering schools at the beginning of the 1970's,

history of technology programs had been established, albeit on an institutionally weak basis. Both the Chalmers Institute of Technology (CTH) and the Royal Institute of Technology (KTH) offered courses for engineering students. Thus, interest in and the need for the new subject was subdivided into two sectors at an early stage, viz. an increasing university interest in *research* and an increasing need for basic *education* at the engineering schools. The situation was further complicated by the presence of a third party in the institutional picture. In 1968, the Royal Swedish Academy of Engineering Sciences (IVA) had established a History of Technology Council. Among other things, the Council collected contemporary documentation by interviewing older engineers (Ljungberg 1976) and published a bibliography of Swedish industrial history (Sandqvist 1979).

Thus, increasing interest in the history of technology was displayed from several different quarters and could not be coordinated in any lasting way. However, the turning point came in 1974 when the National Museum of Science and Technology celebrated its 50th anniversary. Industry then established a fund, the "1974 Museum of Science and Technology Anniversary Fund" whose annual yield was to be used for holding international symposia on the history of technology. One expressed intention was to interest younger scholars in the history of technology. The fund was managed by a board, the symposia committee, with Nils-Eric Svensson as its chairman.

In retrospect, we can see that the symposia committee's composition was highly favorable. It had representatives of all the history of technology activities that had emerged at universities, engineering schools, the National Museum of Science and Technology and the IVA in the 1970's. All the interested parties were gathered in an organization able to take concerted action. The Museum's first international symposium, "Technology and Its Impact on Society", at Hässelby Castle in 1977, was also the first time all these groups had assembled. Here, for example, Gunnar Eriksson, Rolf Torstendahl and Nils Runeby presented the results of their project "Engineers and Scientists in the Industrial Revolution", and Sven Tägil reported on plans for the new Tema T research organization at Linköping University (Strandh 1979).

However, the most important aspect of the symposium was that Sweden had its first opportunity to meet representatives of the international community of historians of technology, scholars from the U.S. in particular. The symposium was attended by a number of well-known members of the Society for the History of Technology (SHOT), the discipline's main international organization. For example, Eugene S. Ferguson, Thomas P. Hughes and the legendary Melvin Kranzberg, editor of the journal *Technology and Culture*, participated in the symposium. This was important because the contents of international research in history of technology are defined by this society and its journal. Here, there are a number of common concepts and issues, and a continuous debate has been conducted in *Technology and Culture* and at SHOT's annual meetings ever since the end of the 1950's. The encounter with the American historians of technology gave several important impulses for the emerging Swedish research. Another result was a realization of the subject's strong institutional position at U.S. universities and engineering schools. Practical information on how to devise teaching programs in Sweden was a further result (Lindqvist 1981).

## The network and its institutionalization

As a result of the 1977 symposium in Hässelby, an informal network developed in Sweden, a network that cut across departmental and institutional boundaries. Personal contacts were established between universities, engineering schools, IVA, the

National Museum of Science and Technology and other museums.

One concrete product of the expanded interest was the foundation of the Center for the History of Technology at the CTH with representatives from Göteborg University and the Industry Museum. The Center's chairperson was Jan Hult, professor in mechanics of materials at the CTH. The Center for the History of Technology held courses in the history of technology at Chalmers and published a bulletin, *Teknikhistoriska notiser,* that became a connecting link in the new network. At the KTH, where Torsten Althin had served as a teacher in the history of technology after retiring from the National Museum of Science and Technology, a teaching appointment was established in 1978 to ensure continuity. After Althin's death in 1982, the Knut and Alice Wallenberg Foundation made a donation to the KTH. Activities could then be made permanent through the acquisition of new offices and the opening of a department for the history of technology. So the engineering schools now had the foundation for institutional establishment of the new subject but with the emphasis on the subject's role in undergraduate training.

As a result of the increased contacts between Sweden and international research in history of technology, Swedish general historians, economic historians and historians of ideas now developed an interest in the new subject and the way it should be defined as a history discipline (Glete 1980, Lönnroth 1983, Olsson 1980, Schiller 1983). Representatives of industry also pointed out the need for research in history of technology so as to shed light on the role played by technology in social and economic development (Rydberg 1981, Waldenström 1983).

The National Museum of Science and Technology's symposia committee continued to hold symposia on the history of technology. Thus, the new network continued to grow, and contacts with international research were strengthened (Sörbom 1980, *Daedalus* 1984, *Daedalus* 1986). The "Flying

Symposium" in 1980 was of particular importance in spreading interest in the history of technology (Lindqvist and Sörbom 1982). The symposia committee, reinforced with two foreign historians of technology, Melvin Kranzberg and Alex Keller, visited six university towns in the course of two weeks, i.e. Linköping, Göteborg, Lund, Umeå, Uppsala and Stockholm. In each town, lectures and discussions were held on motives and means in history of technology. A total of nearly 700 people from universities and engineering schools all over Sweden attended these sessions.

As a subject on the Swedish academic map, the history of technology lies somewhere between the history of ideas and economic history. At the beginning of the 1980's, the first Swedish theses (with technology as the main focus) were published in these two disciplines: Sundin (1981) and Lindqvist (1984) in the history of ideas and Berglund (1982) and Gadd (1983) in economic history. Boel Berner's thesis in sociology, i.e. a study of technological change and engineering traditions in Swedish industry, was also influenced by international research in the history of technology (Berner 1981).

The increased interest in the subject in the years after the Hässelby symposium achieved its institutional embodiment in 1982 through the formation of the Swedish National Committee for the History of Technology (SNT) under the aegis of the IVA and the Royal Swedish Academy of Sciences. The committee included representatives of all the universities, engineering schools and the National Museum of Science and Technology. The establishment of the SNT represented institutionalization of the network that had developed as a result of the 1977 symposium. Thanks to the SNT, Swedish research became a part of the International Committee for the History of Technology (ICOHTEC).

The national committee's first chairperson was Sven Rydberg, a historian of ideas from Uppsala and a former director of the Stora Kopparberg company and a well-known author on industrial history. The SNT took important initiatives during its first three years. One such initiative entailed a national inventory on ongoing research, *Teknikhistoria i Sverige 1982*. A second was the decision to publish a book describing the evolution of technology in Sweden through the ages, a general survey that could serve as a textbook and introduction to the subject. A third initiative concerned the starting of the journal *Polhem Tidskrift för teknikhistoria* (published quarterly since 1983 and edited by Jan Hult). The appearance of *Polhem* gave the subject an academic identity, a forum for the publication of papers and reviews.

International contacts with the discipline were intensified at the beginning of the 1980's when a number of foreign scholars visited Sweden to hold seminars and lectures; two of these scholars were invited to spend an extended period of time in Sweden. In the spring of 1983, the American historian of technology, Merritt Roe Smith, professor at MIT, was a Fulbright Scholar at Tema T in Linköping. In the autumn of 1984, the British historian of technology Angus Buchanan from the University of Bath held the CTH jubilee professorship. During their stays in Sweden, both Smith and Buchanan also gave seminars at other Swedish universities and engineering schools. The internationalization of emerging research and the subject's institutional establishment at the beginning of the 1980's might therefore be described as good. There were international contacts, a scientific journal and a national committee. But there was also a major difference. All the other national committees had equivalents in established disciplines at universities and engineering schools. However, the new national committee had no disciplinary base but was a collaborative body for different disciplines and institutions interested in the history of technology.

The position of the subject at this time is illustrated by the following event. A multiparty bill submitted to the 1982 Riksdag by five Members of Parliament (Soc., Agrar., Lib., Cons.)

proposed that the "Riksdag ask the Government for proposals on ways of strengthening the position of the history of technology subject in relation to other historical disciplines" (1981/82:358). However, the Education Committee suggested that the Riksdag reject the bill for the following reasons:

> "The history of technology is part of our general culture and a part of the history of ideas and learning. Development of the subject has started at the engineering schools, e.g. by including teaching in the subject in some *civilingenjör* (roughly equivalent to a Master of Science degree in engineering) curricula. With a view to the bill, the education committee would like to point out that it is primarily the responsibility of local and central authorities to decide in their planning work on the need for reinforcement of a particular subject field and on the assignment of priorities to different subject fields".

## Organization of Swedish higher education

The interdisciplinary nature of the history of technology encompasses tension between technology and history, a polarity making research in the field particularly dynamic. Scholars need knowledge and understanding of both technical aspects and the general historical context. But the introduction of this kind of interdisciplinary subject in the Swedish higher education system caused special problems.

Advocates of the history of technology had long pointed out that the subject was an established discipline abroad, albeit deeply aware of a decisive difference between Sweden and other countries. Foreign engineering schools are generally an integral part of a larger university that also has departments in the humanities and social sciences. When foreign engineering schools are independent institutions, they almost always include departments for subjects such as history, modern languages, philosophy and other disciplines in the humanities. However, the humanities are not represented at Swedish engineering schools, so limited opportunities are available there for interdisciplinary work on the basis of internal competence.

So even if interest in the history of technology had increased considerably in Sweden since the beginning of the 1980's, this interest was spread among multiple institutions. Interest in *research* in history of technology predominated at university departments representing the humanities and social sciences, resulting in theses in disciplines such as the history of ideas, economic history and sociology. At the engineering schools, the predominant interest was in *teaching* on the undergraduate level as a phase in the broadening of engineering curricula. As a result of the way Swedish higher education is organized, it was hard to attain the necessary linkup between research and teaching that is a prerequisite for the establishment of a new discipline at one and the same institute.

## Guest professorship at the KTH

Thomas P. Hughes is a professor in the history of technology at the Department of History and Sociology of Science at the University of Pennsylvania. He is one of the internationally most prominent historians of technology. Thus, two of his books have received the Dexter Prize, the subject's most prestigious award (Hughes 1971, Hughes 1983). In the 1970's, Hughes became known as an advocate of the importance of technological change in terms of technological systems, rather than as a series of inventions. A characteristic feature of Hughes is his view that these systems have been strongly shaped by prevailing cultural values and social circumstances. This means, Hughes maintains, that technological systems in different countries display distinct national differences that are not the product of technical restraints. At the Hässelby symposium in 1977, he introduced his concept "technological style" and spoke of the importance of studying regional and national aspects of technological change (Strandh 1979). In his acclaimed book *Networks of Power: Electrification in Western Society, 1880-1930* he showed how electrical power systems in the U.S., Germany and Great Britain acquired different configurations because of cultural and social differences (Hughes 1983).

Hughes was invited to Sweden in 1983 by the IVA to hold a seminar for the Academy's Man-Technology-Society committee. During his stay, he also held a seminar at Tema T in Linköping and at the Department of the History of Science and Technology at the KTH. This resulted in discussions on the possibility of acquiring his services for Sweden on a more permanent and continuous basis. Nils-Eric Svensson and the KTH's rector at the time, the present University Chancellor, Gunnar Brodin, were behind this initiative. As previously noted, a guest professorship was established at the KTH in 1984 with funds from the Foundation, i.e. the "Torsten Althin Chair in the History of Technology and Society". As a result of this administrative innovation, this history subject, a humanistic-social science discipline, gained entry to an engineering school.

For four years, Thomas P. Hughes gave a graduate course at the KTH, "Technology and Culture, 1870-1970". It was in every sense of the word research-related, since material for the lectures consisted of the manuscript of a book Hughes was working on at the time. The book evolved during the four years in which he gave the course and lent his lectures particular vitality. His lecture notes were always the latest version of a chapter, usually disgorged by a printer the same morning. The book, *American Genesis: A Century of Inventions and Technological Enthusiasm, 1870-1970*, was published in the spring of 1989. Recently, it was one of three nominees for the prestigious Pulitzer Prize in history.

Hughes' course was attended each year by an audience of more than a hundred (the course was originally planned for 15 participants/year). Over the four years, a total of 284 students complied with attendance and reading requirements. The majority, 150, were doctoral candidates in science and technology at the KTH. The others were senior year engineering students, doctoral candidates at Tema T in Linköping and doctoral candidates in humanities and social sciences at the universities in Stockholm, Uppsala and Göteborg. The course also received an enthusiastic response from students at the Stockholm School of Economics.

The large number of attenders showed that courses in the history of technology meet a need on the graduate level at Swedish engineering schools. Interest in the course did not abate with time. The number of applications from KTH doctoral candidates actually increased every year in which the course was given. The response from students at the universities and the School of Economics showed that the history of technology is a humanistic-social science subject. General, overriding issues were at the fore, not individual aspects requiring technical prior knowledge that would make the course incomprehensible or uninteresting to students enrolled at non-technical university departments. However, Hughes did not treat technical content as irrelevant. Quite the opposite! But he did emphasize the general aspects.

The fact that Hughes proved to be an uncommonly skilled teacher contributed to the course's success, in addition to the thematic structure of the course in which general problems were given priority over chronological narrative. "Lecturing as a divine art" is a virtually extinct art form, especially at our engineering schools, but something Hughes demonstrated in ample measure. Course evaluations showed that Hughes was a very popular lecturer. One thing Hughes emphasized each year was the difference between a problem and an issue. Teaching at Swedish engineering schools concentrates on problem-solving. This means that all training promulgates a particular view of the world to some extent, i.e. that all issues can be framed as problems and that all problems have solutions. It implies that the technical, instrumental methods taught at the engineering schools provide the best answers. But from the humanities point of view, posing the question of *who* framed a problem and *why* is more interesting, since different groups in society frame problems in different ways. Indeed, problem framing is relative and affected by cultural and social factors. Like all cultural phenomena, it changes in the course of time. (For example, Swedish attitudes towards exploitation of its rivers in the far north have changed over the years and differ considerably even among different groups today.) Some issues cannot be framed as problems, but this does not stop us from increasing our understanding of their complexity by discussing them from various points of view.

This was a distinction that only eluded students in exceptional instances. However, one or two KTH students a year found the literature "verbose" and demanded more concrete answers to issues. E.g. "The humanities people have a lot to learn from us engineers about presentation stringency." But, as noted above, these students only constituted a fraction of the hundreds who understood the difference between a "problem" and an "issue". Hughes underlined the importance of this distinction by pointing out that they, his audience, were the people who would one day change the world by virtue of their roles as engineers in leading positions.

In addition to the courses he taught at the KTH, Hughes also held an annual seminar at Tema T in Linköping and the Department for the History of Science at Uppsala University. He also held several seminars at the IVA under the auspices of the Man-Technology-Society committee. Moreover, he held occasional lectures at e.g the Royal Academy of Sciences and the Swedish Collegium for Advanced Study in the Social Sciences (SCASSS). In 1987, Hughes was elected a foreign member of the IVA.

## Large-scale research information

A course given for a fifth and final academic year (1988/89) would have indeed been important to the hundred or so students able to take the course, but the temptation to try something new that fifth year was great. In qualitative respects, the project had already achieved its objective. So results could then only be improved in quantitative respects. The Foundation's instructions to grant applicants underline the importance of disseminating research findings beyond the research community. We took this to heart and suggested that the Swedish Broadcasting Company (SBC) do a program with Hughes on the contents of his course "Technology and Culture, 1870-1970". The SBC agreed. The program is being produced by Christian Stannow of Channel 1 and will be part of his "In the light of history" series.

The main theme of the television program is the same as in the course, i.e. the major technological systems that evolved during industrialism. Under this heading, the same general issues will be examined as in the course, issues such as the driving forces and consequences of technological change, technology transfer, national styles, systems dynamics and vulnerability. The general issues will be illustrated with examples taken from a number of different technologies: railways, canals, telecommunications, electric power, sewage disposal, agriculture etc. The idea is to convey the new view of technology that has emerged in history of technology since the 1970's. Technology is currently viewed as an expression of society's structure and values and not, as before, as an autonomous force that imposes itself on society from the outside. This makes a comparative perspective important in illuminating the ways in which national cultural and social differences have influenced technological developments. In order to shed light on the latter, the program is based on a comparison between Sweden and Pennsylvania, a dialogue apparently unrelated by time and space. The development of technology in Hughes' own state actually displays both similarities and disparities in relation to Sweden, opening up opportunities for many interesting comparisons. Thus, the Amish People, a sect in Lancaster County (outside Philadelphia) that eschews most of the aids offered by modern technology, will be compared to a large farm in Sweden's Sörmland County.

At the time of writing, half the program has been filmed in the U.S.. The second half will be filmed in Sweden in the spring of 1990. The one-hour long program will be broadcast in the autumn of 1990. Studies have shown that programs of this kind attract about 300 000 viewers. Thus, course contents will reach an audience about 3 000 times larger than when proffered in a KTH lecture hall. However, the audience will not be the same as students at the KTH. And this is the whole point of the exercise! The history of technology has namely two important tasks. One is to serve as an integrative subject at universities and engineering schools, a subject capable of unifying perspectives and insights across departmental boundaries. But the subject can also play a major general educational role, viz. to convey a holistic view of the development of technology to the "general public", a group for whom the concept "general education" does not traditionally encompass technology.

## Research in history of technology today

The position of history of technology in Sweden is currently very different than at the beginning of the 1970's, i.e. before the programs described above were launched. As previously noted, research in history of technology in different disciplines now has a collaborative body, the SNT, and an academic forum in the national committee's journal *Polhem*. The SNT recently published *Svensk teknikhistoria*, the first overview of Sweden's technological development (Hult et al. 1989). A textbook on the history of technology in Western civilization has also been published

(Hansson 1987), and several more are in press.

The interdisciplinary approach that was the aim of the new research organization at Linköping University was a success for history of technology. Since the middle of the 1980's, Tema T students have published no fewer than five theses on history of technology subjects (Kylhammar 1985, Kaijser 1986, Hagberg 1986, Lindgren 1987, Sandström 1989). Their subjects cover a wide field. However, all relate to varying degrees to international research in the history of technology, and all have broadened and deepened Swedish research. Thus, Arne Kaijser's thesis *Stadens ljus: Etableringen av de första svenska gasverken* was not merely a historical study of the development of a technological system. Kaijser's analysis of the technical, financial, organizational and legal factors influencing the 19th century gas distribution network is also relevant to our understanding of the large-scale system society of today.

History of technology theses have also been written at other university departments. In the history of science and ideas at Göteborg University, Mikael Hård defended a thesis on the "pre-scientific" phase of refrigeration technology at the end of the 19th century, a development he interpreted in terms of Weber's rationalization concept (Hård 1988). Anna Götlind's history thesis at Göteborg University dealt with the importance of the Cistercian Order to technology transfer in medieval Sweden (Götlind 1988). Sven Widmalm's history of science and ideas thesis at Uppsala University examined the importance of the Field Survey Corps to the support and dissemination of technological knowledge in the 19th century (Widmalm 1990).

The first Nordic symposium on "Theories and Methods in Modern Nordic History of Technology" was held in April 1990. Bosse Sundin at the Department of the History of Ideas at Umeå University was responsible for the symposium, held under the auspices of the research committee (formerly called the symposia committee) of the National Museum of Science and Technology. About 30 young historians of technology from Denmark,

Finland, Norway and Sweden participated in the symposium whose emphasis was on concepts and theories for the purpose of developing a comparative view of technological developments in the Nordic countries in more recent times.

A few years ago, the research committee at the National Museum of Science and Technology also invited 20 foreign historians of technology to give their views on accomplishments in Swedish history of technology. They were also asked to submit suggestions on how the subject should be developed. Mikael Hård published an analysis of their replies in "The History of Technology in Sweden – A Field with a Future!" (Hård 1989). The research committee has also engaged the geographer Torsten Hägerstrand, regarded by many as Sweden's foremost social scientist, to perform a critical evaluation of Swedish research in history of technology. Hägerstrand will be examining material published in the subject in the 1980's and propose new paths for the subject's theoretical and methodological development.

The emergence of Swedish research in history of technology on an international level since the mid-1970's is best reflected in the following. The international Society for the History of Technology (SHOT) has held its annual meetings in the U.S. or Canada ever since its inception in 1958. But SHOT has now decided to hold a meeting outside North America for the first time. In competition with France and Great Britain, Sweden gained the honor of holding SHOT's first meeting in Europe. It will be held in Uppsala from 16th-21st August 1992. About 400 participants from all over the world are expected to attend.

## Dichotomies and discipline

The research that has emerged as described above is conducted within different disciplines, i.e. by scholars who address history of technology issues from the point of view of their particular

disciplinary perspectives but who all utilize the common concepts, problems and literature. Research in history of technology is currently encountered in disciplines such as the history of
ideas, economic history, sociology and at Tema T. This very
abundance of perspectives has constantly enriched the field, and
it is sometimes a hallmark for SHOT and its journal *Technology
and Culture*. For example, cultural anthropologists have shed
new light on issues such as the diffusion of innovations. In a
corresponding manner, historians of technology with an engineering background and technical experience have contributed
new insights and overriding concepts to the subject.

The emergence even in Sweden of an interdisciplinary
plentitude that has found an institutional form is a fortunate
development. But in contrast to the situation in other countries,
the subject in Sweden has long lacked a disciplinary base, as
previously noted. However, the subject's establishment as a
discipline is also necessary to research continuity and the
recruitment of future scholars. This demands a combination of
basic education and graduate training in the same university
department, something previously impossible because of dichotomies in Swedish higher education, as noted above, i.e. the
subdivision of teaching and research in history of technology
into separate institutions. However, this problem was resolved
in the Government's latest science policy bill submitted to the
Riksdag in February 1990 (Prop. 1989/90:90, p. 286):

"Research in history of technology is an important complement to
technical research and forges a strong link between the latter and the
cultural sciences. In its Bill no. 1989/90:100, Appendix 10, page 224,
the Government indicated its intention to perform a review of engineering education. In this context, the role of non-technical subjects will
also be accorded special attention. The history of technology is an
important subject of this kind. So the Government feels that the subject
should be given a more established position in research and higher
education".

These lines occur in the section of the bill dealing with allocations for research and graduate teaching in engineering schools.
The reason stated was that research in history of technology is
"an important complement to technical research". The bill also
noted that the subject constitutes a strong link between technical
research and the cultural sciences. All the dichotomies depicted
in the present paper are hereby resolved: the earlier contradic-
tions between technology/humanities, research/education,
engineering schools/universities etc. are integrated and assigned a disciplinary base through the definition of the history
of technology as a *humanistic-social science discipline at
engineering schools.*

Underlying statements in this bill was awareness of the
importance of non-technical aspects in technological developments (and thus in engineering education) that have emerged
since the 1960's. More concretely, the bill was also inspired by
the KTH's 1987 decision to establish an extra chair in the
history of technology in order to ensure continuity after Thomas
P. Hughes' guest professorship had ended. The extra professor
was appointed in 1989 and financed with funding from the
Swedish National Board for Technical Development (STU). In
the research bill, the Government proposed that the extra
professorship should be made a permanent position. The importance of the subject was also underlined, i.e. shown to be a
national priority, when the professorship in the history of
technology at the KTH was the only new chair proposed at *any*
of the country's engineering schools.

As this paper shows, the establishment of the history of
technology as an academic discipline was preceded by a broad
range of developments in different quarters after the middle of
the 1970's, i.e. an *internationalization* of the emerging research
and an *institutionalization* of various interdisciplinary forms of
collaboration. This paper also shows that many of the projects
in the field were initiated by and/or supported by the Foundation. Its 1984 support for a guest professorship in the history of

technology at the KTH was of the greatest importance in legitimizing the science policy bill's solution to the dichotomies that long served as an obstacle to the subject's establishment as a discipline. That support demonstrated that research in history of technology is a humanistic-social science discipline but simultaneously a subject for engineering schools. The guest professorship grant therefore constituted support, proffered at the right time, for an unconventional project.

*Tore Frängsmyr*

# Sweden in the world – on the internationaliza- tion of research

In our time, it has become increasingly common to speak of the "internationalization of research". By this we naturally mean that conditions for intellectual endeavors are identical the world over, that the laws of physics apply both in the Soviet Union and in the United States and that human logic displays the same patterns in England as in Japan.

However, the picture becomes somewhat more complex when the effects of research are viewed. The situation is drastically transformed when results can be translated into money. Countries compete with one another in advanced mili-tary research, and people pursuing "international collaboration" are called spies. Even commercial enterprises keep some things secret. The familiar term "industrial espionage" shows that the phenomenon is not unknown.

Thankfully, not all research is linked to economic gain and national prestige. In most instances, at least in respect to basic research, scientists all over the world are addressing similar problems. The scientists at large laboratories can, individually or collectively, attend international congresses and discuss matters with colleagues from other countries. They can read about one another's results in scientific journals, and research findings can be openly evaluated by scholars and prize commit-tees.

This type of internationalization is particularly important to a small country like Sweden. This has always been the case and will always remain the case. The aim of such a country is not merely to establish a domestic research organization but even to access the intellectual resources available in international science.

Our objective in the project to be presented was to shed light on prerequisites for international collaboration and dependency. We were interested in seeing how they functioned in past eras and procure background and perspective on the presentday situation. So we applied what we referred to as a "double perspective". This means that we studied both Swedish and foreign research relationships in different historical circumstances and even involved foreign scholars in our ongoing studies. In this manner, we hoped we would be able to avoid provincial myopia and, instead, attain breadth and diversity.

It should be noted that this was an "umbrella" project. This means that we attempted to stimulate different kinds of activities working towards the same general end, as well as conduct a number of special studies. Thus, we supported research in progress, started new projects, encouraged young scholars to participate in international conferences and invited foreign scholars to Sweden. We collaborated in the establishment of an international summer school and published our research results in foreign languages to a greater degree than was previously the case.

## *Historical background*

The nature of international research collaboration has remained generally unchanged throughout history, since personal contacts are decisive to it. But work forms, prevalence and intensity have varied, like results.

*Study trips* have been the most common form of contact. As early as the Middle Ages, Swedish students often visited intellectual centers in Europe. In the 17th century, Olof Rudbeck travelled to Holland and returned both with seeds for the botanical garden he subsequently established and philosophical ideas resulting in the Cartesian controversies. In their essence, these ideas concerned conflicts between old and new views of the world, between theologians and scientists. Once the dust had settled, the way had been paved for Newton's description of the world, a description that was to gain ascendancy in the 18th century. Scholars intensified their travelling during this century. It is safe to say that all academics with serious, scholarly ambitions felt compelled to undertake a multi-year study and educational trip. The young Emanuel Swedenborg went to London and sent reports home to friends and colleagues in Uppsala about all the new things happening in the world of science. Mårten Triewald learned the new physics and mechanics in the same city and began, after returning to Sweden, disseminating his new knowledge in public lectures.

But the study visits soon turned into pure *research trips*. When Anders Celsius, as a newly appointed professor of astronomy, began his four-year sojourn abroad (1732-36), his purpose was to establish research contacts and discuss his theories and findings with others. Via Nurnberg and Bologna he traveled to Rome where the Pope provided him with space in the Quirinal for photometric studies. When he went to Paris, he found himself in the midst of the scientific controversy about the shape of the earth. The French Academy of Science decided to despatch two expeditions to investigate the matter further. Since northern Sweden was the destination of one of the expeditions, it was natural for the Academy to engage Celsius. This circumstance alone was enough to give him an international reputation. Carl Linnaeus went to Holland primarily to take a doctorate in medicine, a degree unavailable in Sweden at the time. But he ended up staying for three years in order to conduct research and publish books in Latin.

After returning to Sweden, Linnaeus began organizing research trips for his students. Thanks to a network of contacts, both in Sweden and abroad, he succeeded in despatching students to all five continents. They returned with collections of flora and fauna, travel reports and notes. At that time, Linnaeus still entertained the notion that all nature could be inventoried and a list prepared of every plant on earth. He ultimately realized that this was impossible but still collected a vast amount of material. The Linnean journeys were pioneering ventures and served as models for other scientists. In addition, Linnaeus' work enhanced the prestige of the sciences in Sweden and the reputation of Swedish science abroad.

There are numerous other examples. The period from 1740 to 1780 was especially rich in travelling scholars. In the 19th century, Berzelius instituted a new era of greatness for Swedish science. Nowadays, it is natural for a scholar, at least in natural science and medicine, to spend a year abroad.

However, Linnaeus and Berzelius should inspire us to consider the reverse situation, i.e. visits to Sweden by *foreign guest scholars*. They have often been young scientists interested in learning from a Swedish professor. In the present century, The Svedberg, Manne Siegbahn and Arne Tiselius have attracted such interest. Swedish scholars like these have created scientific settings that have greatly contributed to making Sweden an important part of the international research network.

International *natural science meetings* evolved in the 19th century. They were analogous in function to presentday conferences and symposia. Nordic natural science meetings began to be held, and major gatherings were held in Germany. The enthusiasm felt by these early participants when meeting colleagues and obtaining opportunities to discuss problems of common interest with fellow scientists is not hard to imagine. Communications were still rather limited at that time.

*Academies of science* naturally played a major role. Right from its inception in 1739, the Royal Swedish Academy of Sciences sought to establish contacts with foreign academies. Collaboration ultimately commenced. Agreements on the exchange of publications and information were reached with e.g. the Royal Society in London and the Académie des Sciences in Paris. The Swedish Academy of Sciences employed permanent representatives who purchased instruments and books on its behalf. Even in countries with which they had no formal agreements, the academies developed personal contacts. During his 34 years (1749-83) as the Academy's Permanent Secretary, Pehr Wilhelm Wargentin maintained links with virtually the entire world of science. One way of establishing such links was to elect colleagues from other countries as foreign members. In the beginning, the idea was for each foreign member to have an Academy sponsor. This practice did not survive, but the exchange still remained substantial.

*Scientific prizes* have undoubtedly had a special function in Academy work. Most prizes are awarded to domestic scholars. But international prizes have become increasingly common. It is surely no exaggeration to claim that the Nobel Prize has played a major role. The importance of this prize to Swedish science cannot be designated in specific terms, but the prize's major contributions to putting Swedish science on the international map are incontestable.

*More rapid communications* have also had an impact on this process. A study trip in Linnaeus' time generally took 3-4 years. But scholars of today can often jet to and from an international meeting in the space of a single day. Other forms of communications have also become more commonplace in recent years, in addition to travel. Some scientists in different countries are interlinked in a computer network, results are often transmitted by telex of telefax etc. Experiments are also being made with international computer conferencing and discussion. The world has shrunk almost incomprehensibly in this respect. Whether this *always* has positive effects remains to be seen. Creativity may not always be enhanced by facilitated conferencing, since quantity is often the enemy of quality.

## Some sub-studies

The most comprehensive sub-study bears the working name "The Quantification Project" and was carried out on a collaborative basis by history of science scholars in Uppsala and Berkeley. It got off to a modest start in 1984 and was based on the circumstance that the project leaders, John Heilbron and Tore Frängsmyr, both shared an interest in studying natural sciences in the 18th century. Two aspects were of particular interest. First of all, the position of the natural sciences in the 18th century has not been studied as extensively as the position of the sciences in the 17th and 19th centuries. The 17th century witnessed a breakthrough for the Scientific Revolution. And another revolution occurred in the 19th century, i.e. the industrial revolution, with an impact on the sciences. It was here that the results of science began to generate financial profit. In this way, the 18th century can be viewed as an interim period. Observers have frequently noted that the new science consolidated its position in this century, and this was important to Enlightenment. But the 18th century has otherwise been described as a dull, rather uneventful period. This is enough in itself to justify further study. Second of all, Sweden played a particularly interesting role during this period. Swedish science blossomed, especially from 1740 to 1780. In this period, the Swedish society acquired a strongly economic bias. Sweden seemed to display a concentration of tendencies extant in Europe at the time. Little Sweden apparently served as a reflector of developments elsewhere in Europe.

We were aware that we had to concentrate on some special aspect of this broad subject, so we selected "quantification thinking". The most consistent feature of the scientific revolution was the use of mathematics. Mathematics became virtually synonymous with "rationalism", "science", "enlightenment" and other fashionable terms of the time. Counting, enumeration, quantifying etc. developed into a refined scientific method but also became a political method and a philosophical outlook. The result of this process was actually more interesting and astonishing than we had anticipated. In the first half of the 18th century, intoxication with mathematics was total. Numbers were transformed into philosophy. Data became science, and statistics was employed as a political instrument. Political arithmetic was viewed as a device for predicting the future.

But by the 1760's, the visionaries all seemed to run out of steam. No mathematical utopia ever materialized. Philosophy had been defeated. Statistics was regarded as capricious and highly unreliable and political arithmetic as naive. But this did not mean that quantitative thinking no longer had any role to play. Instead, it was transferred to the scientific laboratory, to economic calculations, to vital statistics, into concrete reality. Sweden adopted ideas from abroad and refined them. The two eras of quantification paralleled one another in Sweden and abroad.

The Quantification Project has now been completed and resulted in a number of papers and two books, Karin Johanisson's "Det mätbara samhället" (1988) and the anthology "The Quantifying Spirit in the Eighteenth Century", edited by Tore Frängsmyr, John Heilbron and Robin Rider (1990).

The Quantification Project studied an entire epoch, whereas the "Berzelius Project" concentrated on a single person. The starting point was an examination of the way a distinguished scientist and powerful personality functioned as a channel between his homeland and the international research community. Berzelius possessed all the characteristics necessary for such a study. He was the world's foremost chemist and had propounded epochal theories and methods. For thirty years he was the Swedish Academy of Sciences' Permanent Secretary. He kept in touch with the entire scientific world, corresponded extensively and travelled widely. Most of his writings were translated into the main Western languages. Young foreign scientists flocked to Sweden to learn from Berzelius at first hand. Every year, he published a summary of events in the various scientific disciplines. In this way, he became something of an arbiter of scientific taste.

Berzelius was certainly unusual, arguably unique. So he might appear to be an unsuitable subject for a study of this kind, since drawing any general conclusions from the study's findings would be difficult. However, I still believe that conclusions can indeed be drawn. Berzelius was admittedly a kind of "one-man show", but his numerous activities make it possible to view him as a whole group. The fact that his activities were so "international" appears to be decisive to his position and contributions. He was at the "cutting edge" of international science, as our results showed. Despite the distances involved and slowness of communications, he still maintained contacts with colleagues in other countries. In addition, his conclusions always included philosophical reflections; laboratory findings always had to fit some philosophy. Thanks to international interest, Berzelius was able to provide a boost for Swedish science as a whole. His personal successes benefitted the entire country. When conditions changed, new results also appeared.

Most of the project's studies were included in an anthology with contributions from about 10 scholars (4 of whom Swedes) from different countries. The preliminary title is "Berzelius as an International Scientist". The book is due for publication in 1990 or 1991 and is being edited by Evan Melhado of the University of Illinois at Urbana-Champaign and Tore Frängsmyr, Uppsala University.

A third sub-project concerns "Eugenics in the Nordic countries". It comprises four sub-studies, one each for Denmark, Finland, Norway and Sweden. The idea is to compare the spread of the eugenics ideology in Nordic countries from the end of the 19th century down to the 1930's. The studies have concentrated on prescribed sterilization; this was as much a political as a medical issue at the time. The subject is particularly suitable for any study of the relationship between politics and science. The final years of this period also encompassed nazism. Developments in the Nordic countries displayed signs of definite external influences, but advocates of eugenics were also able to build on domestic traditions, thus international versus national perspectives. The studies are being led by Bent Sigurd Hansen (Denmark), Marjatta Hietala (Finland), Nils Roll-Hansen (Norway) and Gunnar Broberg (Sweden). The book is due for publication in 1991.

A fourth sub-project is called "Swedish Polar Research up to 1930". Polar research was part of the breakthrough for glacial theory in the middle of the 19th century. Swedish geologists were anxious to test Louis Agassiz's startling glaciation theory, first propounded in 1837. It was found that Sweden and the Swedish landscape constituted an uncommonly appropriate subject for study as the result of its numerous eskers, roches moutonnés and glacial striations. But the theory was so new and encountered such stiff resistance that scientists departed for areas in which glaciers could be studied at close quarters. This is the reason why the young geologist Otto Torell began Swedish polar research in the 1850's. A culmen was achieved with Adolf Erik Nordenskiöld's crossing of the Northeast Passage in 1878-79 and his triumphant return journey home, punctuated by tributes and ovations at each stop. Every country became interested in polar research, and the first international polar year was instituted from the summer of 1882 to the summer of 1883. This was the first big international collaboration in scientific investigation. Eleven countries participated, twelve expeditions conducted studies around the North Pole and two expeditions went to the Antarctic. A second polar year was held, although not without difficulty, from 1932 to 1933.

Swedish polar research after Nordenskiöld assumed two forms. It either involved purely scientific expeditions with geologists, mineralogists, hydrologists, botanists and zoologists in different groupings. Or it entailed the mining or harvesting of natural resources. Some success was achieved by both forms, at least initially. The research performed important studies and investigations. One result of this work can be seen in the numerous Swedish names for islands, capes and mountain peaks. Many of these expeditions were the fruit of international collaboration. Crews were from different countries in other instances. Even though heavy competition sometimes made itself felt, the scientists themselves were apparently able to get along quite well together. Mining was of some importance in and around 1910, but the difficulties soon became overwhelming. Operations at the last arctic mine terminated at the end of the 1920's.

From 1840 to 1880, polar research was a purely scientific venture. From 1880 to 1930, economic interests entered the picture. In both instances, work was conducted in competition or close collaboration with other countries. The international perspective constituted a decisive part of everything undertaken by Sweden in this field. This sub-project was designed in collaboration with the Swedish Polar Research Secretariat and its chief Anders Karlqvist. The main results will consist of the dissertation Urban Jonsson is writing about the period from 1880 to 1930. Tore Frängsmyr previously wrote a book, *Upptäckten av istiden* for the period from 1840 to 1880. An expanded and revised edition will be published in English. This work is at an advanced stage and will probably be concluded in 1990.

I would like to include one more project under our "umbrella", even though funds from our grant were not used for financing it. It concerns the "250th Anniversary of the Swedish Academy of Sciences" in 1989. Since I was in charge of many of the anniversary activities, it was natural for me to utilize my international contact network. The biggest event was a one-week Nobel Symposium on the subject "Solomon's House Revisited: The Organization and Institutionalization of Science". One important subtopic concerned the national perspective versus the international perspective. This topic was the subject of special discussion in a session on "big science". About 40 scholars attended, nearly half of whom from abroad. The lectures will be published in the autumn of 1990 under the title "Solomon's House Revisited".

Another major symposium addressed the "Cultural connections between Sweden and France in the 18th century". French and Swedish scholars elucidated various aspects of scientific, literary and other cultural relationships. The findings will also result in a book, probably published in France. Its editors are Jean Dhombres and Sverker Sörlin.

## Other activities

In addition to normal research projects, we were able to pursue a number of other activities for the purpose of stimulating international collaboration. The most important of these activities is arguably the "International Summer School in History of Science", established as a joint project by the universities of Bologna, Uppsala and Berkeley. The idea is to enable young scholars to convene for joint discussion of common problems, although in another way than at a conventional conference. Thus, the school is to be combined with research and discussions in small groups. The concentration on a particular subject results in a natural selection of participants.

The first International Summer School was held in Bologna in 1988, the same year the university there commemorated its 900th anniversary. The topic was "Science and the Enlightenment", six lecturers participated and 25 young scholars attended. The outcome was very good. The impact was obviously greatest for scholars who attended both weeks. But even those who only attended one week appeared to be satisfied. The second school was held in Uppsala in June 1990. The topic this time was "Science and Society from 1850 to 1914". This school also utilized the services of six prominent international lecturers and 40 scholars participated.

The exchange of both guest scholars and doctoral candidates has developed new impetus. The difficulty encountered in recruiting distinguished scholars almost invariably concerns money. Since we have been awarded funds for the stimulation of international exchanges, this difficulty was not a major problem for us. We were able to establish fruitful contacts by carefully selecting the scholars to be invited. As a result, an increased number of young scholars have been invited to participate in international projects or contribute to scientific journals. The exchange of doctoral candidates has not been formalized as yet but will be implemented in one of two forms. A doctoral candidate in one country will either transfer all her/his studies to the other country's university. Or she/he will spend some time studying at that university, i.e. from one month up to one year. We have tested and are continuing to test both models. Experience has hitherto been extremely good. Exchanges have been conducted with Italy and the U.S. Initial talks have begun with France and England.

New forms of collaboration have also been tested on a departmental basis. A national contact network is a prerequisite for the development of an international contact network. There are strong links and close collaboration in Swedish history of science research, i.e. the history of ideas and learning in the broad sense of the term. This means that our external contacts can offer far more than a single university department is able to do. Foreign guest lecturers can e.g. be invited to Sweden by more than one university. The advantage of a small country is that everyone quickly gets to know everyone else in a particular field. This greatly simplifies the maintenance of personal contacts.

The Center for History of Science at the Swedish Academy of Sciences was founded on 1st January 1988. It is a research institute that primarily works with the Academy's extensive archives and large collection of instruments. Here, scholars can spend varying periods of time. A number of both Swedish and foreign scholars have made use of this facility. Foreign scholars are usually most interested in the Nobel Archives, but other Academy records have also been the subject of study.

The History of Technology and Science Department of the Royal Institute of Technology is another relatively new institute. In only a brief space of time it has become a valuable center for history of technology research in Sweden. The international research there ensures the maintenance of very good contacts. As a result of close collaboration with this institute and its head, Svante Lindqvist, the History of Science Department in Uppsala is also able to offer tutoring in the history of technology.

A third new albeit somewhat different type of institute is the museum opened in the old Stockholm Astronomical Observatory building. Here, instruments from primarily the Swedish Academy of Sciences will be on display in permanent and temporary exhibitions. Other activities will also be arranged, such as symposia. The Observatory and the Center for History of Science held a well-attended symposium on scientific instruments in September 1989.

## Planning and implementation

Since the umbrella project contains so many different sub-projects, the project has employed different work forms. Major collaboration with the Berkeley group has been the most comprehensive and stimulating activity. It all began with a chat, evolved into a project encompassing 13 scholars and continued for six years before a final book was published.

A primary requirement was that group members had to meet from time to time. But before this, the two people behind the initiative drew up a preliminary program declaration and division of labor. We utilized a holistic structure, i.e. in regard to what we wished to cover, and the specialties of prospective members as our starting point. In certain instances, our wishes and a particular scholar's specialty failed to coincide, so we had to use some gentle arm-twisting. Each member then submitted an outline on the envisaged paper. Thereafter, both groups gathered in Berkeley for 10 days. Seminars at which various ideas were discussed were held every weekday there. Each member had a chance to serve as the chairperson and lead discussions. In their leisure time, members mixed to greater and lesser degrees. These personal contacts were of considerable importance. By getting to know one another, members eliminated any of the disagreement heated discussions might have caused.

The work was delayed when the Berkeley group needed to take time out to arrange the XVIIth International Congress in the History of Science. Since the Swedish group attended this Congress, we naturally had a chance for new discussion of the project. By the summer of 1986, all the scholars had completed their papers. This meant that we could start the "final" processing of the papers and propose changes and modifications in relation to the anthology as a whole. In June 1986, both groups convened in Uppsala and held a 10-day series of seminars, as at the first gathering. It was here that difficulties began in earnest. It is easier for an individual scholar to accept suggestions about an outline than about a finished paper. The idea of resuming work on something previously regarded as "completed" was psychologically unappealing. Attitudes varied in the two groups. The Americans were undoubtedly more accustomed to discussions and revisions than the Swedes. We undoubtedly have something to learn here.

Thereafter, the editors assumed total responsibility for the project work. They proposed changes and had talks with both authors and one another. Inter-group differences in attitudes were discernible even here. The American authors apparently found it easier to accept major cuts or changes in papers than the Swedes. And the American editor took on more responsibility than the Swedish editor. The former felt an overall responsibility for the entire book, whereas the latter editor left more of the responsibility to the individual authors. Another circumstance is worthy of note: book publishers are no longer much interested in anthologies, symposium reports and the like. Many readers view these reports as conventional and stereotyped and often find it hard to detect any common denominator in them. So our ambition was to edit the papers into a cohesive totality and show that the papers addressed a common topic. The American editor proved to have considerable experience in this respect. The final result was far more uniform than was the case from the beginning. The book, accepted for publication by the University of California Press and highly praised by the referees appeared in June 1990.

The study of eugenics in the Nordic countries was performed in a similar manner, the difference here being that the subject was Nordic. This group also began with brief outlines that gradually expanded after each meeting and discussion. To keep the project from becoming too narrowly Nordic, the group occasionally invited outside scholars to comment on its work. Like the previous project, the Eugenics Project has also taken a long time. This is because individual scholars had other commitments in addition to this project. In many instances, project work had to be conducted in the scholar's spare time. However, the fact that the project had time to mature actually counteracted the disadvantages of delay (at least to some extent). Scholars had time for careful thinking and re-thinking in the course of their work.

The Berzelius Project utilized a different approach. The two editors knew right from the start where the world's leading Berzelius specialists were to be found. The editors were anxious to elucidate certain aspects of the subject and began by writing to these specialists, asking them whether or not they were interested in participating. With only one exception they all replied affirmatively. So we were able to plan an ideal (from our point of view) book from the very beginning. It was also obvious that we would not need to make any major cuts in papers. We knew what the various contributions would contain. Instead, the editors conferred with one another and with individual contributors. Ordinary correspondences supplemented these verbal discussions. The editing work itself was somewhat easier, since the subjects and project structure were more uniform.

The sub-project on polar research was administratively even easier. Here, we had a two-man project, both scholars attached to the same university department. They achieved a natural division of labor from the beginning. But even if the project was conducted by two Swedes at a Swedish university department, important international contacts were still taken. The reference group contained members of the Swedish Polar Research Secretariat. The group's members participated in international symposia on polar research and prepared articles and lectures that were discussed on these occasions.

In conjunction with the Swedish Academy of Sciences' 250th anniversary symposium, another part of the umbrella project's resources were brought to bear. This concerned our network of personal contacts. A symposium of this kind cannot succeed without special preparations. For example, invited lecturers must be selected with great care for quality to be on a high level. Lecturers should also complement one another and, conceivably, stimulate one another in discussions. Thanks to our project, we had a very good idea about the scholars who should be invited. (This obviously did not mean that there were no other qualified scholars who could have been invited to this symposium.) Meeting so many distinguished foreign colleagues gave a real boost to Swedish scholars.

## Results and experience gained

The extensive umbrella project has not been completed as yet, but a sufficient number of sub-projects have been finished to permit comment on results and experience gained.

Concrete results obviously comprise greater insight into certain historical processes. The history of science, like other history, encompasses a number of assumptions, here involving the way the sciences worked (and work) in society. We have been able to supplement (and even change in certain instances) these assumptions on science in society and on the conditions and effects of intellectual endeavors. Traditional history of science long concentrated mainly on the major theories and the internal development of the sciences. In our studies, the emphasis was instead placed on the social perspective, science in everyday life, if you like. This is sometimes referred to as "intellectual history" in other countries, roughly what we call the "study of intellectual milieus".

The project's stimulating impact on research on the history of science cannot be overestimated. Project work has given us an opportunity to become a part of the international research frontier and participate in scientific discussions all over the world. It has also given us a chance to participate in projects, establish personal contacts and publish our findings in foreign languages. Professors and senior researchers, with the aid of some administrative skill, are able to accomplish all this anyway, but opportunities are limited for young scholars. As a result of this project, young post-doctoral scholars and doctoral candidates were able to participate in international exchanges. They held lectures and took part in discussions. They became a part of collaborative ventures and were evaluated by foreign colleagues. Experience of this kind is bound to enhance maturation of the scientific judgement so essential to the production of theses.

We also obtained valuable insights in respect to the goals and methods of research. Collaboration with American research groups is one example. Swedish history of science scholars generally have a background in the humanities. Those with an education in science usually underwent strictly humanities-oriented doctoral training. So a broad social and history of ideas view of science is a natural starting point for us. Scholars in a small country are forced to cover large historical areas and are afraid of becoming too specialized, too "narrow". But an American history of science scholar often has some scientific subject in her/his background. She/he may be e.g. a specialist in the history of physics *or* the history of chemistry *or* the history of geology, and this could conceivably make her/him more interested in how a particular scientific discipline evolved. Both types of scholars are obviously needed and complement one another. Without access to specialized studies, we cannot readily draw any general conclusions about the circumstances of science in society. On the other hand, the specialist must take political processes or philosophical teachings into account. Our projects have encompassed both confrontations and fruitful discussion of these issues. Waging war on one another was never the objective though, as was sometimes the case in method discussions in the 1950's and 1960's, but to understand, to complement and expand our views. When a scholar completes a piece of work, she/he often enjoys the feeling of having gained valuable experience, perhaps even of having become a better scholar.

Feelings such as these, encouraging continued research, may well be the most important product of the international exchange of knowledge.

# REFERENCES

## N. Stjernquist, The Riksdag from a research point of view

Note. In addition to titles mentioned in the text.

Arter, D. (1984). *The Nordic parliaments*. London: C. Hurst & Company.
Fiskesjö, B. (1987). Konstitutionsutskottets granskning av regeringen. In L-G Stenelo (Ed.), *Statsvetenskapens mångfald*. (pp. 67-79). Lund: Lund University Press.
Holmberg, S., & Esaiasson, P. (1988). *De folkvalda*. Stockholm: Bonniers.
Jansson, J.-M. (1989). The Finnish riksdag – a common heritage. In N. Stjernquist (Ed.), *The Swedish riksdag in an international perspective*. (pp. 44-50). Stockholm: Riksbankens Jubileumsfond.
Johansson, F. (1989). KU-utfrågningarna i TV. In S.Holmberg & L. Weibull (Eds.), *Åttiotal. Svensk opinion i empirisk belysning*. (pp. 135-148). Göteborg: Statsvetenskapliga institutionen.
Schück, H. (1987). Sweden's early parliamentary institutions from the thirteenth century to 1611. In M.F. Metcalf (Ed.), The Riksdag: A history of the Swedish parliament. (pp.5-60). New York: St. Martins Press.

## L. Lewin, Rationality and selfishness

*I. Publications within the PARA program*

1. Lewin, L. (1979). *Det politiska spelet*. Stockholm: Rabén & Sjögren.
2. Petersson, O. (1979). *Regeringsbildningen 1978*. Stockholm: Rabén & Sjögren.
3. Vedung, E. (1979). *Kärnkraften och regeringen Fälldins fall*. Stockholm: Rabén & Sjögren.
4. Henning, R. (1980). *Partierna och Stålverk 80. En studie av industripolitiskt beslutsfattande*. Stockholm: Liber.
5. Hadenius, A. (1981). *Spelet om skatten*. Stockholm: Norstedts.
6. Wedin, J. (1982). *Spelet om trafikpolitiken*. Stockholm: Norstedts.
7. Holmström, B. (1983). *Äganderätt och brukningsansvar. Idéer och intressen i svensk jordbrukspolitik*. Stockholm: Almqvist & Wiksell International.
8. Hadenius, A. (1983a). *Medbestämmandereformen*. Stockholm: Almqvist & Wiksell International.
9. Hadenius, A., Henning, R., & Holmström, B. (1984). *Tre studier i politiskt beslutsfattande*. Stockholm: Almqvist & Wiksell International.
10. Nordfors, L. (1985). *Makten, hälsan och vinsten. Politik från arbetarskydd till arbetsmiljö*. Lund: Studentlitteratur.
11. Johansson, W. (1985). *Husläkaren som försvann*. Uppsala universitet: Statsvetenskapliga institutionen. (manuskript)
12. Gustavsson, S. (1985). *Den sociala bostadspolitiken*. Uppsala universitet: Statsvetenskapliga institutionen. (manuskript)
13. Lewin, L. (1984). *Ideologi och strategi. Svensk politik under 100 år*. Stockholm: Norstedts.
14. Lewin, L., & Vedung, E. (Eds.), (1980). *Politics as rational action. Essays in public choice and policy analysis*. Dordrecht, Boston and London: Reidel.
15. Hadenius, A. (1983b). The verification of motives. *Scandinavian Political Studies, 6*, 125-150.
16. Lewin, L. (1988b). *Ideology and strategy. A century of Swedish politics*. Cambridge, New York, New Rochelle, Melbourne and Sydney: Cambridge University Press.

*II. Other literature.*

Allison, G.T. (1971). *The essence of decision. Explaining the Cuban missile crisis*. Boston: Little, Brown & Co.
Althusser, L. (1968). *För Marx*. Lund: Cavefors.
Arrow, K.J. (1963). *Social choice and individual values*. New Haven and London: Yale University Press. (Orig. 1951)

Axelrod, R. (1984). *The evolution of cooperation.* New York: Basic Books.
Black, D. (1958). *The theory of committees and elections.* Cambridge: Cambridge University Press.
Brecht, A. (1959). *Political theory: The foundations of twentieth-century political thought.* Princeton, New Jersey: Princeton University Press.
Brusewitz, A. (1951). *Kungamakt, herremakt, folkmakt. Författningskampen i Sverige 1906-1918.* Stockholm: Prisma.
Buchanan, J. M., & Tullock, G. (1962). *The calculus of consent. Logical foundations of constitutional democracy.* Ann Arbor: University of Michigan Press.
Condorcet, M.J.A.N.C. (1785). *Essai sur l'application de l'analyse à la probabilité des décisions rendues à la pluralité des voix.* Paris.
Downs, A. (1957). *An economic theory of democracy.* New York: Harper & Row.
Hessler, C.A.(1956). *Stat och religion i upplysningstidens Sverige.* Uppsala och Stockholm: Almqvist & Wiksell.
Hessler, C.A. (1964). *Statskyrkodebatten.* Stockholm, Göteborg och Uppsala: Almqvist & Wiksell.
Key Jr, V.O. (1966). *The responsible electorate. Rationality in presidential voting 1936-1960.* Cambridge, Massachusetts: The Belknap Press of Harvard University Press.
Lewin, L. (1970). *Folket och eliterna. En studie i modern demokratisk teori.* Stockholm: Almqvist & Wiksell.
Lewin, L. (1988a). *Det gemensamma bästa. Om egenintresset och allmänintresset i västerländsk politik.* Stockholm: Carlssons.
Machiavelli, N. (1958). *Fursten.* Stockholm: Natur och Kultur. (Orig. Il principe, 1513)
Mosca, G. (1939). *The ruling class.* New York: McGraw-Hill. (Orig. Elementi di scienza politica, 1896)
Popper, K. R. (1963). *Conjectures and refutations. The growth of scientific knowledge.* London: Routledge & Kegan Paul.
Poulantzas, N. (1970). *Politisk makt och sociala klasser.* Stockholm: Coeckelberghs.

Rapoport, N., & Chammah, A.M. (1965). *Prisoner's dilemma.* Ann Arbor: University of Michigan Press.
Rawls, J. (1971). *A theory of justice.* Cambridge, Massachusetts: The Belknap Press of Harvard University Press.
Riker, W.H., & Ordeshook, P.C. (1973). *An introduction to positive political theory.* Englewood Cliffs, New Jersey: Prentice-Hall.
Tingsten, H. (1941). *Den svenska socialdemokratiens idéutveckling.* Stockholm: Tiden.

## E. Allardt,
## Social structure and social change

Ahrne, G., & Leiulfsrud, H. (1984). De offentligt anställda och den svenska klassstrukturen. *Häften för kritiska studier, 17,* 48-66.
Alestalo, M. (1989). Den offentliga sektorns tillväxt. *Norden förr och nu.* (pp. 127-137). (18:e Nordiska statistikermötet, Stockholm)
Alestalo, M., Bislev, S., & Furuåker, B. (1990). Public employment and class formation. In J.E. Kolberg (Ed.), *Between work and social citizenship.* Armonk, New York: M.E. Sharpe.
Alestalo, M., Bislev, S., & Furuåker, B. (1990). Public and welfare state employment. In J.E. Kolberg (Ed.), *Between work and social citizenship.* Armonk, New York: M.E. Sharpe.
Allardt, E. (1975) *Att ha, att älska, att vara. Om välfärd i Norden.* Kalmar: Argos.
Allardt, E. (1987). *Samhället Finland, omvandlingar och traditioner.* Hangö: Holger Schildts förlag.
Björkman, T., & Sandberg, Å. (1988). Lönearbetets villkor – teknik och organisering i arbetslivet. In U. Himmelstrand, & G. Svensson (Eds.), *Sverige – vardag och struktur.* Södertälje: Norstedts.
Dich, J. (1973). *Den herskende klasse.* Odense: Borgen.
Erikson, R., Hansen, E.J., Ringen, R., & Uusitalo, H. (1987). *The Scandinavian model. Welfare states and welfare research.* New York: M.E. Sharpe.
Erikson, R. (1984). Den sociala strukturen och dess förändring. In R. Erikson & R. Åberg (Eds), *Välfärd i för-*

ändring. Levnadsvillkor i Sverige 1968-1981. Arlöv: Bokförlaget Prisma.

Esping-Andersson, G., & Korpi, W. (1987). From poor relief to institutional welfare states: the development of Scandinavian social policy. In R. Erikson, E.J. Hansen, S. Ringen, & H. Uusitalo (Eds.), The Scandinavian model. Welfare states and welfare research. New York: M.E. Sharpe.

Furuåker, B. (1985). Offentlig sektor och samhällsförändring i Sverige. (Research Reports from the Department of Sociology, University of Umeå No 82).

Haavio-Mannila, E. (1981). The position of women. In E. Allardt et. al. (Eds.), Nordic democracy. Copenhagen: Det Danske Selskab.

Hernes, G., & Martinussen, W. (1980). Demokrati og politiske resurser. (Levekårsundersøkelsen, NOU 1980:07).

Hirdman, Y. (1987). The Swedish welfare state and the gender system: A theoretical and empirical sketch. The study of power and democracy in Sweden. (English series report No. 9). Uppsala: Maktutredningen.

Hoff, J. (1985). The concept of class and public employees. Acta Sociologica, 28, 207-226.

Johansen, L.N., & Kolberg, J.E. (1985). Welfare state regression in Scandinavia? The development of the Scandinavian welfare states from 1970 to 1980. In S.N. Eisendstadt, & O. Ahimeir (Eds.), The welfare state and its aftermath. Totowa, New Jersey: Barnes & Noble Books.

Kandolin, I., & Uusitalo, H. (1980). Scandinavian men and women. A welfare comparison. (Research reports. Research group for comparative sociology No 28). University of Helsinki.

Kennessey, Z. (1985). The primary, secondary, tertiary, and quarternary sectors of the economy. Papers of the nineteenth conference of the International Association for Research in Income and Wealth. Nordwijherkout, Netherlands.

Knutsen, O. (1986). Sosiale klasser og politiske verdier i Norge. Tidskrift for Samfunnsforskning, 27, 263-287.

Kosonen, P. (1987). From collectivity to individualism in the welfare state. Acta Sociologica, 30, 281-293.

Kosonen, P. (1987). Hyvinvointivaltion haasteet ja pohjoismaiset mallit. Tampere: Vastapaino. (The challenges of the welfare state and the Nordic models).

Lafferty, W.M., & Knutsen, O. (1984). Leftist and rightist ideology in a social democratic state: An analysis of Norway in the midst of a conservative resurgence. British Journal of Political Science, 14, 369-392.

Liljeström, R. (1988). Släkt, kön och familj. In U. Himmelstrand, & G. Svensson (Eds.), Sverige – vardag och struktur. Södertälje: Norstedts.

Nordiska Ministerrådet och Nordiska Statistiska Sekretariatet. (1987). Nordisk statistisk årsbok. 26. Stockholm: Liber.

Nordiska Rådet och Nordiska Statistiska Sekretariatet. (1983). Levnadsnivå och ojämlikhet i Norden. En komparativ analys av de nordiska levnadsnivåundersökningarna. Göteborg.

Paakkolanvaara, E. (1988). Informaatioyhteiskunta ja informaatioammatit. (Studies 145). Helsinki, Finland: Central statistical office. (Information society and information occupations).

Porat, M.U. (1977). The information economy: Definition and measurement. Washington D.C.: US Department of Commerce, Office of Telecommunications.

Rogoff Ramsøy, N., & Kjølsrød, L. (1986). Velferdsstatens yrker. In L. Alldén, N Rogoff Ramsøy, & M. Vaa (Eds.), Det norske samfunn, 3. Oslo: Gyldendal norsk forlag.

Skard, T., & Haavio-Mannila, E. (1986). Equality between sexes – myth or reality in Norden? In S.R. Graubard (Ed.), Norden – the passion for equality. Oslo: Universitetsforlaget.

Statistiska centralbyrån (1985). Folkets datavanor. Stockholm: SCB.

Svallfors, S. (1984). Vem älskar välfärdsstaten? Attityder, organiserade intressen och svensk välfärdspolitik. Lund: Arkiv

Zetterberg, H. (1985). Första valen med offentligtförsörjda i majoritet. Svenska Dagbladet, (23/6)

Österberg, C., & Hedman, B. (1989) Kvinnor och män i Norden. Fakta om jämställdheten i går, i dag och i morgon. *Norden förr och nu.* (pp. 171-197). (18:e Nordiska statistikermötet, Stockholm).

**T. Hägerstrand,**
**Urbanization processes**

Note. In addition to titles mentioned in the text.

Bentzel, R. (1972). Några synpunkter på regionalpolitikens mål. *Regioner att leva i. Elva forskare om regionalpolitik och välstånd.* (pp. 17-34). Stockholm: Publica, Allmänna förlaget.

Buttimer, A. (1990). Mirrors, masks and diverse milieux. In F. Boal, & D. Livingstone (Eds.), *The behavioural environment* (pp. 253-276). London: Routledge and Kegan Paul.

Godlund, S. (1954). *Busstrafikens framväxt och funktion i de urbana influensfälten.* (Meddelanden från Lunds universitets geografiska institution, serie avhandlingar XXVIII). Lunds universitet: Geografiska institutionen.

Hedbom, O., Norling, G., & Pålsson, E.(1964). *Befolkningens fördelning 1960 i Sverige.* Stockholm: Kartografiska institutet.

Kristensson, F. (1967). *Människor, företag och regioner. En strukturekonomisk analys.* Stockholm: Ekonomiska forskningsinstitutet.

Meidner, R. (1961). Missförstånd i den lokaliseringspolitiska debatten. *Tiden, 10,* 581-586.

Olsson, R. (1965). Den nya lokaliseringspolitikens innehåll och organisation. *Plan,* 19, 190-194.

Thorngren, B. (1967). *Regional external economics.* Stockholm: Ekonomiska forskningsinstitutet.

Törnqvist, G. (1972). Kontaktbehov och resemöjligheter. Några Sverigemodeller för studier av regionala utvecklingsalternativ. *Regioner att leva i. Elva forskare om regionalpolitik och välstånd.* (pp. 245-284). Stockholm: Publica, Allmänna förlaget.

William-Olsson, W. (1946). *Ekonomisk geografisk karta över Sverige.* Stockholm: Nordisk Rotogravyr.

**B. Gustafsson,**
**Expansion of public sector**

Florman, C. (1976). Bakgrunden till standardiseringskommissionens bildande. (Stencil). Uppsala: Ekonomisk-historiska institutionen.

Forsman, A. (1980). *En teori om staten och de offentliga utgifterna.* (Uppsala Studies in Economic History 22). Uppsala: Almqvist & Wiksell International.

Forsman, A. (1984). *Det nya tjänstesamhället. De offentliga tjänsternas framväxt och framtid.* Stockholm: Gidlund.

Forsman, A., Rodriguez, E., Waara, L., & Wickman, K. (1978). *Offentlig sektors tillväxt. Företagsamheten, den statliga företagssektorn och den ekonomiska planeringen.* Malmö: Liber

Gustafsson, B. (1974). Perspektiv på den offentliga sektorn under 1930-talet. In *Kriser och krispolitik i Norden under mellankrigstiden.* Nordiska historikermötet i Uppsala. (Mötesrapporter). Uppsala.

Gustafsson, B. (Ed.), (1977). *Den offentliga sektorns expansion. Teori och metodproblem.* (Uppsala Studies in Economic History 16). Uppsala: Almqvist & Wiksell International.

Gustafsson, B. (Ed.), (1979). *Post-industrial society.* London: Croom Helm.

Gustafsson, B. (1983). *The causes of the expansion of the public sector in Sweden during the 20th century.* (Uppsala Papers in Economic History No 1). Uppsala: Ekonomisk-historiska institutionen.

Gustafsson, B. (1987). Hur vägarna blev en kollektiv nyttighet. In J. Norrlid (Ed.), *Över gränser. Festskrift till Birgitta Odén.* Lund: Historiska institutionen.

Gustafsson, B. (1988). *Den tysta revolutionen. Det lokala välfärdssamhällets framväxt. Exemplet Örebro 1945-1982.* Stockholm: Gidlund

Gårestad, P. (1982). Jordskatteförändringar under industrialiseringsperioden 1861-1914. *Historisk Tidskrift,* 45, 516-539.

Gårestad, P. (1987). *Industrialisering och beskattning i Sverige 1861-1914.* (Uppsala Studies in Economic History 28). Uppsala: Almqvist & Wiksell International.

Rodriguez, E. (1980). *Offentlig inkomst-expansion. En analys av drivkrafterna bakom de offentliga inkomsternas utveckling i Sverige under 1900-talet.* Lund: Liber.

Rodriguez, E. (1981). *Den svenska skattehistorien.* Lund: Liber.

Waara, L. (1980). *Den statliga företagssektorns expansion. Orsaker till förstatliganden i ett historiskt och internationellt perspektiv.* Stockholm: Liber.

Wickman, K. (1980). *Makro-ekonomisk planering – orsaker och utveckling.* (Uppsala Studies in Economic History 23). Stockholm: Almqvist & Wiksell International.

**A. Lindbeck,
Internationalization process**

Note. IIES = Institute of International Economic Studies.

Black, S. W. (1979). The political assignment problem and the design of stabilization policies in open economies. In A. Lindbeck (Ed.), *Inflation and unemployment in open economies.* (pp. 249-267). Amsterdam: North-Holland.

Branson, W. H. (1979). Exchange rate dynamics and monetary policy. In A. Lindbeck (Ed.), *Inflation and unemployment in open economies.* (pp. 189-224). Amsterdam: North-Holland.

Branson, W. H., & Myhrman, J. (1976). Inflation in open economies: Supply-determined versus demand-determined models. *European Economic Review, 7,* 15-34. (Reprint No 50. Stockholm: IIES)

Branson, W. H., & Myhrman, J. (1979). Inflation in Sweden. In L. B. Krause, & W. S. Salant (Eds.), *Worldwide inflation – Theory and recent experience.* Washington, D. C.: Brookings Institution.

Calmfors, L. (1978). *Prices, wages and employment in the open economy.* (Monograph series No 10). Stockholm: IIES.

Calmfors, L. (1979). Real wages, inflation and unemployment in the open economy. In A. Lindbeck (Ed.), *Inflation and unemployment in open economies.* (pp. 41-69). Amsterdam: North-Holland.

Calmfors, L. (1983), Output, inflation and the terms of trade in a small open economy. *Kyklos, 36,* 40-65. (Reprint No 208. Stockholm: IIES)

Calmfors, L., & Herin, J. (1979). Domestic and foreign price influences: A disaggregated study of Sweden. In A. Lindbeck (Ed.), *Inflation and unemployment in open economies.* (pp. 269-306.) Amsterdam: North-Holland.

Calmfors, L., & Viotti, S. (1982). Wage indexation, the Scandinavian model and macroeconomic stability in the open economy. *Oxford Economic Papers, 34,* 546-566. (Reprint No 196. Stockholm: IIES)

Grassman, S. (1973). A fundamental symmetry in international payment patterns. *Journal of International Economics, 3,* 105-116. (Reprint No 30. Stockholm: IIES)

Grassman, S. (1976). Det flytande växelkurssystemets inverkan på utrikeshandeln. *Långtidsutredningen.* (SOU 1976:27).

Grassman, S. (1980). Long term trends in openness of national economies. *Oxford Economic Papers, 32,* 123-133. (Reprint No 127. Stockholm: IIES)

Grassman, S., & Herin, J. (1976). De korta kaptialrörelsernas bestämningsfaktorer. *Långtidsutredningen.* (SOU 1976:27).

Hamilton, S., & Söderström, H. T. (1981). Technology and international trade: A Heckscher-Ohlin approach. In S. Grassman, & E. Lundberg (Eds.), *The world economic order: Past and prospects.* London: Macmillan. (Reprint No 162. Stockholm: IIES)

Herin, J., Lindbeck, A., & Myhrman, J. (1976). *Flexible exchange rates and stabilization policy.* London: Macmillan.

Kouri, P. J. (1979). Profitability and growth in a small open economy. In A. Lindbeck (Ed.), *Inflation and unemployment in open economies.* (pp. 129-142). Amsterdam: North-Holland.

Krauss, M. B. (1975). *International trade and economic welfare.* (Monograph

series No 6). Stockholm: IIES.
Lindbeck, A. (1973). The national state in an international world economy. (Seminar paper No 26). Stockholm: IIES. (Lecture at Conjunto Universitario Candido Mendes, Rio de Janeiro)

Lindbeck, A. (1975). The changing role of the national state. *Kyklos, 28,* 23-46. (Reprint No 36. Stockholm: IIES)

Lindbeck, A. (1976). Stabilization policy in open economies with endogenous politicians. *The American Economic Review, 66* (2), 1-19. (Reprint No 56. Stockholm: IIES)

Lindbeck, A. (1978). Economic dependence and interdependence in the industrialized world. *From Marshall plan to global interdependence.* (pp. 59-68). Paris: OECD. (Reprint No 90. Stockholm IIES)

Lindbeck, A. (Ed.), (1979a). *Inflation and employment in open economies.* Amsterdam: North-Holland.

Lindbeck, A. (1979b). Imported and structural inflation and aggregate demand: The Scandinavian model reconstructed. In A. Lindbeck (Ed.), *Inflation and unemployment in open economies.* (pp. 13-40). Amsterdam: North-Holland.

Lundgren, N. (1974). Multinational firms and economic stability. In A. W. Sijthoff (Ed.), *Multinational enterprises – financial and monetary aspects.* Leiden. (Reprint No 35. Stockholm: IIES)

Lundgren, N. (1975). Internationella koncerner i industriländerna. Samhällsekonomiska aspekter. *Koncentrationsutredningen.* (SOU 1975:50).

Michaeli, M. (1978). Analysis of devaluation. Purchasing power parity, elasticities and absorption. (Seminar Paper No 112). Stockholm: IIES.

Myhrman, J. (1975). *Monetary policy in open economies.* (Monograph series No 5). Stockholm: IIES.

Myhrman, J. (1979). The determinants of inflation and economic activity in Sweden. In A. Lindbeck (Ed.), *Inflation and unemployment in open economies.* (pp. 307-335). Amsterdam: North-Holland.

Nyberg, L. (1979). Imported and homemade inflation under fixed and floating exchange rates. In A. Lindbeck (Ed.), *Inflation and unemployment in open economies.* (pp. 145-168). Amsterdam: North-Holland.

Nyberg, L., & Viotti, S. (1974). Optimal reserves and adjustment policies. *The Swedish Journal of Economics, 76,* 415-433. (Reprint No 37. Stockholm: IIES)

Nyberg, L., & Viotti, S. (1975). *A control systems approach to macroeconomic theory and policy in an open economy.* (Monograph series No 4). Stockholm: IIES.

Nyberg, L., & Viotti, S. (1979). Unemployment, inflation and the balance of payments: A dynamic analysis. In A. Lindbeck (Ed.), *Inflation and unemployment in open economies.* (pp. 99-127). Amsterdam: North-Holland.

Purvis, D.D. (1979). Wage responsiveness and the insulation properties of a flexible exchange rate. In A. Lindbeck (Ed.), *Inflation and unemployment in open economies.* (pp. 225-245). Amsterdam: North-Holland.

Svedberg, P. (1978). The portfolio-direct composition of private foreign investment in 1914 revisited. *The Economic Journal, 88,* 763-777.

Söderström, H. T. (1974). *Studies in the microdynamics of production and productivity change.* (Monograph series No 2). Stockholm: IIES.

Söderström, H. T., & Brundell, P. (1983). Macroeconomic causes of unbalanced productivity growth in open economies. (Seminar Paper No 252). Stockholm: IIES.

Söderström, H. T., & Viotti, S. (1979). Money, wage disturbances and the endogeneity of the public sector in an open economy. In A. Lindbeck (Ed.), *Inflation and unemployment in open economies.* (pp. 71-98). Amsterdam: North-Holland.

Wihlborg, C. (1976). *Risk capital market integration and monetary policy under different exchange rates regimes.* (Monograph series No 7). Stockholm: IIES.

Wihlborg, C. (1978). *Currency risks in international financial markets.* (Princeton Studies in International Finance No 44).

Wihlborg, C. (1979). Flexible exchange

rates, currency risks and the integration of capital markets. In A. Lindbeck (Ed.), *Inflation and unemployment in open economies.* (pp. 169-187). Amsterdam: North-Holland.

Wihlborg, C., & Wijkman, P. (1981). Outer space resources in efficient and equitable use: New frontiers for old principles. *Journal of Law and Economics, 24,* 23-43. (Reprint No 165. Stockholm: IIES)

Wijkman, P. (1976). Det internationella utbytet av varor och tjänster: Utvecklingstendenser och handelsvillkor. *Den internationella bakgrunden.* (SOU 1976:26)

Wijkman, P. (1980). Effects of cargo reservation: A review of UNCTADs code of conduct for liner conferences. *Marine Policy, 4,* 271-289. (Reprint No 142. Stockholm: IIES)

Wijkman, P. (1982a). UNCLOS and the redistribution of ocean wealth. *Journal of World Trade Law, 16,* 27-48. (Reprint No 177. Stockholm: IIES)

Wijkman, P. (1982b). Managing the global commons. *International Organization, 36,* 511-536. (Reprint No 186. Stockholm: IIES)

## S. Carlsson, Emigration and family history

Note. SHU = Studia Historica Upsaliensia.

Beijbom U. (1971). *Swedes in Chicago. A demographic and social study of the 1846-1880 immigration.* (SHU 38).

Berggren, H. (1966). *Förenta staternas historia.* Stockholm: Wahlström & Widstrand

Blomfelt, F. (1968). Emigrationen från ett skärgårdslandskap. Emigrationen från Åland 1856-1918 med särskild hänsyn till Finström och Föglö socknar. (Licentiatavhandling). Uppsala universitet: Historiska institutionen.

Bondestad, K. (1967). Det amerikanska inbördeskriget i svensk opinion. (Licentiatavhandling). Uppsala universitet: Historiska institutionen.

Bondestad, K. (1968). The American civil war and Swedish public opinion. *Swedish Pioneer Historical Quarterly, 19,* 95-115.

Brattne, B. (1973). *Bröderna Larsson. En studie i svensk emigrantagentverksamhet under 1880-talet.* (SHU 50).

Carlsson, S. (1966-67). Emigrationen från Småland och Öland 1861-1930. Social och regional fördelning. *Historielärarnas förenings årsskrift, 1966-67,* 41-63.

Carlsson, S (1967). Frikyrklighet och emigration. Ett bidrag. *Kyrka, folk, stat. Festskrift till Sven Kjöllerström.* (pp. 118-131). Lund: Gleerups.

Carlsson, S. (1968). Från familjeutvandring till ensamutvandring. En utvecklingslinje i den svenska emigrationens historia. In M. von Platen (Ed.), *Emigrationer. En bok till Vilhelm Moberg 20.8.1968.* (pp. 101-122). Stockholm: Bonniers.

Carlsson, S. (1970). *Skandinaviska politiker i Minnesota 1882-1900. En studie i den etniska faktorns roll vid politiska val i en immigrantstat.* (Folia Historica Upsaliensia 1). Uppsala universitet: Historiska institutionen.

Carlsson, S. (1971). Scandinavian politicians in Minnesota around the turn of the century. A study of the role of the ethnic factor in an immigrant state. In H. Naess, & S. Skard (Eds.), *Americana Norvegica III.* (pp. 237-271). Olso: Universitetsforlaget.

Carlsson, S. (1973). Skandinaviska politiker i Minnesota. In A-S Kälvemark (Ed.), *Utvandring. Den svenska emigrationen till Amerika i historiskt perspektiv. En antologi.* (pp. 211-243). Stockholm: Wahlström & Widstrand.

Carlsson, S. ( 1976). Chronology and composition of Swedish emigration to America. In H. Runblom, & H. Norman (Eds.), *From Sweden to America.* (pp. 114-148). Minneapolis & Uppsala: Minnesota University Press & Acta Universitatis Upsaliensis.

Carlsson, S. (1977). *Fröknar, mamseller, jungfrur och pigor. Ogifta kvinnor i det svenska ståndssamhället.* (SHU 90).

Carlsson, S. (1978). Kvinnoöden i Mälardalen under 1800-talet – en jämförelse mellan land och stad. *Annales Academiae Regiae Scientiarum Upsaliensis, 21,* 80-125.

Carlsson, S. (1980). Scandinavian poli-

ticians in the United States. In I.
Semmingsen, & P. Seyersted (Eds.),
*Scando-Americana. Papers on Scan-
dinavian emigration to the United Sta-
tes.* (pp. 153-166). University of Oslo:
American Institute.
Carlsson, S. (1988). *Swedes in North
America 1638-1988. Technical, cul-
tural, and political achievements.*
Stockholm: Streiffert. (Utförlig biblio-
grafi)
Dahlgren, S., & Norman, H. (1988).
*The rise and fall of New Sweden.
Governor Johan Risingh's journal
1654-1655 in its historical context.*
Uppsala: Acta Bibliothecae R. Universitatis Upsaliensis XXVII.
De Geer, E. (1977). *Migration och in-
fluensfält. Studier av emigration och
intern migration i Finland och Sverige 1816-1972.* (SHU 97).
Ebbeson, U. (1968). Emigrationen från
en bruksbygd i Östergötland. Utvandringen till Amerika åren 1868-1893
från Risinge socken med Finspångs
styckebruk. (Licentiatavhandling),
Uppsala universitet: Historiska institutionen.
Eriksson, I., & Rogers, J. (1978). *Rural
labor and population change. Social
and demographic developments in east-
central Sweden druing the nineteenth
century.* (SHU 100).
Gunnlaugsson, G. (1988). *Family and
household in Iceland 1801-1930. Studies in the relationship between demographic and socio-economic development, social legislation and household structures.* (SHU 154).
Halldin Norberg, V. (1977). *Swedes in
Haile Selassi's Ethiopia 1924-1952.
A study in early development co-operation.* (SHU 92).
Hasselmo, N. (Ed.). (1978). *Perspectives on Swedish immigration: Proceedings of the international conference
on the Swedish heritage in the Upper
Midwest, April 1-3, 1976, University
of Minnesota, Duluth.* Chicago: Swedish Pioneer Historical Society. (Med
bidrag från sex forskare inom Uppsa-
la-projektet)
Höjfors Hong, M. (1986). *Ölänningar
över haven. Utvandring från Öland
1840-1930, bakgrund, förlopp, effekter.* (SHU 143).

Hörsell, A. (1983). *Borgare, smeder
och änkor. Ekonomi och befolkning i
Eskilstuna gamla stad och Fristad
1750-1850.* (SHU 131).
Kronborg, B,. & Nilsson, T. (1975).
*Stadsflyttare. Industrialisering, migra-
tion och social mobilitet med utgångspunkt från Halmstad 1870-1910.* (SHU
65).
Kronborg, B., Nilsson, T., & Svale-
stuen, A. (Eds.). (1977). *Nordic population mobility. Comparative studies
of selected parishes in the Nordic
countries, 1850-1900.* Oslo: Universitetsforlaget.
Kälvemark, A-S. (1972). *Reaktionen
mot utvandringen. Emigrationsfrågan
i svensk debatt och politik, 1901-1904.*
(SHU 41).
Kälvemark, A-S. (1973). *Utvandring.
Den svenska emigrationen till Amerika i historiskt perspektiv. En antologi.*
Stockholm: Wahlström & Widstrand.
Kälvemark, A-S. (1980). *More children of better quality? Aspects on
Swedish population policy in the 1930's.*
(SHU 115).
Kälvemark, A-S. (1983). Utvandring
och självständighet. Några synpunkter på den kvinnliga emigrationen från
Sverige. *Historisk Tidskrift, 108,* 140-
174.
Larsson, J. (1977). *Diplomati och indu-
striellt genombrott. Svenska export-
strävanden på Kina 1906-1916.* (SHU
94).
Lindmark, S. (1971). *Swedish America,
1914-1932. Studies in ethnicity with
emphasis on Illinois and Minnesota.*
(SHU 37).
Lithell, U-B. (1981). *Breast-feeding and
reproduction. Studies in marital ferti-
lity and infant mortality in 19th century Finland and Sweden.* (SHU 120).
Lithell, U-B. (1988). *Kvinnoarbete och
barntillsyn i 1700- och 1800-talets
Österbotten.* (SHU 156).
Lucas, R. B. (1974). *Charles August
Lindbergh, Sr. A case study in political insurgency.* (SHU 61).
Lunander, E. (1988). *Borgare blir för-
etagare. Studier kring ekonomiska,
sociala och politiska förhållanden i
förändringens Örebro under 1800-
talet.* (SHU 155).
Lundbäck, B-M. (1982). *En industri*

kommer till stan. Hudiksvall och trä-varuindustrin 1855-1880. (SHU 123).

Nelson, M. (1988). Bitter bread. The famine in Norrbotten 1867-1868. (SHU 153).

Nilsson, F. (1970) Emigrationen från Stockholm till Nordamerika, 1880-1893. En studie i urban utvandring. (SHU 31).

Nilsson, R. (1982). Rallarliv. Arbete, familjemönster och levnadsförhållanden för järnvägsarbetare på banbyggena i Jämtland-Härjedalen, 1912-1928. (SHU 127).

Norberg, A. (1980) Sågarnas ö. Alnö under industrialiseringen 1860-1910. (SHU 116).

Noreen, P. (1987). Emigrationen från Sundals härad i Dalsland 1860-1895. Emigrationens orsaker och förlopp. Mellerud: Vasa Orden av Amerika Logen Mellerud nr 644. (Licentiatavhandling, Uppsala universitet, Historiska institutionen, 1967)

Norman, H. (1974). Från Bergslagen till Nordamerika. Studier i migrationsmönster, social rörlighet och demografisk struktur med utgångspunkt från Örebro län, 1851-1915. (SHU 62).

Norman, H. (Ed.). (1980). Demografisk-historisk forskning i Uppsala. (Meddelanden från familjehistoriska projektet nr 2). Uppsala universitet: Historiska institutionen. (Andra reviderade upplaga 1984.)

Norman, H. (Ed.) (1983). Den utsatta familjen. Liv, arbete och samlevnad i olika nordiska miljöer under de senaste tvåhundra åren. Stockholm: LT.

Norman, H., & Rogers, J. (1986). Familj och hushåll i förändrade produktionsmiljöer. Familien i forandring i 18- og 1900-tallet & mødeberetning. Rapport till den XIX nordiske historikerkongres Odense 1984. Bind 3 Odense: Odense universitetsforlag.

Norman, H., & Runblom, H. (Eds.) (1980a). Nordisk emigrationsatlas. Del 1: Atlas. Del 2: Texter och kommentarer. Gävle: Cikada.

Norman, H., & Runblom, H. (Eds.). (1980b). Amerikaemigrationen i källornas belysning. Gävle: Cikada.

Norman, H., & Runblom, H (1988). Transatlantic connections. Nordic emigration to the New World after 1800. Olso: Norwegian University Press.

Ohlander A-S. (1986). Kärlek, död och frihet. Historiska uppsatser om människovärde och livsvillkor i Sverige. Stockholm: Norstedts.

Rogers, J., & Norman, H. (Eds.) (1985). The Nordic family. Perspectives on family research. Reports to the round table session: The family in history at the 16th international congress of historical sciences, Stuttgart 25 August – 1 september 1985. (Meddelanden från familjehistoriska projektet nr 4). Uppsala universitet, Historiska institutionen.

Rolén, M. (1979). Skogsbygd i omvandling. Studier kring befolkningsutveckling, omflyttning och social rörlighet i Revsunds tinglag, 1820-1977. (SHU 107).

Rondahl, B. (1972). Emigration, folkomflyttning och säsongsarbete i ett sågverksdistrikt i södra Hälsingland 1865-1910. Söderala kommun med särskild hänsyn till Ljusne industrisamhälle. (SHU 40).

Runblom, H. (1971). Svenska företag i Latinamerika. Etableringsmönster och förhandlingstaktik. (SHU 35).

Runblom, H. (1977). Svenskarna i Canada. En studie i låg etnisk medvetenhet. In L-G. Tedebrand (Ed.), Historieforskning på nya vägar. Studier tillägnade Sten Carlsson 17.12.1977. (pp. 213-228). Lund: Studentlitteratur.

Runblom, H., & Norman, H. (Eds.) (1976). From Sweden to America. A history of the migration. (SHU 76) Minneapolis & Uppsala: Minnesota University Press & Acta Universitatis Upsaliensis.

Samson, M. L. (1977.). Population mobility in the Netherlands 1880-1910. A case study of Wisch in the Achterhoek. (SHU 87).

Stenbeck, K. (1973). Utvandringen från Sverige till Brasilien 1868-1891. (Licentiatavhandling). Uppsala universitet: Historiska institutioner.

Sundin, J. (1973). Främmande studenter vid Uppsala universitet före andra världskriget. En studie i studentmigration. (SHU 45).

Tedebrand, L-G. (1972). *Västernorrland och Nordamerika, 1875-1913. Utvandring och återinvandring.* (SHU 42).

Tedebrand, L-G. (Ed.). (1977). *Historieforskning på nya vägar. Studier tillägnade Sten Carlsson 17.12.1977.* Lund: Studentlitteratur.

Wester, H. (1977) *Innovationer i befolkningsrörligheten. En studie av spridningsförlopp i befolkningsrörligheten utgående från Petalax socken i Österbotten.* (SHU 93)

Åkerman, S. (1971). Intern befolkningsomflyttning och emigration. *Emigrationen fra Norden indtil 1. Verdenskrig. Rapporter til det Nordiska historikermøde i København 1971.* (pp. 61-107). Köpenhamn.

Åkerman, S. (1975). From Stockholm to San Fransisco. The development of the historical study of external migrations. *Annales Academiae Regiae Scientiarum Upsaliensis, 19,* 5-46.

Åkerman, S. (1976). Theories and methods of migration research. In H. Runblom, & H. Norman (Eds.), *From Sweden to America.* (pp. 19-73). Minneapolis & Uppsala: Minnesota University Press & Acta Universitatis Upsaliensis.

Åkerman, S. et. al. (1973). *Aristocrats, farmers and proletarians. Essays in Swedish demographic history.* (SHU 47)

List compiled by H. Norman and H. Runblom

## B. Odén,
## Studying the elderly in society

Andréasson, E. (1983). Ålderdom och engagemang i ett föränderligt samhälle. In B. Odén, A. Svanborg, & L. Tornstam (Eds.), *Äldre i samhället förr, nu och i framtiden. Del 2: Probleminventeringar.* (pp. 233-255). Stockholm: Liber.

Berggren, L., & Olsson, L. (1988). Arbetsmiljö, hälsa och arbetarskydd. *Metall 100 år – fem uppsatser.* (pp 53-82). Stockholm: Svenska metallindustriarbetareförbundet.

Blom, C. (1987). Bilden av de äldre.

(Arbetsrapport nio 26). Lunds universitet, Historiska institutionen.

Brocklehurst, J.C. (Ed.). (1975). *Geriatric care in advanced societies.* Lancaster: Medical and Technical Publishing.

Carlsson-Wetterberg, C. (1988). Kvinnor, arbete och åldrande. Textilarbeterskor i Malmö 1870-1918. *Scandia, 54* (2), 235-250.

Carlsson-Wetterberg, C. (1989). Likhet och särart. *Arbetarhistoria, 3,* 47-54.

Delegationen för långsiktsmotiverad forskning. (1978). *Äldre i samhället – förr, nu och i framtiden – ett forskningsprogram om de äldre som resurs, personligt, kulturellt, kunskapsmässigt och ekonomiskt.* (Information från delegationen för långsiktsmotiverad forskning nr 13). Stockholm: Forskningsrådsnämnden.

Edgren, L. (1982). *Hantverk och åldrande. Hantverkets äldre män och kvinnor i Malmö 1820.* (Arbetsrapport n:o 9). Lunds universitet, Historiska institutionen.

Edgren, L. (1983). Hantverkaränkor på äktenskapsmarknaden. Änkekonservering inom Malmöhantverket 1816-1840. *Ale, 4,* 1-17.

Edgren, M. (1987). Befolkningsomflyttningens betydelse för ålderdomstryggheten. *Ale, 4,* 11-19.

Elvander, N. (1982). Pensionärspolitik. In L. Tornstam, B. Odén, & A. Svanborg (Eds.), *Äldre i samhället förr, nu och i framtiden. Del 1: Teorier och forskningsansatser.* (pp. 218-263). Stockholm: Liber.

Eriksson, B.G., Mellström, A., & Svanborg, A. (1978). Medical-social intervention in a 70-year-old Swedish population. *Comprehensive Gerontology, 1,* 49-56.

Gaunt, D. (1976). Familj, hushåll och arbetsintensitet. *Scandia, 42,* 32-58.

Gaunt, D. (1977). I slottets skugga. *Ale, 2,* 15-30.

Gaunt, D. (1983). Arv och generationskonflikter. *Familjeliv i Norden.* (pp. 144-173). Malmö: Gidlunds.

Gaunt, D. (1983). Den pensionerade jordbrukaren: Dennes egendom och familjeförhållanden sedan medeltiden:

Norra och centrala Europa. In B. Odén, A. Svanborg, & L. Tornstam (Eds.), *Äldre i samhället förr, nu och i framtiden. Del 2: Probleminventeringar.* (pp. 137-167). Stockholm: Liber. (Engelsk version: In R. Wall (Ed.), (1983). *Family forms in historic Europe.* (pp. 249-279) Cambridge. Tysk version: In M. Mitterauer & R. Sieder (Eds.) (1982). *Historische Familienforschung.* (pp. 156-191) Frankfurt.)

Glimstedt, H. (1984). *Förståelse och metodintegration i muntlig historieforskning. Några reflexioner kring intervjuer med äldre i Göteborg.* (Arbetsrapport n:o 16). Göteborgs universitet, Historiska institutionen.

Jansson, T. (1985). *Adertonhundratalets associationer.* Uppsala: Almqvist & Wiksell International.

Jansson, T. (1987). *Agrarsamhällets förändring och landskommunal organisation.* Uppsala: Almqvist & Wiksell International.

Johansen, H.C. (1976). The position of the old in the rural household. *Scandinavian Economic Review, XXIV:2,* 129-142.

Johansson, U. (1984). *Fattiga och tiggare i Stockholms stad och län under 1700-talet.* Stockholm: Liber.

Kjellman, G. (1981). *De gamlas bostad – fattig-åldringskulturen.* (Arbetsrapport n:o 5). Lunds universitet, Historiska institutionen.

Kjellman, G. (1984). *Kultur och åldrande. En etnologisk studie av boendemönster och livsformer bland äldre på svensk landsbygd.* (Arbetsrapport n:o 17). Lunds universitet, Historiska institutionen.

Kjellman, G. (1987). *Åldringskultur i urbana miljöer.* (Arbetsrapport n:o 28). Lunds universitet, Historiska institutionen.

Kälvemark, A-S. (1977). Att vänta barn när man gifter sig. *Historisk tidskrift, 97* (2), 181-199.

Kälvemark, A-S. (1978). Äktenskap och familj i Sverige i historiskt perspektiv. *Historielärarnas Förenings Årsskrift.* (pp. 28-31). Skara.

Nilsson, U. (1986). *Pensionärer och studieverksamhet.* Lund: Pedagogiska institutionen.

Odén, B. (1978). De äldre i samhället –

förr, nu och i framtiden. *Humanistisk forskning 1,* 2-5.

Odén, B. (1983a). Åldrandet, familjen och de sociala relationerna. En introduktion. In B. Odén, A. Svanborg, & L. Tornstam (Eds.), *Äldre i samhället förr, nu och i framtiden. Del 2: Probleminventeringar.* (pp. 125-136). Stockholm Liber.

Odén, B. (1983b). Åldrandet och åldringar i olika kulturer och tider. In K. Lidmar-Reinius (Ed.), *Forskare om åldrande och boende.* (Byggforskningsrådet T 13:1983). Stockholm: Statens råd för byggforskning.

Odén, B. (1983c). De äldre i samhället – ett kulturellt och jämförande perspektiv. *Äldreomsorg i samverkan –forskning och praktik.* (Socialstyrelsen 56/83). Stockholm: Socialstyrelsen

Odén, B. (1985). Uppväxt-, utvecklings-, och åldringsprocesser från historievetenskaplig synvinkel. In *De äldre i samhället – förr.* (Arbetsrapport n:o 22). Lunds universitet, Historiska institutionen.

Odén, B. (1986). Familjen igår och idag. *Socialmedicinsk tidskrift, 1986:5-6,* 200-207.

Odén, B. (1987) Planering inför ålderdomen i senmedeltidens Stockholm. In B. Sawyer, & A. Göransson (Eds.). *Manliga strukturer och kvinnliga strategier.* (Meddelande från Historiska institutionen i Göteborg nr 33). Borås.

Odén, B. (1988a). Vem har makt och inflytande i ett äldre samhälle – de gamla eller de unga? *Gerontologia, 1,* 3-17.

Odén, B. (1988b). The role of the family and state in old-age support: the Swedish experience up to 1913. *Comprehensive Gerontology, 2,* 42-46.

Olsson, L. (1983a). Industrialiseringen, de äldre arbetarna och pensioneringen. In B. Odén, A. Svanborg, & L. Tornstam (Eds.), *Äldre i samhället förr, nu och i framtiden. Del 2: Probleminventeringar.* (pp. 81-96). Stockholm: Liber.

Olsson, L. (1983b). *En typ bland typer i Lund. En livslinjestudie av en lundatypografs liv i helg och söcken.* Lund: Grafiska fackföreningen i Lund.

Olsson, L. (1984). Altern im gesellschaftlichen Wandel – Ein interdiziplinäres Forschungsprojekt über Schweden im 19. und 20. Jahrhundert. *Zeitschrift für Gerontologie, 17*, 6-12.

Olsson, L. (1986). *Gamla typer och nya produktionsförhållanden. Om rationalisering och medbestämmande, åldrande och solidaritet bland typografer i Sverige från slutet av 1800-talet till omkring 1960.* Lund: Luciters Förlag.

Olsson, L. (1988a). Våra gamla kolleger, yrkesveteraner, de som passerat 35-års-strecket. *Arbetets historia 2.* Lund: Arbetshistoriska seminariet.

Olsson, L. (1988b). Arbeitsbedingungen und Lebensdauer unter schwedischer Typographen 1900-1970. *Arbeiterklasse in Deutschland zur Zeit der Weimarer Republik.* Rostock: Wilhelm-Pieck-Universität.

Olsson, L. (1989). Dödsorsaker bland metallarbetare i Stockholm 1890-1926. *Studier och handlingar rörande Stockholms historia VI.* Stockholm: Stockholms stadsarkiv.

Pikwer, P. (1986). *Äldres beroende av anhörigvård.* (Arbetsrapport n:o 25). Lunds universitet, Historiska institutionen.

Pikwer, P., Arvidsson, A., & Holmberg, I. (1984). *Omvårdnaden om äldre.* (Arbetsrapport n:o 18). Lunds universitet, Historiska institutionen.

Pulma, P. (1985). *Fattigvård i frihetens Finland.* Helsingfors: Suomen Historiallinen Seura.

Stenkula, C. G. (1983). *Gammal i Lund.* Malmö: Gleerup.

Thomas, K. (1976). Age and authority in early modern England. *Proceedings of the British academy, LXII.* (pp. 205-248). Oxford: Oxford University Press.

Tornstam, L. (1978). Attityder, värderingar och samhälle. In C. Ström, & Y. Zotterman (Eds.), *Attityder och åldrande.* Stockholm: Liber.

Tornstam, L. (1984). *Sociala attityder till äldre.* (Arbetsrapport n:o 19). Uppsala universitet, Sociologiska institutionen.

Tornstam, L. (1985). *Känslomässiga attityder till äldre.* (Arbetsrapport n:o 20). Uppsala universitet, Sociologiska institutionen.

Tornstam, L. (1989). Abuse of the elderly in Denmark and Sweden: Results from a population study. *Journal of Elder Abuse and Neglect, 1*, 35-44.

Udvardy, M. (1983). Att bli änka bland några östafrikanska bantufolk. In C. Ström, & D. Ottoson (Eds.), *Att bli lämnad ensam.* (pp. 15-21). Vadstena: Allmänna Förlaget.

Winberg, C. (1988). Några anteckningar om historisk antropologi. *Historisk tidskrift, 1*, 1-29.

Zitomersky, J. (1983). Familjen som vårdresurs för de äldre. En historiskkonceptuell ansats. In B. Odén, A. Svanborg, & L. Tornstam (Eds.), *Äldre i samhället förr, nu och i framtiden. Del 2: Probleminventeringar.* (pp. 168-181). Stockholm: Liber.

Zitomersky, J. (1987). Ecology, class or culture? Explaining family residence and support of the elderly in the Swedish agrarian past. *Scandinavian Journal of History, 12*(2), 117-160.

Åkerman, S. (1977). En befolkning före den demografiska transitionen. In J. Cavallie (Ed.), *Karolinska förbundets årsbok.* (pp. 66-113). Lund.

Åkerman, S. (1981). *De stackars pensionärerna.* (Arbetsrapport n:o 3). Umeå universitet, Historiska institutionen.

Åman, A. (1976). *Om den offentliga vården.* Stockholm: Liber.

See also Notes.

**L. Furuland,**
**Swedish sociology of literature**

Bennich-Björkman, B. (1970a). *Författaren i ämbetet. Studier i funktion och organisation av författarämbeten vid svenska hovet och kansliet 1550-1850.* Stockholm: Svenska bokförlaget.

Bennich-Björkman, B. (1970b). *Termen litteratur i svenskan 1750-1850.* Uppsala: Avdelningen för litteratursociologi.

Bennich-Björkman, B. (1988). Jacob Gustaf Björnståhl – sago- och viskung i Stockholm på 1820-talet. *Litteraturens vägar. Litteratursociologiska studier tillägnade Lars Furuland.* (pp. 93-135). Stockholm: Gidlund.

Bennich-Björkman, B., & Furuland, L.

(1988). Vad folket sjöng och läste. In L. Lönnroth, & S. Delblanc (Eds.), Den svenska litteraturen. III (pp. 269-299). Stockholm: Bonniers.

Blanck, A. (1935). Ur samma synvinkel. Tidshändelser i diktens spegel. Stockholm: Gebers.

Edström, V., & Furuland, L. (1976). Projektet Barn- och ungdomslitteratur i Sverige. Humanistisk forskning, 1976, 2, 31-35.

Furuland, L. (1971). Folkhögskolan – en bildningsväg för svenska författare. Stockholm: Utbildningsförlaget. (Först publicerad i något kortare form i Svensk folkhögskola 100 år, IV. Stockholm: Liber, 1968)

Furuland, L. (1976). Statarnas ombudsman i dikten. En bok om Ivar Lo-Johansson. Stockholm: LTs förlag.

Furuland, L. (1984). Ljus över landet. Elektrifieringen och litteraturen. Daedalus, 53, 11-36.

Furuland, L. (1989a). Folkrörelser och arbetardikt. In L. Lönnroth, & S. Delblanc (Eds.), Den svenska litteraturen. IV (pp. 229-254). Stockholm: Bonniers.

Furuland, L. (1989b). Autodidakter och arbetardiktare. In L. Lönnroth, & S. Delblanc (Eds.), Den svenska litteraturen. V (pp. 105-148). Stockholm: Bonniers.

Furuland, L. (1989c). Literacy in Sweden: two essays. (The Nordic Roundtable Papers, vol 3). University of Minnesota: The Center for Nordic studies.

Furuland, L. (1989d). Litteratur och samhälle. In E. Munch-Petersen (Ed.),Litteratursociologi. En antologi. (pp. 11-48). København: Bibliotekscentralen.

Johannesson, K. (1968). I polstjärnans tecken. Studier i svensk barock. Uppsala: Almqvist & Wiksell.

Rehn, M. (1974). Jack London i Sverige. Studier i marknadsföring och litterärt inflytande. Uppsala: Avdelningen för litteratursociologi.

Schön, E. (1973). Jan Fridegård och forntiden. En studie i diktverk och källor. Uppsala: Avdelningen för litteratursociologi.

Svanberg, V. (1943-46). Medelklassrealism. Samlaren. 1943-46. (I bokform Stockholm: Gidlund, 1980)

Svanberg, V. (1980) Romantikens samhälle. Stockholm: Gidlund.

Svedjedal, J. (1987). Almqvist – berättaren på bokmarknaden. Berättartekniska och litteratursociologiska studier i C.J.L. Almqvists prosafiktion kring 1840. Uppsala: Avdelningen för litteratursociologi.

Åkerstedt, J. (1967). Den litterate arbetaren. Bildningssyn och studieverksamhet i ABF 1912-1930. Uppsala: Avdelningen för litteratursociologi.

See also Notes.

## E. Dahmén and K.-G. Mäler, Environment, natural resources and society

Andreasson, I. (1988). Costs of controls on farmers' use of nitrogen. Stockholm: Ekonomiska forskningsinstitutet.

Ayres, R., & Kneese, A.V. (1969). Production, consumption and externalities. American Economic Review, 59, 282-297.

Bergman, L. (1977). Energy and economic growth. Stockholm: Ekonomiska forskningsinstiutet.

Bergman, L., Mäler, K.G., Nordström, T., & Ysander, B. (1983). Energy and economic adjustment. Stockholm: Industins utredningsinstitut och Ekonomiska forskningsinstitutet.

Bergman, L., Mäler, K.G., & Ståhl, I. (1987). Överförbara utsläppstillstånd. En studie av kolväteutsläpp i Göteborg. Stockholm: Ekonomiska forskningsinstiutet.

Bergström, C. (1985). Supply disruptions and the allocation of emergency reserves. Stockholm: Ekonomiska forskningsinstitutet.

Dahmén, E. (1965). Planerar vi för den ekonomiska utvecklingen på längre sikt som vi verkligen vill ha? Svensk ekonomisk tillväxt. Stockholm: Finansdepartementet.

Dahmén, E. (1968). Sätt pris på miljön. Stockholm: Studieförbundet Näringsliv och Samhälle.

Dahmén, E. (1971) Environmental control and economic systems. Swedish Journal of Economics, 73, 67-75.

Facht, J. (1976). Emission control costs

*in Swedish industry.* Stockholm: Industrins utredningsinstitut.

Freeman, M. (1979). *The benefits of environmental improvement.* Baltimore: Johns Hopkins University Press.

Georgescu-Roegen, N. (1971) *The entropy law and the economic process.* Cambridge: Harvard University Press.

Lundgren, S. (1985). *Model integration and the economics of nuclear power.* Stockholm: Ekonomiska forskningsinstitutet.

Mäler, K.G. (1971). A method of estimating social benefits from pollution control. *Swedish Journal of Economics, 73,* 120-133.

Mäler, K.G. (1974). *Environmental economics – A theoretical inquiry.* Baltimore. Johns Hopkins University Press.

Mäler, K.G. (1985). Welfare economics and the environment. In A.V. Kneese, & J.L. Sweeney (Eds.), *Handbook of natural resource and energy economics.* Amsterdam: North Holland.

Mäler, K.G., & Wyzga, R. (1976). *Economic measurement of environmental damage functions.* Paris: OECD.

Pigou, A.C. (1932). *The economics of welfare.* London: Macmillan (4th ed)

Stevens, J. (1966). Recreational benefits from water pollution control. *Water Resources Research, 2,* 167-182.

**A. Rapp, Soil conservation for survival**

Andersson, I. (1982). *Wells and handpumps in Shinyanga region, Tanzania.* (Research Paper 77). University of Dar es Salaam.

Bennet, H. H. (1939). *Soil conservation.* New York: McGraw – Hill.

Blaikie, P., & Brookfield, H. (1987). *Land degradation and society.* London: Methuen.

Chagula, W. K. (1972). Foreword to the DUSER project report. *Geografiska Annaler, 54 A,* I-II.

Christiansson, C. (1972). Notes on morphology and soil erosion in Kondoa and Singida districts, Tanzania. *Geografiska Annaler, 54 A,* 319-324.

Christiansson, C. (1981). *Soil erosion and sedimentation in semi-arid Tanzania.* Uppsala: Scandinavian Institute of African Studies.

Christiansson, C. (1988). Degradation and rehabilitation of agropastoral land. Perspectives on environmental change in semi-arid Tanzania. *Ambio, 17(2),* 144-152.

Christiansson, C. (1989). Rates of erosion in the East African savanna environment. In D. B. Thomas et. al. (Eds.), *Soil and water conservation in Kenya.* (pp. 99-114). University of Nairobi: Department of Agricultural Engineering.

Fries, J. (1988). Västafrikas savanner – är de på väg att bli öken? *Ymer, 108,* 90-109.

Gillman, C. (1940). *Water consultant's report 6.* Dar es Salaam: Government Printer.

Harrison, E. (1937). *Soil erosion, a memorandum.* (pp. 1-22). London: Government of Tanganyika Territory Crown Agents.

Helldén, U. (1988). Desertification monitoring: Is the desert encroaching? *Desertification Control Bulletin, 17* (pp. 8-12). Nairobi: UNEP.

Hudson, N. (1989). *Success and failure of soil conservation programmes.* (6th ISCO Conference Abstract, session 6, Addis Abeba)

Jacks, B. V., & Whyte, R. O. (1939). *The rape of the earth.* London: Faber & Faber.

I.S.C.O.6. (1989). *Soil conservation for survival.* (6th International Conference on Soil Conservation, Abstracts, Ethiopia and Kenya)

Klemm, W. (1989). *Runoff farming experiences with locally adapted farming techniques in Mali.* (6th ISCO Conference, Addis Abeba)

Lundgren, B. (1978). *Soil conditions and nutrient cycling under natural and plantation forests in Tanzanian highlands.* (Report No 31). Uppsala: Department of Forest Soils, Swedish University of Agricultural Science.

Lundgren, B. (1985). Global deforestation, its causes and suggested remedies. *Managing global issues.* (pp. 89-102). (The Club of Rome Conference, Helsinki)

Lundgren, L. (1980) *Soil erosion in Tanzanian mountain areas. Case stu-*

dies of land degradation and recovery. (Research report 39). University of Stockholm: Department of Physical Geography.

Lundgren, L. (1989). Kan agroforestry och markvård minska trycket på de tropiska skogarna? Ymer, 109, 85-102.

Lundgren, L., & Rapp, A. (1974). A complex landslide with destructive effects on the water supply of Morogoro town, Tanzania. Geografiska Annaler, 56 A, 251-260.

Murray-Rust, H. (1972). Soil erosion and reservoir sedimentation in a grazing area west of Arusha, northern Tanzania. Geografiska Annaler, 54 A, 325-344.

Olsson, L. (1985). An integrated study of desertification. (Avhandling 98). Lunds unviersitet: Geografiska institutionen.

Rapp, A. (1976) An assessment of soil and water conservation needs in Mwanza region, Tanzania. (Rapporter och Notiser 31). University of Lund: Department of Physical Geography.

Rapp, A., Berry, L., & Temple, P. H. (Eds.). (1972). Studies of soil erosion and sedimentation in Tanzania. Geografiska Annaler, 54 A, 105-379.

Rapp, A., Axelsson, V., Berry, L., & Murray-Rust, D. H. (1972). Soil erosion and sediment transport in the Morogoro river catchment, Tanzania. Geografiska Annaler, 54 A, 125-155.

Rapp, A., Murray-Rust, D. H., Christiansson, C., & Berry, L, (1972). Soil erosion and sedimentation in four catchments near Dodoma, Tanzania. Geografiska Annaler, 54 A, 255-318.

Rapp, A., Le Houérou, H. N., & Lundholm, B. (Eds.). (1977). Can desert encroachment be stopped? Ecological Bulletins, 24 Stockholm: Swedish Natural Science Research Council.

Rapp, A., & Håsteen, A. (1990). Improved management of drylands by water harvesting in Third World countries. In J. Boardman, J. Dearing, & I. D. L. Foster (Eds.), Soil erosion on agricultural lands. (pp. 496-511). Chichester: J. Wiley & Sons.

Reij, C. (1989). Basic information about the Sub-Saharan water harvesting study. (Circular letter, 6th ISCO Conference, Addis Abeba)

Roose, E. (1989). Diversity of traditional and modern strategy for soil and water conservation. (6th ISCO Conference Abstract, Session 4, Addis Abeba)

Staples, R. R. (1939). Run-off soil erosion tests in semi-arid Tanganyika territory. (3rd Report, Animal Husbandry). Dar es Salaam: Government Printer.

Strömquist, L. (1976). Land systems of the Great Ruaha drainage basin upstream of the Mtera dam site. In D. Johansson (Ed.), Ecological studies of the Mtera basin. Stockholm: SWECO.

Sundborg, Å., & White, W. (Eds.). (1982). Sedimentation problems in river basins. (Studies and reports in hydrology 35). Paris: UNESCO.

Sundborg, Å., & Rapp, A. (1986). Erosion and sedimentation by water: Problems and prospects. Ambio, 4, 215-225.

Temple, P. H. (1972). Soil and water policies in the Uluguru mountains, Tanzania. Geografiska Annaler, 54 A, 110-123.

Temple, P. H., & Rapp, A. (1972). Landslides in the Mgeta area, Western Uluguru mountains, Tanzania. Geografiska Annaler, 54 A, 157-194.

Temple, P. H., & Sundborg, Å. (1972). The Rufiji river, Tanzania. Hydrology and sediment transport. Geografiska Annaler, 54 A, 345-368.

W.C.E.D. (1987). Our common future. World commission on environment and development. Oxford: Oxford University Press.

Östberg, W. (1986). The Kondoa transformation. Coming to grips with soil erosion in Central Tanzania. (Reseach Report 76). Uppsala: Scandinavian Institute of African Studies.

## J.-E. Kihlström,
## Environmental pollutants

Bishop, E.L. (1949). Effects of DDT mosquito larviciding on wildlife. III. The effects on the plankton population of routine larviciding with DDT. Public Health Reports, 62, 1263-1268.

Brunström, B. (1989). Toxicity of co-planar polychlorinated biphenyls in avian embryos. Chemosphere, 19, 765-768.

Brunström, B., & Andersson, L. (1988). Toxicity and 7-ethoxyresorufin 0-deethylase-inducing potency of coplanar polychlorinated biphenyls (PCBs) in chick embryos. *Archives of Toxicology, 62*, 263-266.

Brunström, B., & Darnerud, P.O. (1983). Toxicity and distribution in chick embryos of 3,3',4,4'-tetrachlorobiphenyl injected into eggs. *Toxicology, 27*, 103-110.

Brunström, B., Darnerud, P.O., Brandt, I., & Örberg, J. (1982). Distribution, metabolism and toxicity of 2,2',4,5'-tetrachlorobiphenyl after injection into the yolk of embryonated hens' eggs. *Ambio, 11*, 212-214.

Brunström, B., & Lund, J. (1988). Differences between chick and turkey embryos in sensitivity to 3,3',4,4'-tetrachlorobiphenyl and in concentration/affinity of the hepatic receptor for 2,3,7,8-tetrachlorodibenzo-p-dioxin. *Comparative Biochemistry and Physiology, 91C*, 507-512.

Brunström, B., & Reutergårdh, L. (1986). Differences in sensitivity of some avian species to the embryotoxicity of a PCB, 3,3',4,4'-tetrachlorobiphenyl, injected into eggs. *Environmental Pollution (Series A), 42*, 37-45.

Crouter, R.A., & Vernon, E.H. (1959). Effects of black-headed budworm control on salmon and trout in British Columbia. *Canadian Fish Culturist, 24*, 23-40.

Eriksson, G., Jensen, S., Kylin, H., & Strachan, W. (1989). The pine needle as a monitor of atmospheric pollution. *Nature, 341*, 42-44.

Eriksson, P., Archer, T., & Fredriksson, A. (in press). Altered behaviour in adult mice exposed to a single low dose of DDT and its fatty acid conjugate as neonates. *Brain Research.*

Eriksson, P. (1984). Age-dependent retention of 14C1DDT in brain of the postnatal mouse. *Toxicology Letters, 22*, 323-328.

Eriksson, P., Falkeborn, Y., Nordberg, A., & Slanina, P. (1984). Effects of DDT on muscarine- and nicotine-like binding sites in CNS of immature and adult mice. *Toxicology Letters, 22*, 329-334.

Eriksson, P., & Darnerud, P.O. (1985). Distribution and retention of some chlorinated hydrocarbons and a phtalate in the mouse brain during the pre-weaning period. *Toxicology, 37*, 185-203.

Eriksson, P., Nilsson-Håkansson, L., Nordberg, A., Aspberg, A., & Fredriksson, A. (in press). Neonatal exposure for DDT and its fatty acid conjugate – Effects on cholinergic and behavioural variables in the adult mouse. *Neurotoxicology.*

Eriksson, P., & Nordberg, A. (1986). The effect of DDT, DDOH-palmitic acid and a chlorinated paraffin on muscarinic receptors and the sodium-dependent choline uptake in the central nervous system of immature mice. *Toxicology and Applied Pharmacology, 85*, 121-127.

George, J.L., & Frear, D.E.H. (1966). Pesticides in the Antarctic. *Pesticides in the environment and their effects on wildlife. Journal of Applied Ecology, 3* (suppl.), 155.

Helle, E., Olsson, M., & Jensen, S. (1976a) DDT and PCB levels and reproduction in ringed seal from the Bothnian Bay. *Ambio, 5*, 188-189.

Helle, E., Olsson, M., & Jensen, S. (1976b). PCB levels correlated with pathological changes in seal uteri. *Ambio, 5*, 261-263.

Hoffman, C.H., & Merkel, E.P. (1948). Fluctuations in insect populations associated with aerial applications of DDT for forests. *Journal of Economic Entomology, 41*, 464-473.

Jensen, S. (1966). Klorerade bifenyler i naturen. *Nordforsk biocid-information, 7*, 1.

Jensen, S. (1972). The PCB story. *Ambio, 1*, 123-131.

Jensen, S., Kihlström, J.E., Olsson, M., Lundberg, C., & Örberg, J. (1977). Effects of PCB and DDT on mink (Mustela vision) during the reproductive season. *Ambio, 6*, 239.

Kihlström, J.E. (1986). *Gifter i naturen.* Stockholm: Liber.

Kihlström, J.E., Lundberg, C., Örberg, J., Danielsson, P.O., & Sydhoff, J. (1975). Sexual functions of mice neonatally exposed to DDT or PCB. *Environmental and Physiological Biochemistry, 5*, 54-57.

Kihlström, J.E., Örberg, J., Lundberg, C., & Danielsson, P.O. (1974). Postnatal growth in mice sucking milk containing PCB or DDT. *Ambio, 3*, 231-233.

Naturvårdsverket. (1988). *Biologiska effekter av blekeriavlopp.* (Rapport 3498). Solna: Naturvårdsverket.

Nikolaidis, E., Brunström, B., & Dencker, L. (1988). Effects of TCDD and its congeners 3, 3',4,4'-tetrachloroazoxybenzene and 3,3',4,4'-tetrachlorobiphenyl on lymphoid development in the thymus of avian embryos. *Pharmacology & Toxicology, 63*, 333-336.

Olsson, M., & Reutergårdh, L. (1986). DDT and PCB pollution trends in the Swedish aquatic environment. *Ambio, 15*, 103-109.

Peterle, T.J. (1969). DDT in Antarctic snow. *Nature, 224*, 620.

Ratcliffe, D.A. (1967). Decrease in eggshell weight in certain birds of prey. *Nature 215*, 208-210.

Rudd, R.L., & Genelly, R.E. (1955). Avian mortality from DDT in California rice fields. *Condor, 57*, 117-118.

Sladen, W.J.L., Menzie, C.M., & Reichel, W.L. (1966). DDT residues in Adelic penguins and crabeater seal from Antarctica. *Nature, 210*, 670-675.

Stearns, L.A., Lynch, E.E., Krafchick, B., & Woodmansee, C.W. (1947). Report of the use of DDT and Paris green on muskat marshes. *Proceedings of the 34th Annual Meeting of New Jersey Mosquito Extermination Association.* (pp. 82-95).

Wigglesworth, V.B. (1945). DDT and the balance of nature. *Atlantic Monthly, 176*, 107-113.

Wragg, L.E. (1954). The effect of DDT and oil on muskrats. *Canadian Field-Naturalist, 68*, 11-13.

**D. Ingvar, On alcohol research**

Note. Publications referred to by numbers

1. Arendt, T. (1989). Cholinergic system and memory in the rat. Effects of chronic ethanol. *Neuroscience, 33*, 435-462.

2. Arvidsson, O. (Ed.). (1982). *Risken att bli alkoholist.* Stockholm: Riksbankens Jubileumsfond.

3. Bailar III, J.C. (1987-1988). Rethinking the war on cancer. *Issues, 4*(1), 16-21.

4. Bejerot, N. (1972). *Addiction, an artificially induced drive.* Springfield, Illinois: Charles C. Thomas.

5. Berglund, M., Ingvar, D. H. (1976). The cerebral blood flow and its regional cerebral distribution in chronic alcoholism and in Korsakoff's psychosis. *Journal of Studies on Alcohol, 37*, 586-597.

6. Eckhardt, M.J. (1988). Acute ethanol administration selctively alters localized cerebral glucose metabolism. *Brain Research, 444* (53-58).

7. Engel, J. (Ed.), (1987). *Brain reward systems and abuse.* New York: Raven Press. (VII Berzelius symposium, Göteborg 1986)

8. Engel, J., & Liljequist, S. (1983). The involvement of different central neurotransmitters in mediating stimulatory and sedative effects of ethanol. In L.Å. Pohorecky, & J. Brick (Eds.), *Stress and alcohol use.* Amsterdam: Elsevier.

9. Freund, G. (1975). Impairment of memory after prolonged alcohol consumption in mice. In M.M. Gross (Ed.), *Alcohol intoxication and withdrawal.* New York: Plenum Press.

10. Goodman, L.G., & Gilman, A. (1965). *The pharmacological basis of therapeutics.* New York: MacMillan. (4th ed)

11. Hemmingsen, R (1981). *Cerebrale mekanismer ved ethanol-intoxikation og abstinens.* University of Copenhagen: Fadl's forlag.

12. Hibell, B., Romelsjö, H., & Rydberg, U. (1989) Utvecklingen av alkoholkonsumtion och alkoholskadorna i Sverige. Ur artikelserien: Alkohol – ett evigt problem. *Läkartidningen, 86*, 17-25.

13. Ingvar, D. H. (Ed.) (1977). *Att dricka. Fakta och diskussioner om alkohollens verkan på kropp och själ.* Stockholm: Bonniers.

14. Ingvar, D. H. (1985). "Memory" of the future. An essay on the temporal organization of conscious awareness. *Human Neurobiology, 4*, 127-136.

15. Johannesson, G., Berglund, M., &

Ingvar, D. H. (1980). EEG and cerebral blood flow in chronic alcoholism. *Electroencephalography & Clinical Neurophysiology, 49*, 79-81.

16. Kalant, H. (1987). Current trends in biomedical research on alcohol. *Alcohol and Alcoholism, Suppl 1*, 1-12.

17. Kissin, B., & Begleiter, H. (Eds.), (1972). *The biology of alcoholism. Vol. I-III* New York: Plenum Press.

18. Liebman, J. M., & Cooper, S. J. (Eds.), (1989). *The neuropharmacological basis of reward.* Oxford: Clarendon Press.

19. Lishman, W. H. (1978). *Organic psychiatry.* Oxford: Blackwell.

20. Magnusson, N. (Ed.), (1985). *Alkoholpolitiken.* (Socialstyrelsen 109/85). Stockholm: Socialstyrelsen.

21. Olds, J., & Milner, P. (1954). Positive reinforcement produced by electrical stimulation of septal area and other regions of rat brain. *Journal of Comparative Physiology and Psychology, 47*, 419-427.

22. Persson, J. (1989). *The excessive drinker in somatic and outpatient care.* University of Lund.

23. Rankin, J.G. (Ed.). (1975). *Alcohol, drugs and brain damage.* Toronto, Canada: Addiction Research Foundation.

24. Rydberg, U. (Ed.). (1985). *Alcohol and the developing brain.* New York: Raven Press. (III International Berzelius symposium, Stockholm, 1984)

25. Schuckitt, M.A., & Gold, E. O. (1988). A simultaneous evaluation of multiple markers of ethanol/placebo challenges in sons of alcoholics and in controls. *Archives of General Psychiatry, 45*, 211-216.

26. Stellar, J. R., & Stellar, E. (1985). *The neurobiology of motivation and reward.* Heidelberg: Springer Verlag.

27. Treml, V. G. (1982). *Alcohol in the USSR.* Durham, N.C.: Duke University Press.

28. Wallgren, H., & Barry III, H. (1970). *Actions of alcohol. Vol I-II* Amsterdam: Elsevier.

29. Victor, M., Adams, R. D., & Collings, G. H. (1971). *The Wernicke Korsakoff syndrome.* Oxford: Blackwell.

## B. Pernow, Attempts to prevent cardiovascular disease

Brown, M.S., & Goldstein, J.L. (1984). How LDL receptors influence cholesterol and atherosclerosis. *Scientific American, 251*(5), 52-60.

Grundy, S. M. (1986). Cholesterol and coronary heart disease. State of the art review. *Journal of the American Medical Association, 256*, 2849-2858.

Hanson, B.S. (1988). *Social network, social support and health in elderly men.* Lund: Studentlitteratur.

Hjärt-lungfonden. (1988). *Riktlinjer för behandling av hyperkolesterolemi.* Stockholm.

Knutsson, A. (1989). Shift work and coronary heart disease. *Scandinavian Journal of Social Medicine, 44* (suppl.), 1-36.

Lannerstad, O. (1978). *Död och sjukdom bland medelålders män.* Lunds universitet, Allmänna sjukhuset, Malmö: Institutionerna för klinisk fysiologi, patologi, socialmedicin och kirugi.

Lannerstad, O., Isacsson, S. & Lindell, S. (1979). Risk factors for premature death in men 56-60 years old. *Scandinavian Journal of Social Medicine, 7*, 41-47.

Socialstyrelsen *Folkhälsorapport.* (1987). Stockholm.

Svärdsudd, K., & Wilhelmsen, L. (1984). Prevention av hjärt-kärlsjukdomar. En kunskapsöversikt. *Att förebygga hjärt- och kärlsjukdom – ett hälsopolitiskt handlingsprogram.* (HS 90, SOU 1984:43). Stockholm.

Theorell, T. (1982). Review of research on life events and cardiovascular illness. In H. Denolin (Ed.), *Psychological problems before and after myocardial infarction. Advances in cardiology. 29* (pp. 140-153). Basel: Karger.

Wilhelmsen, L., Berglund, G., Elmfeldt, D., Tibblin, G., Wedel, H., Pennert, K., Vedin, A., Wilhelmsen, C., & Werkö, L. (1986). The multifactor primary prevention trial in Göteborg, Sweden. *European Heart Journal, 7*, 278-288.

Wilhelmsen, L., Wedel, H., & Tibblin, G. (1973). Multivariate analysis of risk factors for coronary heart disease. *Circulation, 48,* 950-958.

## D. Magnusson,
## Individual development

Andersson, T., Bergman, L.R., & Magnusson, D. (1989). Patterns of adjustment problems and alcohol abuse in early adulthood: A prospective longitudinal study. *Development and Psychopathology, 2,* 119-131.

Bergman, L.R. (1987). You can't classify all of the people all of the time. *Multivariate Behavioral Research, 23,* 425-441.

Bergman, L.R. (1988). Modelling reality: Some comments. In M. Rutter (Ed.), *Studies of psychosocial risk.* Cambridge: Cambridge University Press.

Bergman, L.R., & Magnusson, D. (1984a). *Patterns of adjustment problems at age 10: An empirical and methodological study.* (Reports from the Department of Psychology, University of Stockholm No 615).

Bergman, L.R., & Magnusson, D. (1984b). *Patterns of adjustment problems at age 13: An empirical and methodological study.* (Reports from the Department of Psychology, University of Stockholm No 620).

Gustafson, S.B., & Magnusson, D. (in press). Female life careers (vol 3). In D. Magnusson (Ed.), *Paths through life.* Hillsdale, NJ: Erlbaum

Hinde, R.A., & Dennis, H. (1986). Categorizing individuals: An alternative to linear analysis. *International Journal of Behavioral Development, 9,* 105-119.

af Klinteberg, B., & Magnusson, D. (1989). Aggressiveness and hyperactive behavior as related to adrenaline excretion. *European Journal of Personality, 3,* 81-93.

Loevinger, J. (1966). Models and measures of developmental variation. *New York Academy of Sciences, 134,* 585-590.

Magnusson, D. (1981). Some methodology and strategy problems in longitudinal research. In F. Schulzinger, S.A. Mednick, & J. Knop (Eds.), *Longitudinal research. Methods and uses in behavioral science.* (pp. 192-215). Boston: Nijhoff.

Magnusson, D. (1985). Implications of an interactional paradigm of research on human development. *International Journal of Behavior and Development, 8,* 115-137.

Magnusson, D. (1987). Adult delinquency in the light of conductant physiology at an early age: A longitudinal study. In D. Magnusson, & A. Öhman (Eds.), *Psychopathology: An interactional perspective.* New York: Academic Press.

Magnusson, D. (1988). Individual development from an interactional perspective: A longitudinal study (vol 1). In D. Magnusson (Ed.), *Paths through life.* Hillsdale, NJ: Erlbaum.

Magnusson, D., & Allen, V. (Eds.). (1983). *Human development: An interactional perspective.* New York: Academic Press.

Magnusson, D., & Bergman, L.R. (1988). Individual and variablebased approaches to longitudinal research on early risk factors. In M. Rutter (Ed.), *Studies of psychological risk: The power of longitudinal data.* (pp. 45-61). Cambridge: Cambridge University Press.

Magnusson, D., & Bergman, L.R. (in press). A pattern approach to the study of pathways from childhood to adulthood. In L. Robbins, & M. Rutter (Eds.), *Straight and devious pathways from childhood to adult life.* New York: Cambridge University Press.

Magnusson, D., & Dunér, A. (1981). Individual development and environment: A longitudinal study. In S.A. Mednick, & A.E. Baert (Eds.), *Prospective longitudinal research: An empirical basis for the primary prevention of psychosocial disorders.* (pp. 111-122). Oxford: Oxford University Press.

Magnusson, D., Dunér, A., & Zetterblom, G. (1975). *Adjustment: A longitudinal study.* Stockholm: Almqvist & Wiksell.

Magnusson, D., Stattin, H., & Allen, V.L. (1985). Biological maturation and social development: A longitudinal study of some adjustment processes from mid-adolescence to adulthood.

*Journal of Youth and Adolescence,* *14,* 267-283.

Magnusson, D., Stattin, H., & Allen, V.L. (1986). Differential maturation among girls and its relation to social adjustment: A longitudinal perspective. In P. Baltes, D. Featherman, & R. Lerner (Eds.), *Life span development,* 7 (pp. 134-172). New York: Academic Press.

Stattin, H., & Magnusson, D. (1989). Social transition in adolescence: A biosocial perspective. In A. de Ribaupierre (Ed.), *Transition mechanisms in child development: The longitudinal perspective.* (pp. 147-190). Cambridge: Cambridge University Press.

Stattin, H., & Magnusson, D. (1990). Pubertal maturation in female development (vol 2). In D. Magnusson (Ed.), *Paths through life.* Hillsdale, NJ: Erlbaum.

**T. Husén, Swedish education in an international perspective**

Conant, J.B. (1970). *My several lives: Memoirs of a social inventor.* New York: Harper and Row.

Husén, T. (1973). *Svenska skolan i internationell belysning I: Naturorienterande ämnen.* Stockholm. Almqvist & Wiksell.

Husén, T. (1979). An international research venture in retrospect: the IEA surveys. *Comparative Education Review, 23*(3), 371-385.

Husén, T. (1986). *Tryckta skrifter 1981-1985. Supplement.* Stockholm: Institutionen för internationell pedagogik.

Husén, T. (1987). Policy impact of IEA research. *Comparative Education Review, 31*(1), 29-46.

Husén T. (1988). *Skolreformen och forskningen.* Stockholm: Verbum-Gothia.

Husén, T. (1989). Samhällsvetenskaperna: På väg mot en egen identitet. In I. Lindqvist, & A-K. Wentzel (Eds.), *Dagens forskning och morgondagens.* (pp. 30-41). Stockholm: Författarförlaget Fischer & Rye.

Husén, T., & Kogan, M. (1984). *Educational research and policy: How do they relate?* Oxford: Pergamon Press.

Härnqvist, K. (1975). The international study of educational achievement. In

F.N. Kerlinger (Ed.), *Review of Research in Education. 3* (pp. 85-109). Washington, D.C.: American Educational Research Association.

Inkeles, A. (1978). The international evaluation of educational achievement. *Proceedings of the National Academy of Education. 4* (pp. 212-227). Washington, D.C.: National Academy of Education.

Keeves, J. (1990). *Changes in science education and achievement: 1970-1984.* Oxford: Pergamon Press.

Kelly, A. (1978). *Girls and science: An international study of sex differences in school science achievements.* Stockholm: Almqvist & Wiksell International.

Postlethwaite, T.N., & Lewy, A. (Eds.). (1979). *Annotated bibliography of IEA publications 1962-1978.* Stockholm: IEA, University of Stockholm.

Walker, D.A. (1976). *The IEA six subject survey: An empirical study of education in twenty-one countries.* Stockholm: Almqvist & Wiksell International.

**K. Härnqvist, Long-term effects of education**

*I. Publications within the Individual Statistics and LING projects*

Balke-Aurell, G. (1982). *Changes in ability as related to educational and occupational experience.* Göteborg: Acta Universitatis Gothoburgensis.

Bengtsson, J (1972). *Utbildningsval, utbildningsforskning och utbildningsplanering.* Lund: Studentlitteratur.

Björkdahl Ordell, S. (1990). *Socialarbetare. Bakgrund, utbildning och yrkesliv.* Göteborg: Acta Universitatis Gothoburgensis.

Emanuelsson, I., & Svensson, A. (in press). Changes in intelligence during a quarter of a century. *Scandinavian Journal of Educational Research.*

Gustafsson, J-E., & Svensson, A. (1982). *Family size, social class, intelligence and achievement: A study of interactions.* Göteborg: Department of Education.

Härnqvist, K. (in press). Enduring effects of higher education, In B.R. Clark, & G. Neave (Eds.), *Encyclopedia of*

*Higher Education.* Oxford: Pergamon Press.

Härnqvist, K. (1966) Social factors and educational choice. *International Journal of Educational Science, 1,* 87-102.

Härnqvist, K. (1968). Relative changes in intelligence from 13 to 18. *Scandinavian Journal of Psychology, 9,* 50-82.

Härnqvist, K. (1977). Enduring effects of schooling: A neglected area in educational research. *Educational Researcher, 6*(10), 5-11.

Härnqvist, K. (1984). *LING-projektens enkät. Loglineära analyser av enkätsvarens samband med utbildningsnivå, intelligens och social bakgrund.* (LING 5). Göteborg: Pedagogiska institutionen.

Härnqvist, K. (1989). *Background, education and work as predictors of adult skills.* (LING 8). Göteborg: Department of Education and Educational Research.

Härnqvist, K., & Svensson, A. (1980). *Den sociala selektionen till gymnasiestadiet.* (SOU 1980:30). Stockholm: Utbildningsdepartementet.

Reuterberg. S-E. (1984). *Studiemedel och rekrytering till högskolan.* Göteborg: Acta Universitatis Gothoburgensis.

Reuterberg, S-E. (1986). Study assistance and degree completion in Swedish higher education. *Studies in Higher Education, 11*(2), 155-171.

Reuterberg, S-E., & Svensson, A. (1987a). Student financial aid and participation in Swedish higher education I: The effects of background variables on transition to higher education. *Scandinavian Journal of Educational Research, 31,* 139-150.

Reuterberg, S-E., & Svensson, A. (1987b). Student financial aid and participation in Swedish higher education II: Recruitment effects of student financial aid. *Scandinavian Journal of Educational Research, 31,* 151-161.

Reuterberg, S-E., Svensson, A. (1987c). *Studiemedel – medel för jämlikhet? En granskning av studiemedelssystemet.* Stockholm: Universitets- och Högskoleämbetet.

Rubenson, K. (1975). *Rekrytering till vuxenutbildning.* Göteborg: Acta Universitatis Gothoburgensis.

Svensson, A. (1971). *Relative achievement.* Stockholm: Almqvist & Wiksell.

Svensson, A. (1979). *Jämlikhet på gång? Den sociala selektionen till universitet och högskolor under 60- och 70-talet.* Stockholm: Universitets- och Högskoleämbetet.

*II. Other literature*

Brown, J.S., Collins, A., & Duguid, P. (1989). Situated cognition and the culture of learning. *Educational Researcher, 18* (1), 32-42.

Fägerlind, I. (1975). *Formal education and adult earnings: A longitudinal study on the economic benefits of education.* Stockholm: Almqvist & Wiksell.

Husén, T. (1969). *Talent, opportunity and career.* Stockholm: Almqvist & Wiksell.

Hyman, H.H., & Wright, C.R. (1979). *Education's lasting influence on values.* Chicago: The University of Chicago Press.

Hyman, H.H., Wright, C.R., & Reed, J.S. (1975). *The enduring effects of education.* Chicago: The University of Chicago Press.

Jöreskog, K.G., & Sörbom, D. (1986). *LISREL VI.* Moresville, Indiana: Scientific Software.

Tuijnman, A. (1989). *Recurrent education, earnings, and well-being.* Stockholm: Almqvist & Wiksell.

Winkler, D.R. (1987). Screening models and education. In G. Psacharopoulos (Ed.), *Economics of education. Research and studies.* Oxford: Pergamon Press.

# G. Fant, Man's voice and speech

Note. Publications listed in chronological order. STL-QPSR = Speech Transmission Laboratory Quarterly Progress and Status Report.

Fant, G., Galyas, K., Carlson, R., & Granström, B. (1980). Talforskning och handikapp. *Kommunikation – trots handikapp. Människan i kommunikationsteknologin.* (RJ 1980:5). (pp 76-

80). Stockholm: Riksbankens Jubileumsfond.

Fant, G. (1982). *Preliminaries to analysis of the human voice source.* (STL-QPSR 4/1982). (pp. 1-27).

Ananthapadmanabha, T.V., Fant, G. (1982). Calculation of true glottal flow and its components. *Speech Communication, 1*, 167-184.

Fant, G., Liljencrants, J., & Lin, Q. (1985). *A four parameter model of glottal flow.* (STL-QPSR 4/1985). (pp. 1-13).

Gauffin, J. (1983). Voice research at the Department of Speech Communication and Music Acoustics. *Transactions of the Committee on Speech Research, Journal of the Acoustics Society of Japan, S83-06*, 38-45.

Fant, G. (1986). Glottal flow: models and interaction. *Journal of Phonetics, 14*(3/4), 393-399. (Theme issue: Voice acoustics and dysphonia. Gotland, Sweden, Aug. 1985).

Gobl, C. (1988). *Voice source dynamics in connected speech.* (STL-QPSR 1/1988). (pp. 123-159).

Karlsson, I. (1989). *Dynamic voice source parameters in a female voice.* (STL-QPSR 1/1989). (pp. 75-77).

Fant, G. (1988). *Frequency domain interpretation and derivation of glottal flow parameters.* (STL-QPSR 2-3/1988). (pp. 1-21).

Fant, G. (1989). The speech code. In C. von Euler, I. Lundberg, & G Lennerstrand (Eds.), *Brain and reading.* (Wennergren International Symposium series, vol 54). London: Mac Milland.

Fant, G., Nord, L., & Kruckenberg, A. (1986). *Individual variations in text reading. A data-bank pilot study.* (STL-QPSR 4/1986). (pp. 1-17).

Fant, G., & Kruckenberg, A. (1989). *Preliminaries to the study of Swedish prose reading and reading style.* (STL-QPSR 2/1989). (pp. 1-83).

Fant, G., Kruckenberg, A., & Nord, L. (1989). Rhythmical structures in text reading. A language contrasting study. *European Conference on Speech Communication and Technology. 1* (pp. 498-501). Edinburgh: CEP Consultant Ltd.

Nord, L., Kruckenberg, A., & Fant, G. (1989). Some timing studies of prose, poetry and music. *European Conference on Speech Communication and Technology. 2* (pp. 690-693). Edinburgh: CEP Consultant Ltd.

Kruckenberg, A., Fant, G., & Nord, L. (1990). Från prosa till poesiens rytm och meter. Stockholm: Institutionen för talöverföring och musikakustik, KTH. (Manus, Andra Nordiska Metrikkonferensen, Uppsala 1989).

## I. Rosengren,
## Language and pragmatics

Note. S & P = Sprache und Pragmatik. Arbeitsberichte des Forschungsprogramms Sprache und Pragmatik.

Altmann, H. (1987). Zur Problematik der Konstitution von Satzmodi als Formtypen. In J. Meibauer (Ed.), *Satzmodus zwischen Grammatik und Pragmatik.* (pp. 22-56). Tübingen: Niemeyer.

Andric, B., Hansson, K., & Koch, W. (1989). Prozeßsteuerung und Verbsemantik in einem computersimulierten Küchenmodell: Teilen, Mischen und Erwärmen. *S & P, 14*, 1-106.

Bierwisch, M. (1980). Semantic structure and illocutionary force. In J.R. Searle, F. Kiefer, & M. Bierwisch (Eds.), *Speech act theory and pragmatics.* (pp. 1-35). Dordrecht: Reidel.

Bierwisch, M. (1988). On the grammar of local prepositions. In M. Bierwisch, W. Motsch, & I Zimmerman (Eds.), *Syntax, Semantik und Lexikon.* (pp. 1-65). Berlin: Akademie-Verlag. (studia grammatica XXIX)

Blume, C., & Jakob, W. (1983). *Programming languages for industrial robots.* New York: Springer-Verlag.

Brandt, M., Falkenberg, G., Fries, N., Liedtke, F., Meibauer, J., Rehbock, H., Rosengren, I., & Öhlschläger, G. (1989). Die performativen Äußerungen – eine empirische Studie. *S & P, 12*, 1-22 (ZPSK 43/1990)

Brandt, M., Koch, W., Motsch, W., Rosengren, I., & Viehweger, D. (1983). Der Einfluß der kommunikativen Strategie auf die Textstruktur – dargestellt am Beispiel des Geschäftsbriefes. In I. Rosengren (Ed.), *Sprache und Pragmatik.* (pp. 105-135). Stockholm: Almqvist & Wiksell International. (Lunder Symposium 1982)

Brandt. M., Rosengren, I., & Zimmermann, I. (1989). Satzmodus, Modalität und Performativität. *S & P, 13*, 1-42. (ZPSK 43/1990)

Cercone, N., & MacCalla, G. (Eds.) (1987). *The knowledge frontier. Essays in the representation of knowledge.* New York: Springer-Verlag.

Chomsky, N. (1986). *Knowledge of language: Its nature, origin, and use.* New York: Praeger.

Drescher, M., & Kotschi, T. (1988). Das "Genfer Modell". Diskussion eines Ansatzes zur Diskursanalyse am Beispiel der Analyse eines Beratungsgesprächs. *S & P, 8*, 1-42.

Falkenberg, G. (1989a). Explizite Illokutionen. *S & P, 12*, 22-42. (ZPSK 43/1990)

Falkenberg, G. (1989b). Explizite Performative sind nicht indirekt. *S & P, 13*, 55-62. (Även i Linguistische Berichte 124)

Grice, H.P. (1979). Logic and conversation. In G. Meggle (Ed.), *Handlung, Kommunikation, Bedeutung.* (pp. 243-265). Frankfurt am Main: Suhrkamp.

Gülich, E., & Kotschi, T. (1987). Reformulierungshandlungen als Mittel der Textkonstitution. Untersuchungen zu französischen Texten aus mündlicher Kommunikation. In W. Motsch (Ed.), *Satz, Text, sprachliche Handlung.* (pp. 199-261). Berlin: Akademie-Verlag (studia grammatica XXV)

Höhle, T.N. (1982). Explikationen für "normale Betonung" und "normale Wortstellung". In W. Abraham (Ed.), *Satzglieder im Deutschen. Vorschläge zur syntaktischen, semantischen und pragmatischen Fundierung.* (pp. 74-154). Tübingen: Gunter Narr Verlag.

Katz, J.J. (1977). *Propositional structure and illocutionary force.* New York: Crowell.

Koch, W. (1988a). Weltwissen, Sprachsystem und Textstruktur in einem integrierten Modell der automatischen Sprachverarbeitung. Zum Beispiel Kochrezepte. *S & P, 4*, 1-39.

Koch, W. (1988b). Referenz- und Inferenzprobleme im Parsingprozeß. *S & P, 7*, 1-33.

Levinson, S.C. (1983). *Pragmatics.* Cambridge: Cambridge University Press.

Liedtke, F. (1989). Performativität, Sprechhandlung, Wahrheit. *S & P, 12*, 43-67. (ZPSK, 43/1990)

Motsch, W. (1989). Dialog-Texte als modular organisierte Strukturen. *S & P, 11*, 37-67.

Motsch, W., & Pasch, R. (1987). Illokutive Handlungen. In W. Motsch (Ed.), *Satz, Text, sprachliche Handlung.* (pp. 11-80). Berlin: Akademie-Verlag. (studia grammatica XXV)

Motsch, W., Reis, M., & Rosengren, I. (1989). Zum Verhältnis von Satz und Text. *S & P, 11*, 1-36. (Kommer även att publiceras i Deutsche Sprache)

Rehbock, H. (1989). Deklarativsatzmodus und pragmatische Interpretation. *S & P, 15*, 1-69.

Reis, M. (1987). Die Stellung der Verbargumente im Deutschen. Stilübungen zum Grammatik:Pragmatik-Verhältnis. In I. Rosengren (Ed.), *Sprache und Pragmatik.* (pp. 139-177). Stockholm. Almqvist & Wiksell International. (Lunder Symposium 1986)

Reis, M. (1990). Zur Grammatik und Pragmatik von Echo-w-Fragen. Universität Tübingen: Deutsches Seminar. (manus, kommer att publiceras i S & P)

Reis, M., & Rosengren, I. (1988). Wh-Imperatives?! *S & P, 10*, 1-49.

Rosengren, I. (1989). w-Interrogativsatz, Skopus und Fokus. Lunds universitet: Tyska institutionen. (S & P 16)

Schank, R.C. (1977). *Scripts, plans, goals and understanding. An inquiry into human knowledge structures.* Hillsdale, N. J. Erlbaum.

Searle, J.R. (1975). A taxonomy of illocutionary acts. In K. Gunderson (Ed.), *Language, mind & knowledge.* (pp. 344-369). Minneapolis: University of Minnesota Press.

Tremblay, J.P., & Sorensen, P.G. (1985). *The theory and practice of compiler writing.* New York: McGraw-Hill.

**S. Allén, From grapheme to lexeme**

*I. Publications in the series Data linguistica*

1. Allén, S. (1970). *Nusvensk frekvensordbok baserad på tidningstext.1. Graford, homografkomponenter.*

2. Allén, S., & Hellberg, S. (1971). *Introduktion i grafonomi, det lingvistiska skriftstudiet.*

3. Thavenius, J. (1971). *Konkordans till Hjalmar Gullbergs lyrik.*

4. Allén, S. (1971). *Nusvensk frekvensordbok baserad på tidningstext 2. Lemman*

5. Gavare, R. (1971). *Graph description of linguistic structure. A linguistic approach to the theory of graphs.*

6. Allén, S. (1971). *Tiotusen i topp. Ordfrekvenser i tidningstext.*

7. Ralph, B. (1972). *Introduktion i historisk språkvetenskap.*

8. Sågvall, A-L. (1973). *A system for automatic inflectional analysis implemented for Russian.*

9. Ljung, M. (1974). *A frequency dictionary of English morphemes.*

10. Allén, S. et al (1975). *Nusvensk frekvensordbok baserad på tidningstext. 3. Ordförbindelser.*

11. Gellerstam, G., & Gellerstam, M. (1977). *Ord och fras i psalmboken.*

12. Berg, S. (1978). *Olika lika ord. Svenskt homograflexikon.*

13. Hellberg, S. (1978). *The morphology of present-day Swedish. Word-inflection, word-formation, basic dictionary.*

14. Allén, S., Berg, S., Järborg, J., Löfström, J., Ralph, B., & Sjögreen, C. (1980). *Nusvensk frekvensordbok baserad på tidningstext. 4. Ordled, betydelser.*

15. Lindvall, L. (1982). *Jean Renart et Galeran de Bretagne. Étude sur un problème d'attribution de textes.*

16. Allén, S. (Ed.). (1982). *Text processing. Text analysis and generation. Text typology and attribution.* (Proceedings of Nobel Symposium 51).

17. Engwall, G. (1984). *Vocabulaire du roman français (1962-1968). Dictionnaire des fréquences.*

18. *Studies in computer-aided lexicology* (1988).

*II. Other literature*

Allén, S. (1965). *Grafematisk analys som grundval för textedering med särskild hänsyn till Johan Ekeblads brev till brodern Claes Ekeblad 1639-1655.* (Nordistica Gothoburgensia 1). Göteborg: Acta Universitatis Gothoburgensis.

Allén, S. (1965). *Johan Ekeblads brev till brodern Claes Ekeblad 1639-1655.* Utg. med inledning, kommentar och register. (Nordistica Gothoburgensia 2). Göteborg: Acta Universitatis Gothoburgensis.

Allén, S. (1976). On phraseology in lexicology. *Cahiers de Lexicologie,* 29, 83-90.

Allén, S. (1977). Text-based lexicography and algorithmic text analysis. *Association for Literary and Linguistic Computing Bulletin,* 5(2), 126-131.

Allén, S (1979). Lexical morphology. A model and an application. In H. Bergenholtz & B. Schaeder (Eds.), *Empirische Textwissenschaft.* Königstein/TS: Scriptor

Allén, S. (1980). The language bank concept. In J. Raben & G. Marks (Eds.), *Data bases in the humanities and social sciences.* Amsterdam, New York, Oxford: North-Holland.

Allén, S. (1981). The lemma-lexeme model of the Swedish lexical data base. In B. Rieger (Ed.), *Empirical semantics 1-2.* Bochum: Studienverlag Brockmeyer.

Allén, S. (1985). Computational linguistics in a future-requirement framework. In S. Bäckman & G. Kjellmer (Eds.), *Papers on language and literature presented to Alvar Ellegård and Erik Frykman.* (Gothenburg Studies in English 60). Göteborg: Acta Universitatis Gothoburgensis.

Allén, S. (Ed.). (1988). *Possible worlds in humanities, arts and sciences. Proceedings of Nobel Symposium 65.* Berlin, New York: Walter de Gruyter.

Allén, S., Hamesse, J., & Zampolli, A. (Eds.). (1988). *Literary & linguistic computing 3 (2).* Oxford: Oxford University Press.

Allén, S. & Petöfi, J.S. (Eds.). (1979). *Aspects of automatized text processing.* Hamburg: Helmut Buske.

*Svensk ordbok.* (1988). Stockholm: Esselte Studium. (2 uppl. Utarbetad vid Språkdata).

## B. Sigurd,
### Social reforms and Newspeak

Bolinger, D. (1975). *Aspects of language*. New York: Harcourt Brace Jovanovich. (2nd ed)

Brown, R. (1958). How shall a thing be called? *Psychological Review*, *65*, 14-21.

Gellerstam, M. (1984). Ord som inte vill dö. *Språkvård*, *1*, 16-21.

Karlström, H. Å. (1978). Examensbenämningar i grundläggande högskoleutbildning. Stockholm. (UHÄ, PM 100-4864-78)

Liedman, S. (1985). Hotade humaniora. *Svenska Dagbladet*, (16/1)

Oksaar, E. (1986). *Berufsbezeichnungen im heutigen Deutsch*. Düsseldorf: Schwann.

Oppenheimer, M. (1961-62). Some linguistic aspects of mind-conditioning by the Sovjet press. *Journal of Human Relations*, *10*, 21-31.

Orrling Welander, A. (1983). Prälle, svartrock, himlalots. *Språkvård*, *2*, 17-28.

Orrling, A. (1990). Förändringar i benämningsskicket för yrken under 1930-1980. Lunds universitet: Institutionen för lingvistik. (manus)

Orrling, A, & Sigurd, B. (1981). Högskolan som verbal reform. *Forskning och Framsteg*, (8), 27-31.

Orwell, G. (1946). Politics and the English language. *Collected essays*. London: Secker & Warburg. (2nd ed)

Protokoll och handlingar från Planeringsberedningen för kultur- och informationsyrken. Stockholm: UHÄ.

Sigurd, B. (1984). Låt kandidaten leva! *Sydsvenska Dagbladet*, (10/4)

Sigurd, B. (1985). Återinför fil kand. *Dagens Nyheter*, (18/4)

Stedje, A. (1989). *Deutsche Sprache gestern und heute*. (UTB 1499). München.

UHÄ. (1985). *Högskolan*. (UHÄ-rapport 1985:6). Stockholm.

UHÄ. (1989). *Ny examensordning i högskolan*. (UHÄ-rapport 1989:3). Stockholm.

Utbildningsdepartementet. (1986). *Bilaga 10 till budgetpropositionen*. (1985/86:100). Stockholm.

## S. Lindqvist,
### History of technology

Berglund, B. (1982). *Industriarbetarklassens formering: Arbete och teknisk förändring vid tre svenska fabriker under 1800-talet*. (Meddelanden från ekonomisk.historiska institutionen 51). Göteborgs universitet: Ekonomisk-historiska institutionen.

Berner, B. (1981). *Teknikens värld: Teknisk förändring och ingenjörsarbete i svensk industri*. (Arkiv avhandlingsserie 11). Lund: Arkiv förlag.

Eriksson, G. (1978). *Kartläggarna: Natuvetenskapens tillväxt och tillämpningar i det industriella genombrottets Sverige 1870-1914*. (Umeå Studies in the Humanities 15). Umeå universitet.

Gadd, C. J. (1983). *Järn och potatis: Jordbruk, teknik och social omvandling i Skaraborgs län 1750-1860*. (Meddelanden från ekonomisk-historiska institutionen 53). Göteborgs universitet: Ekonomisk-historiska institutionen.

Glete, J. (1980). Teknikhistoria – viktig i ekonomisk och historisk forskning. *Tekniska museets årsbok Daedalus*, *49*, 55-65.

Götlind, A. (1988). *Teknikens medeltida apostlar? En studie av cistercienserna som bärare och förmedlare av teknisk kunskap i det medeltida Skandinavien*. Göteborgs universitet: Historiska institutionen.

Hagberg, J.E. (1986). *Tekniken i kvinnornas händer: Hushållsarbete och hushållsteknik under tjugo- och trettiotalen*. (Linköping Studies in Arts and Science 7). Linköpings universitet.

Hansson, S. (1987). *Teknik-Historia: Teknikhistorisk översikt från äldsta tid fram till 1900-talet*. Luleå: Centek.

Hughes, T. P. (1971). *Elmer Sperry: Inventor and engineer*. Baltimore and London: The Johns Hopkins University Press.

Hughes, T.P. (1983). *Networks of power: Electrification in Western society, 1880-1930*. Baltimore and London: The Johns Hopkins University Press.

Hughes, T. P. (1989). *American genesis: A century of invention and technological enthusiasm 1870-1970*. New York: Viking.

Hult, J., Lindqvist, S., Odelberg, W., & Rydberg, S. (1989). *Svensk teknikhistoria*. Hedemora: Gidlunds.

Hård, M. (1988). *In the icy waters of calculation: The scientification of refrigeration technology and the rationalization of the brewing industry in the 19th century*. (Arachne 4). Göteborgs universitet: Institutionen för idé- och lärdomshistoria.

Hård, M. (1989). History of technology in Sweden – A field with a future!? *Polhem Tidskrift för teknikhistoria, 7*, 164-182.

Kaijser, A. (1986). *Stadens ljus: Etableringen av de första svenska gasverken*. (Linköping Studies in Arts and Science 4). Linköpings universitet.

Kylhammar, M. (1986). *Maskin och idyll: Teknik och pastorala ideal hos Strindberg och Heidenstam*. (Linköping Studies in Arts and Science 1). Linköpings universitet.

Lindgren, M. (1987). *Glory and failure: The difference engines of Johann Müller, Charles Babbage and Georg and Edvard Scheutz*. (Linköping Studies in Arts and Science 9). Linköpings universitet.

Lindqvist, S. (1981). *The teaching of history of technology in USA – A critical survey in 1978*. Stockholm: KTH.

Lindqvist, S. (1984). *Technology on trial: The introduction of steam power technology into Sweden, 1715-1736*. (Uppsala Studies in History of Science 1). Uppsala universitet.

Lindqvist, S., & Sörbom, P. (1982). Det flygande symposiet. *Tekniska museets årsbok Daedalus, 51*, 31-34.

Ljungberg, G. (1976). IVA:s teknikhistoriska råd – Verksamheten 1968-1976. *Tekniska museets årsbok Daedalus, 45*, 64-73.

Lönnroth, E. (1983). Behovet av teknikhistoria. *IVA-nytt, 3/4*, 10-11.

Olsson, C. A. (1980). *Teknikhistoria som vetenskaplig disciplin: Några kommentarer*. (Meddelanden från ekonomisk-historiska institutionen 11). Lunds universitet: Ekonomisk-historiska institutionen.

Runeby, N. (1976). *Teknikerna, vetenskapen och kulturen: Ingenjörsundervisning och ingenjörsorganisationer i 1870-talets Sverige*. (Studia Historica Uppsaliensia 81). Uppsala universitet.

Rydberg, S. (1981). Tekniken: Den försummade historien. *Svenska Dagbladet*, (14/5).

Sandqvist, I.-B. (1979). *Litteratur om svenska industriföretag*. (IVA-meddelande 227). Stockholm: Ingenjörsvetenskapsakademien.

Sandström, U. (1989). *Arkitektur och social ingenjörskonst: Studier i svensk arkitektur- och bostadsforskning*. (Linköping Studies in Arts and Science 47). Linköpings universitet.

Schiller, B. (1983). Technology – history- social change: A methodological comment and an outline of a Nordic account. *Scandinavian Journal of History, 8*, 71-82.

Strandh, S. (Ed.). (1979). *Technology and its impact on society*. Stockholm: Tekniska museet.

Sundin, B. (1981). *Ingenjörsvetenskapens tidevarv: Ingenjörsvetenskapsakademien, Pappersmassekontoret, Metallografiska institutet och den teknologiska forskningen i början av 1900-talet*. (Umeå Studies in the Humanities 42). Umeå universitet.

Sörbom, P. (Ed.). (1978). *Attityder till tekniken*. Stockholm: Riksbankens Jubileumsfond.

Sörbom, P. (Ed.). (1980). *Transport technology and social change*. Stockholm: Tekniska museet.

Tekniska museet. (1984). När elektriciteten kom: Tretton uppsatser om elkraftens historia i Sverige. *Daedalus, 53*.

Tekniska museet. (1986). Teknisk forskning i historiskt perspektiv. *Daedalus, 55*.

Torstendahl, R. (1975). *Teknologins nytta: Motiveringar för det svenska tekniska utbildningsväsendets framväxt framförda av riksdagsmän och utbildningsadministratörer 1810-1870*. (Studia Historica Upsaliensia 66). Uppsala universitet.

Waldenström, E. (1983). Näringslivet och den teknikhistoriska forskningen. *IVA-Nytt, 1*, 6-8.

476 · References

Widmalm, S. (1990). Mellan kartan
och verkligheten: Geodesi och kart-
läggning, 1695-1860. (Skrifter 10).
Uppsala universitet: Institutionen för
idé- och lärdomshistoria.

T. Frängsmyr, Sweden in the world

Battail, J. F: (1986). La Suède intellec-
tuelle et savante. Napoli: Prismi. (Även
i Uppsala Studies in History of Science, 3)
Crawford, E. (1984). The beginnings of
the Nobel institution: The science prizes,
1901 – 1915. Cambridge: Cambridge
University Press.
Frängsmyr, T. (1980). Nordenskiöld och
polarforskningen: Den idéhistoriska
bakgrunden. Ymer, 100, 6-38.
Frängsmyr, T. (1986). L'activité scien-
tifique en Suède au XVIIIe siècle dans
son contexte international. Nouvelles
de la République de Lettres, II, 45-54.
Frängsmyr, T (Ed.). (1987). Otto To-
rells reseberättelser 1826-63. Lych-
nos, 1986, 127-148.
Frängsmyr, T. (Ed.). (1989). Science in
Sweden: The Royal Swedish Academy
of Sciences, 1739-1989. Canton, USA:
Science History Publications.
Frängsmyr, T., Heilbron, J. L., & Rider,
R. (Eds.). (1990). The quantifying spirit
in the eighteenth century. Berkeley:
University of California Press. (Även
i Uppsala Studies in History of Science, 7)
Johannisson, K (1988). Det mätbara
samhället: Statistik och samhällsdröm
i 1700-talets Europa. Stockholm:
Norstedts.
Jonsson, U. (1989). Svensk polarforsk-
ning på 1800-talet. Seminarrapport
fra internasjonalt seminar om huma-
nistisk Svalbardforskning. (Longyear-
byen 3-6 Mai, 1989).
Lundgren, A. (1987). Dextran som
blodplasmasubstitut. In T. Frängsmyr
(Ed.), Vetenskap och läkemedel.
Uppsala: Almqvist & Wiksell International.
Sörlin, S. (1989). Scientific travel – the
Linnean tradition. In T. Frängsmyr
(Ed.), Science in Sweden. (pp. 96-
123). Canton, USA: Science History
Publications.
Widmalm, S. (1990). Mellan kartan

och verkligheten: Geodesi och kart-
läggning 1695-1860. Uppsala: Institutionen för idé- och lärdomshistoria.

In press
Broberg, F. et. al. (Eds.). Rashygienen i
Norden.
Dhombres, J. & Sörlin, S. Les relations
entre la France et la Suède au siècle
de lumières.
Frängsmyr, T. (Ed.). Solomon's house
revisited: The organization and insti-
tutionalization of science. Canton, USA:
Science History Publications. (Nobel
Symposium 75)
Melhado, E., & Frängsmyr, T. (Eds.).
Berzelius as an international scien-
tist.

# NOTES

**A.Lindbeck:**
**Internationalization process and national economic policies**

1. This was especially the case for the projects "*En ny ekonomisk världsordning* (A new economic world order), "*Europeiska länders relativa konkurrenskraft*" (The relative competitiveness of European countries), "*Handel, tillväxt, och europeisk integration*" (Trade, growth and European integration), "*Betydelsen av marknadsstruktur och produktionsförhållanden för utrikeshandelns sammansättning och för handels- och industripolitik*" (The importance of market structure and production conditions for the composition of foreign trade and industrial policies), and "*Regler för stabiliseringspolitiken*" (Rules for stabilization policies).

**B.Odén:**
**Studying the elderly in society**

1. E. Reutersvärd (Andréasson). "Kulturell intervention. Ett participatoriskt projekt". Submitted for publication in the report series. No report has as yet been submitted on Henrik Glimstedt's interesting interviews in Göteborg. A *social* intervention was performed in Uppsala and Göteborg.
2. Traditional lectures in history, held at Norra Hospital in Lund, by another project member, Allan Persson, were more successful. They apparently lived up to expectations. Also see U. Nilsson (1986).
3. "Blentarps socken 1901. En kohortstudie med speciell inriktning på äldres boendegemenskap". Submitted for publication in the report series.
4. "Migration och åldrande. Stadsmigrationens effekter för de äldres boendemönster med utgångspunkt från flyttningarna till och från Falkenberg under 1850- och 1870-talen". Submitted for publication in the report series.
5. The transformation of the care-providing institutions was previously examined by Åman (1976).
6. Söderpalm's studies of shifting policies towards the poor in Skåne have still not been published. Also see Pulma (1985).
7. B. Odén, "Lund i välfärdspolitiken". Submitted for publication in *Lund under expansion*, 1990.
8. B. Odén, "Disciplinbildning mellan universitet och samhälle". Submitted for publication in *Liberala perspektiv. Vision och verklighet i historia och politik* (1990).
9. "Attityder och värderingar inom den offentliga vården". Submitted for publication in the report series.

10. B. Odén, "Relationer mellan generationerna". Submitted for publication 1991.

**L. Furuland**
**Swedish sociology of literature**

1. Åkerstedt (1967), Schön (1973), Rehn (1974).
2. Application documents from the Sociology of Literature Section to the Foundation in 1966. Johannesson (1968).
3. Application documents from the Sociology of Literature Section to the Foundation in 1966. Bennich-Björkman (1970 a).
4. Furuland L. Litteratur och samhälle. Litteratursociologiska frågeställningar. In *Forskningsfält och metoder inom litteraturvetenskapen.* Stockholm: Wahlström & Widstrand, 1970, 165-206. Furuland , L. Litteratursociologi. In *Svenskt litteraturlexikon.* Lund: Gleerups, 1970, 340-341. — Information on the international debate and foreign scholars of importance to the emergence of the Sociology of Literature Section is contained in these two publications.
5. Thorsell, L. Den svenska parnassens "demokratisering" och de folkliga bildningsvägarna". *Samlaren* 1957, 53-135. Hansson, G. *Dikten och läsaren.* Stockholm: Bonniers, 1959. Johannesson (1968). Bennich-Björkman (1970 a).
6. The presentation is based on Furuland (1989 d).
7. E.g. Rehn (1974). See Bennich-Björkman & Furuland (1988) for a history of literature overview with elements from reception research.
8. Furuland (1989 a), 250-251.
9. One example is Bennich-Björkman (1988).
10. University of Minnesota. Example of the contents of guest lectures in Furuland (1989 c).

# THE AUTHORS

*Erik Allardt*, Professor of Sociology, Helsinki University, President of the Academy of Finland.

*Sture Allén*, Professor of Computational Linguistics, Göteborg University, Permanent Secretary of the Swedish Academy.

*Sten Carlsson*, Professor emeritus of History, Uppsala University, deceased 1989.

*Erik Dahmén*, Professor emeritus of Economics with Economic and Social History, Stockholm School of Economics.

*Gunnar Fant*, Professor emeritus of Speech Communication, Royal Institute of Technology, Stockholm.

*Tore Frängsmyr*, Professor of History of Science, Uppsala University.

*Lars Furuland*, Professor of Literature, especially Sociology of Literature, Uppsala University.

*Bo Gustafsson*, Professor of Economic History, Uppsala University.

*Torsten Husén*, Professor emeritus of International and Comparative Education, Stockholm University.

*Torsten Hägerstand*, Professor emeritus of Human Geography, especially Geographic Process and System Analysis, Lund University.

*Kjell Härnqvist*, Professor emeritus of Education and Educational Psychology, Göteborg University.

*David H. Ingvar*, Professor of Clinical Neurophysiology, Lund University.

*Jan Erik Kihlström*, Professor of Ecotoxicology, Uppsala University.

*Leif Lewin*, Johan Skytte Professor of Eloquence and Government, Uppsala University.

*Assar Lindbeck*, Professor of International Economics and Director of the Institute of International Economic Studies, Stockholm University.

*Svante Lindqvist*, Professor of History of Technology, Royal Institute of Technology, Stockholm.

*David Magnusson*, Professor of Psychology, Stockholm University.

*Karl-Göran Mäler*, Professor of Economics, Stockholm School of Economics.

*Birgitta Odén*, Professor emeritus of History, Lund University.

*Bengt Pernow*, Professor emeritus of Clinical Physiology, Karolinska Institutet, Stockholm.

*Anders Rapp*, Professor of Physical Geography, Lund University.

*Inger Rosengren*, Professor of German, Lund University.

*Bengt Sigurd*, Professor of General Linguistics, Lund University.

*Nils Stjernquist*, Professor emeritus of Political Science, Lund University.

*Nils-Eric Svensson*, Professor and Executive Director of the Bank of Sweden Tercentenary Foundation.

# CHAIRMEN OF THE BOARD
# AND DIRECTORS OF THE FOUNDATION

## Chairmen of the Board

Professor Torgny Segerstedt
1965-74
Professor Hans Meijer 1974-80
Professor Staffan Helmfrid
1980-86
Professor Kjell Härnqvist 1986-

## Executive Directors

Professor Hans L. Zetterberg
1965-66
Dr. Paul Lindblom 1966-70
Dr. Östen Johansson 1970-73
Professor Nils-Eric Svensson 1974-

## Finance Director

Lars-Erik Klangby 1989-

*Note: A complete list of members of the board, priority assignment committees, special committees and staff is found in the Swedish edition of the book.*